GUIDE
to the 1971
NATIONAL
ELECTRICAL
CODE

by Roland E. Palmquist

THEODORE AUDEL & CO.
a division of
HOWARD W. SAMS & CO., INC.
4300 West 62nd Street
Indianapolis, Indiana 46268

THIRD EDITION

FIRST PRINTING—1972

International Standard Book Number: 0-672-23193-X
Library of Congress Catalog Card Number: 71-186135

Foreword

Many persons whose job is concerned with the installation, operation, or inspection of electrical systems and equipment have often expressed a desire for an interpretation or clarification of certain parts of the National Electrical Code (NEC). This book has been written in an attempt to fulfill this need.

The National Electrical Code is published by the National Fire Protection Association as one of a number of codes, standards, and recommended practices prepared by NFPA Technical Committees. Because of the complexity of all possible electrical installations and equipments, and the necessity for covering any possible contingency, the NEC becomes quite complicated in many areas. For this reason, this Guide has been written to simplify the intent of the Code where needed most.

The NEC is revised approximately every three years to keep up-to-date with new methods and new materials that are constantly being developed. This Guide is based on the 1971 revision of the NEC. The interpretations in this Guide are those of the author and are in no manner to be considered as official NFPA Electrical Code Committee interpretations.

My sincere thanks are given to Mr. Frank Stetka, Secretary of the National Electrical Code Committee, and to Mr. George Tryon, Technical Secretary of the National Fire Protection Association, for their kindness in granting me permission to write this book. I also wish to acknowledge the part that my wife Elsie has played in this matter. Her patience and extreme tolerance in permitting me to devote so much time to this venture must not go unrewarded. I therefore wish to dedicate this book to her.

ROLAND E. PALMQUIST

About the Author . . .

Mr. Palmquist has been active in the electrical field since 1929. He is currently a full-time Electrical Inspector in charge of District D, NE Colorado for the Colorado State Electrical Board. In addition, he is a member of the Electrical Section of the National Fire Protection Association, and serves on the Executive Board of the Rocky Mountain Chapter of the International Association of Electrical Inspectors. Mr. Palmquist has had numerous articles published in the Electrical Construction and Maintenance Magazine and in the IAEI News. He recently revised Audels **Questions and Answers for Electricians Examinations,** and **Answers to Blueprint Reading.**

Contents

Chapter 4. Equipment for General Use

Chapter 7. Special Conditions

Chapter 8. Communication Systems

Chapter 9. Tables and Examples

See NEC

ARTICLE 90—INTRODUCTION

The National Electrical Code was first published in 1897 under the sponsorship of the National Conference of Electrical Rules, the membership of which consisted of delegates from interested national associations. This edition was the forerunner of a very democratic and valuable document that has been responsible in saving many lives and many dollars in property. This organization was disbanded in 1911, at which time the National Fire Protective Association took over the responsibility of writing and publishing the NEC, which it has continued to do since that time. The NEC has also been adopted by the American Standards Association.

A National Electrical Code committee, set up under the NFPA, is headed by the correlating committee which works with the various panels, each panel having the responsibility of certain Articles. This correlating committee and the Code-making panels include dedicated men from all phases of the electrical industry. They are assigned to the particular panel where it is felt they may do the most good. The Code is set up as a minimum standard for electrical installations and for the protection of life and property, without creating undue hardship.

The NEC, as it now exists, is very complete. However, local conditions may dictate some variations, and as we proceed with the text, you will see that, in most instances, these variations have been anticipated and planned for in the Code.

The NEC is divided into chapters covering the different phases of electrical installations, and is preceded by an introduction. **It is not the intention of this book to replace the NEC, but rather to be used in conjunction with it.** Where direct quotes from the National Electrical Code book are made, they will appear in *italic type*. The NEC is also known as NFPA 70, and can be purchased from the National Fire Protection Association, 60 Batterymarch Street, Boston, Mass.

ARTICLE 90

90-1. Purpose—The fundamental purpose of the NEC is to safeguard lives and property from the hazards that arise through the improper installation of wiring and equipment, and to provide standards for the proper installation of electricity for heat, light, power, radio, signaling, and for any other purpose. The standards as set forth in the NEC are considered necessary for safety, and the intention certainly is not that this minimum is to be followed entirely. The intention is that these basic minimums may be enlarged upon, but there must be some minimum safety guides set forth.

If these minimums are not followed, hazards will arise due to over-loading of wiring, improper grounding, improper overcurrent protection, or many other reasons. The NEC is most certainly not intended as a design manual, but in planning a wiring system, the standards should never be less than the minimum NEC requirements. If the rules as stated are followed, a system that is essentially free from hazards will be obtained. The system will be safe, but not necessarily the most efficient, convenient, or adaptable for future expansion.

It is not good practice to install systems that are below Code standards. Always take into consideration the present and future needs of the user and make as good an installation over and above Code regulations as is practical and necessary.

90-2. Scope—

(a) The Code covers the installation of conductors and equipment within or on the following public and private buildings and other premises:

Yards.
Carnivals.
Parking lots.
Industrial substations.
Conductors connecting the installations to the power supply.
Other outside conductors adjacent to the premises.
Mobile homes.
Recreation vehicles.

(b) The following installations are not covered in the Code:

(1) Installations in:
Ships.
Watercraft.
Railway rolling stock.
Aircraft.
Automotive vehicles, (except mobile homes and recreational vehicles.

(2) *Installations in underground mines.*

(3) *Installations of railways for generation, transformation, transmission or distribution of power used exclusively for operation of rolling stock or installations used exclusively for signalling and communication purposes.*

(4) *Installation of communication equipment under exclusive control of communication utilities, located outdoors or in building spaces used exclusively for such installations.*

You will no doubt find that most inspection authorities do not include the wiring in said buildings for lighting, air-conditioning, etc. These items are not used exclusively for communication.

(5) *Installations under the exclusive control of electric utilities for the purpose of communication, metering or for the generation, control, transformation, transmission and distribution of electric energy located in buildings used exclusively by utilities for such purposes or located outdoors on property owned or leased by the utility or on public highways, streets, roads, etc., or outdoors by established rights on private property.*

Again, as in **(4)**, you no doubt will find that inspection authorities do not include the wiring in said locations, for lighting, air-conditioning, etc.

(c) Special Permission. *The authority having jurisdiction for the enforcement of the Code may grant exception for the installation of conductors and equipment, not under the exclusive control of the electric utilities and used to connect the electric utility supply system to the service entrance conductors on the premises served, provided such installations are outside a building or terminate immediately inside a building wall.*

There has been an abundance of work done by utilities and often the work becomes a part of the Code. Should the installation of service laterals, for example, be deemed good engineering practice by utilities, and acceptable by the enforcing authority this practice may by special permission be permitted under the Code. This special permission does not eliminate the **Special Permission** under **Article 100;** it only applies to **Section 90-2.**

90-3. Code Arrangement—The Code is divided into chapters. Chapters 1 through 4 deal with general applications of the Code to wiring and installations. Chapters 5, 6, and 7 supplement or amend the first four chapters, and deal with special occupancies and installations which involve special equipment or special conditions. Chapter 8 deals with communication circuits, and with the equipment and installation of radio and television. Chapter 9 deals with tables not included in, but to be used in conjunction with, the first eight chapters. Also included are examples for figuring minimum requirements for installation. These examples are extremely valuable in the understanding of the preceding chapters.

90-4. Definitions—In **Article 100,** there are definitions which appear in two or more Articles of the NEC. Referral is made to the American Standard Definitions of Electrical Terms (USAS C-42) for any definition or electrical term not included in **Article 100.** For an interpretation of terms or definitions not appearing in **Article 100,** the USAS C-42 pamphlet will be the deciding ruling.

90-5. Fundamental Rules—Fundamental rules appear at the beginning of articles throughout the Code, and are usually termed **Scope.** These rules are followed by more detailed and recognized methods. Reference is often made in this book and in the NEC to another **Section** or **Sections.** These references will be included at the time they are mentioned.

90-6. Interpretation—An NEC committee is set up to render official Code interpretations when these are necessary. In the majority of questions arising on the Code, the interpretations are under the inspectors' jurisdiction, as will be seen in the next Section. However, there may be instances when official interpretations are required. No official interpretations will be made unless the procedures outlined in the Code are followed.

90-7. Enforcement—The NEC is written so that it can be enforced when adopted by agencies having the rights of inspection. The Code's enforcement and interpretation is placed in the hands of the enforcing agency or authority. They decide the answers, but of course good judgment is essential in the interpretations. In many instances, the Code puts the entire responsibility of interpretation on the enforcing authority. For example, you will often find the phrase *by special permission*; this means special permission, in writing, by the Code-enforcing authority.

The enforcing authority is vested with the right to decide upon the approval of equipment and materials. However, listings from the Underwriters' Laboratory or other independent testing laboratory are used for this purpose in many instances. One of the deterrents to Code understanding is the feeling between the inspector and the workmen. Actually, the inspector is the workman's friend, and all he wants is a good safe job. The best advice to offer in this respect is—get acquainted with your inspector. Take your problems to him; you will find him understanding and helpful in most cases.

90-8. Examination of Equipment for Safety—There are independent testing laboratories set up for the testing of equipment and materials. These agencies have the facilities for the job and should be relied upon. The agency having inspection jurisdiction usually adopts one or more of these independent agencies as the guide in determining what materials and equipment are approved or not approved. Check with your inspector to determine what is required.

Factory installed wiring or the construction of equipment is not required to be inspected at the time of installation, except for damage or defects. The above holds true if the equipment has been inspected and approved by a nationally recognized electrical testing laboratory, such as Underwriter's Laboratories.

90-9. Wiring Planning—In the design of electrical systems by electrical engineers, ample provision should be made in the raceways for adequate wiring, as well as distribution and load centers which should be laid out in practical locations, keeping in mind their accessibility. The number of wires in enclosures and boxes should adhere to Code requirements in order to avoid fires and breakdowns and the inconveniences that accompany such troubles.

In reaching the goal of good wiring and installation, there is one requirement—good workmanship. Insulation damage, too many wires, and overfusing are the points that must be carefully watched. Regardless of how good the design of the installation, cutting corners will defeat the intended product.

90-10. Revisions—The NEC is periodically revised—presently every three years. Condition and material changes make revision necessary in order for the Code to fit current situations. The material in this text is based on the 1971 revised edition of the NEC.

Chapter 1. General

ARTICLE 100—DEFINITIONS

The following nomenclature is part of the definitions included in the NEC. They may not be in the order in which they appear in the Code, but they are in the order in which their explanations will be most applicable.

Accessible—There are three definitions under this term.

(1) Accessible (as applied to wiring methods) means that the wiring is not permanently enclosed in the structure or finish of the building, and may be reached without disturbing any part of the building or finish. The definitions of **concealed** and **exposed** may also be incorporated in this definition, without explanation, since these terms are closely related. Conduit in walls or floors that are sealed on both sides is concealed. Also concealed is conduit, Type NM cable, and others located between the floor and the ceiling below it, as well as in sealed walls. As used here, the term **concealed** is the opposite of **accessible**. Wires located in raceways, even though they can be accessible by withdrawing them, are considered to be concealed.

A conduit run on the surface is considered **exposed** and **accessible**, as would any other wiring method under the same condition. Wall boxes are regarded as **concealed** but **accessible**, because you may reach the wiring within the box for maintenance. However, a junction box located in the wall and covered with lath and plaster or Celotex is **concealed** but is **not accessible** because the wall structure must be disturbed to reach the wiring. A junction box in a wall but with its cover exposed so that it can be removed without disturbing the building, is **accessible**, even though it is concealed to some degree. A handy box on the exterior of a wall is **accessible** and **exposed**; a gutter raceway with a removable cover is an **accessible** raceway.

(2) Accessible (as applied to equipment) indicates that the equipment may be reached without having to unlock a door. Such equipment would be manufactured so that it is unnecessary to unlock a panel door to operate the switch

or replace a fuse, and located so that a ladder is not needed to reach the equipment. In other words, the equipment can be reached without undue effort.

(3) **Readily accessible** is actually self-explanatory. This term indicates that the part or parts referred to may be reached quickly for operation, renewal, inspection, or repair without the necessity of climbing over an obstruction or using portable ladders, chairs, or other items to reach the equipment. Readily accessible also applies to equipment not located in a room that would be considered private, such as a bathroom or bedroom. To illustrate, an improperly installed main disconnect would require you to travel downstairs to a remote corner of the basement and then to the opposite side of the building in order to operate the main. In no case would this be considered readily accessible. In the event of a fire, this is the last place you would wish to go to shut off the electrical supply.

Approved—*Acceptable to the authority enforcing this Code.* In many instances this means approval by a private testing laboratory, such as the Underwriters' Laboratories.

Automatic—A type of device that is self-acting; operating by its own mechanism which in turn might be operated by a change in pressure, temperature, time, current or voltage strength, or light. The function is performed without the aid of an individual.

Nonautomatic—As the word implies, a device that requires operation by a person. A magnetic starter with a push button is nonautomatic, even though all you do is push the button. Most equipment has switches which may be operated either automatically or nonautomatically.

Ampacity—This is a term that is rapidly coming into the terminology of the electrical industry, and is the *current-carrying capacity expressed in amperes.*

Bonding Jumper—*A reliable conductor to assure the required electrical conductivity between metal parts required to be electrically connected.*

Bonding Jumper, Circuits—*The connection between portions of a conductor in a circuit to maintain required ampacity of the circuit.*

Bonding Jumper, Equipment—*The connection between two or more portions of the equipment grounding conductor.*

Bonding Jumper, Main—*The connection between the grounded circuit conductor and the equipment grounding conductor at the service.*

Branch Circuits—There are five separate definitions for branch circuits, each with an individual purpose in mind.

(1) *A branch circuit is that portion of the wiring system between the final overcurrent device protecting the circuit and the outlet(s).* This protective device may be a circuit breaker or fuse in the service-entrance equipment, where the particular circuit breaker or fuse does not serve as protection for feeder circuits to the feeder panels, or where feeder panels are used. The branch circuit is that circuit coming from the feeder panel, or as stated above, it may be from the service-entrance equipment. Do not confuse the part that says *beyond the final overcurrent device protecting the circuit.* The part *protecting the circuit* defines what is meant. Thus, in the motor-branch circuit shown in

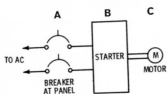

Fig. 100-1. A motor circuit. The branch circuit extends from point **A** to point **C**.

Fig. 100-1, there is a circuit breaker or fuse in the panel feeding the motor. At the motor, or somewhere between the motor and the panel, there is a magnetic starter with overload protection, and finally the motor. The starter provides the motor with overcurrent protection but no protection to the branch circuit, so the branch circuit originates at the panel and extends to the motor.

(2) A branch circuit (as applied to **appliances)** is a circuit designed for the sole purpose of supplying an appliance or appliances; nothing else can be connected to this circuit, including lighting. The lighting that is an integral part of the appliance is not considered as lighting in this instance.

(3) A branch circuit for **general purpose** includes circuits that supply lighting and appliances. An illustration of this might be circuits supplying appliances and lighting but would not include appliance circuits for kitchens, etc. General-purpose circuits have certain limitations on loads that will be explained later in the text.

(4) A branch circuit **individual** is a circuit that supplies just one piece of equipment, such as a motor, an air conditioner, or a furnace.

(5) A branch circuit **multiwire** (Fig. 100-2A and 2B) is a circuit

consisting of two or more underground conductors with a potential difference between them, and a grounded conductor with an equal potential between it and any one ungrounded conductor. This may be a 120/240-volt three-wire circuit or a wye-connected circuit with two or more phase wires and a neutral. It is not a circuit using two or more wires connected to the same phase and the neutral (Fig.

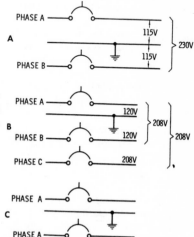

Fig. 100-2. Variations of a multiwire branch circuit. Circuit **C** is not a multiwire branch circuit because it utilizes two wires from the same phase in conjunction with the neutral conductor.

100-2C). The potential between the neutral and the wild leg would not be the same as between the neutral and the other two phases. Neither is a branch circuit multiwire a four-wire delta circuit for the reason that the potential between the neutral and the wild leg will not be the same as between the other two phase legs and the neutral. (See Fig. 100-2)

Branch-Circuit Selection Current—*See* **Section 440-3(c)**, *Sealed (hermetic-type) motor-compressors or equipment containing such compressor(s) in which the protection system, approved for the use with the motor-compressor which it protects, permits continuous current in excess of the specified percentage of nameplate rated-load current given in* **Section 440-52 (b) (2)** *or* **(b) (4)** *shall also be marked with a branch-circuit selection current that complies with* **Section 440-52 (b) (2)** *or* **(b) (4)**. *This marking shall be on the nameplate(s) where the rated-load current(s) appear.* See NEC.

Building—A building is defined as *a structure that stands alone or which is cutoff from adjoining structures by fire walls with all openings therein protected by approved fire doors.* Pipes, if they are properly sealed, will not affect the classification. For example, there are three separate two-story buildings on a lot. However, the brick fire wall does not extend through the roof between each section, and there is a hallway on the second floor without the protection of fire doors. This type of structure is to be construed as one building.

Cells—Cells, as applied to raceways, are defined as *the hollow spaces of cellular metal floors, together with suitable fittings, which may be approved as enclosures for electrical conductors; a cell shall be defined as a single, enclosed tubular space in a cellular metal floor member, the axis of the cell being parallel to the axis of the metal floor member.* In **Section 356-1** and **Section 358-1**, the same is implied for precast cellular concrete floor raceways. The only difference is that one cell type is metal, and the other type is concrete.

Conductor—There are two classifications for conductors:

(1) **Bare.** This, of course, means a conductor that is without any insulation.
(2) **Covered.** This is a conductor that has one or more layers of nonconducting material (insulation) over the conductor.
(3) **Insulated**. *An insulated conductor is one covered with material recognized as insulation.*

There is considerable confusion over the term **conductor** and the term **cable**. A conductor is one wire, while a cable means that there are two or more current-carrying conductors enclosed within an outer covering or jacket. This might appear to be a fine point, but in interpreting the Code, it is of the utmost importance.

Connectors, Pressure (solderless)—These are devices that are used to connect wires together by means of pressure, but without the use of solder. When using this type of connector, make certain that they are the approved type and are made of the same material as that of the conductor. Otherwise, electrolysis may set in and cause the conductors to loosen, or oxidization may take place and cause high-resistance connections and heating.

Continuous Load—*This is a load where the maximum current is expected to continue for three hours or more.*

Control Circuit—Refer to **Section 430-71**. *The control circuit of a control apparatus or system is the circuit which carries the electric signals directing the performance of the controller, but does not carry the main power circuit.* The control circuit may or may not be at the same potential as the main power circuit. The control circuit is often powered from a foreign source or at a reduced potential which might be obtained from a stepdown transformer.

Controller—*A device, or group of devices, which serves to govern,* *in some predetermined manner, the electric power delivered to the apparatus to which it is connected.* Motor starter switches of many types are considered controllers.

Demand Factor—Demand factor may be applied to an entire electrical system, or any part of an electrical system. It is *the ratio of the maximum demand of the system, or part of a system, to the total connected load of the system, or of the part of the system under consideration.* The loads on a system are practically never thrown on at the same time due to the diversity of uses. Somewhere between the maximum connected load and the actual usage is a load that may be considered the maximum demand. This fact is often used in determining the size of conductors or overcurrent devices. The demand factor is usually determined by a series of tests, and then after it is proved it is added to the Code. Examples will appear later in this text.

Device—*A unit of an electrical system which is intended to carry but not utilize electric energy.* This definition is often misapplied. Bear in mind that it says *not utilize electric energy.*

Equipment—This is a general term referring to practically every part of an electrical system, including the parts consuming electrical energy. Devices are also included in this category.

Explosion-Proof Apparatus—An apparatus enclosed in a case which is capable of withstanding an explosion from within, and capable of preventing internal explosion from igniting gases or vapors surrounding the equipment. This apparatus must also be capable of being operated at a temperature low enough to prevent ignition of surrounding flammable atmospheres.

Explosion-proof boxes and fittings have threaded connections, threaded lids, or ground-joint lids. The theory is that the gases that have exploded may leak out through the threads or ground joint, but in so doing, their temperature is reduced to a point that will not cause further ignition.

Feeder—*A feeder is the circuit conductors between the service equipment, or the generator switchboard of an isolated plant, and the branch circuit overcurrent device.* We must always have service equipment, but it is not always necessary to have feeders. For instance, the average home does not have feeders; the branch circuits are taken from the overload devices in the service-entrance equipment. When we have a large area to cover, the usual practice is to extend feeder circuits from the service-entrance equipment to the proper locations for distribution to the branch circuits. Thus, the conductors from the service equipment to the distribution location are termed *feeders.*

Fittings—These are accessories that are not current-carrying parts, that are for a mechanical rather than an electrical function, such as

19

locknuts and bushings. As you will recall, devices were the current-carrying parts.

Ground—*A ground is a conducting connection, whether intentional or accidental, between an electrical circuit or equipment and earth, or to some conducting body which serves in place of the earth.* Note that a ground may be *intentional* or *accidental*. When intentional, its purpose is for safety; when accidental, the system should be designed so as to trip the overcurrent devices and disconnect the circuit, actuating grounding lights or in some other manner indicate that a ground is present on the system. **Ground** is a broad term, and its usage should be employed properly.

Grounded—*Grounded means connected to earth or to some conducting body which serves in place of the earth.*

Grounded Conductor—*A system or circuit conductor which is intentionally grounded.* Conductors pertaining to grounding are so often misinterpreted and it is so essential for the understanding of the Code that the proper terminology be used. In addition to *Grounded Conductor,* there are now four additional definitions, namely: *Grounding Conductor; Grounding Conductor, Main; Grounding Conductor, Common Main;* and *Grounding Conductor, Equipment.* See NEC.

Grounding Conductor, Equipment—This may be a conductor, or, might be metallic raceways, used to connect noncurrent-carrying parts (metal) of electrical equipment, raceways, devices, etc., to the grounded system conductor at the service to the building or structure and/or the grounding electrode conductor. In order to have a safe system, great care must be exercised in the grounding.

Grounding Electrode Conductor—*The conductor used to connect the grounding electrode to the equipment-grounding conductor and/or to the grounded conductor of the circuit at the service.*

Identified—This term is used when referring to a conductor or terminal, and is employed only in reference to the conductors or terminals recognized as grounded.

Location—In the past there have been questions as to classification of damp, dry, and wet locations. The 1971 NEC has added definitions to cover this subject. A very fine job has been done on these definitions which will be explained at this point.

Damp Location—*Partially protected locations under canopies, marquees, roofed open porches, and like locations, and interior locations subject to moderate degrees of moisture, such as some basements, some barns and some cold-storage warehouses.* This is quite important so as the proper classified fixtures and other equipment might be used.

Dry Locations—*A location not normally subject to dampness or wetness. A location classified as dry may be temporarily subject to dampness or wetness, as in the case of a building under construction.* **Section 110-11, Deteriorating Agencies,** can apply to buildings under construction.

Wet Location—*Installations underground or in concrete slabs or masonry in direct contact with the earth, and locations subject to saturation with water or other liquids, such as vehicle washing areas, and locations exposed to weather and unprotected.* This has been badly needed. Too much has been left to the inspection authority and often discussions developed.

Qualified Person—*One familiar with the construction and operation of the apparatus and the hazards involved.* This term will be referred to in numerous instances, and great care should be taken in electrical design to consider whether or not a qualified person will be available for maintenance after installation has been made. There will be definite situations where certain installations require that maintenance be performed only by qualified persons.

Rainproof—*So constructed, protected, or treated as to prevent rain from interfering with the successful operation of the apparatus.* This was a proposal in the 1971 reprint, submitted by NEMA, and I will submit their supporting comment, which I heartily agree with. This will give a better understanding of the why of the submittal. *So-called* **Raintight** *equipment as now approved and manufactured is really only* **Rainproof** *since UL standards allow the entrance of rain below the lowest live part so that conduit knockouts can be used. Manufacturers feel that the suffix* **tight** *should not be used unless rain is completely excluded. A definition of* **Rainproof** *is needed in the Code to establish the distinction and give UL a basis for changing their terminology.*

Raintight—*So constructed or protected that exposure to a beating rain will not result in the entrance of water.* Raintight should also be considered with the definitions of **watertight** and **weatherproof**, and should be evaluated with them.

Watertight—*So constructed that moisture will not enter the enclosing case.*

Weatherproof—*So constructed or protected that exposure to the weather will not interfere with successful operation.* **Raintight and watertight** may serve as **weatherproof**, but, as the note under **weatherproof** in the Code states, *raintight or watertight equipment may fulfill the requirements for "weatherproof." However, weather conditions vary and consideration should be given to conditions resulting from snow, ice, dust, or temperature extremes.* These conditions must always be considered in the use of weatherproof materials. The final decision for the use of the correct term is up to the enforcing authority, and he should be aware of the possible prevailing weather conditions in the area involved. **Raintight** is based on the direction that rain falls, usually directly down or at an angle; this must be taken into consideration. However, in some areas, the rain fall might be accompanied by tornadoes or hurricanes, and these conditions would certainly alter the interpretation of what would be considered **raintight**. There are conditions where **watertight** is extremely important, since moisture can seriously affect the operation of electrical devices and equipment.

Service—*The conductors and equipment for delivering energy from the electricity supply system to the wiring system of the premises served.* This definition is very complete and applies to all wiring and equipment extending from the last pole or underground distribution system through the service equipment. The following definitions will give the breakdown of the separate parts or sections of a service.

Service Cable—The service conductors in the *form of a cable*. Refer back to the definition of **conductors** which explains the difference between conductors and cables.

Service Conductors—*The supply conductors which extend from the street main, or from transformers to the service equipment of the premises supplied.* Therefore, service conductors are the conductors defined under **Service**.

Service Drop—*The overhead service conductors between the last pole or other aerial support and the first point of attachment to the building or other structure.* In rural areas, the utility company often locates a meter pole in the yard; this may or may not have an overcurrent device installed. The service drop does not stop at the meter pole, but continues on to the building or buildings or other structures that it serves, as shown in Fig. 100-3.

Service Entrance Conductors, Overhead System—The service entrance includes the conductors from the service equipment to a point outside the building, clear of the building walls. They are attached to the service drop at this point by either tap or splice. The meter housing and meter, if on the building wall, are not considered as parts of the service-entrance equipment.

Service Entrance Conductors, Underground System—*The service conductors between the terminals of the service equipment and the point of connection to the service lateral. Where service equipment is located outside the building walls, there may be no service-entrance conductors, or they may be entirely outside the building.* See Fig. 100-4 for a sketch showing the possible conditions.

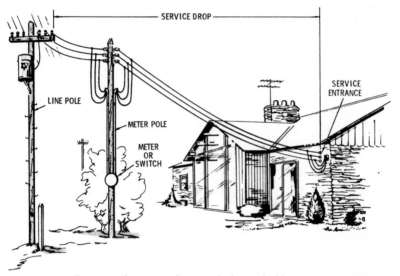

Fig. 100-3. Illustrating the service drop attached to a building or other structure.

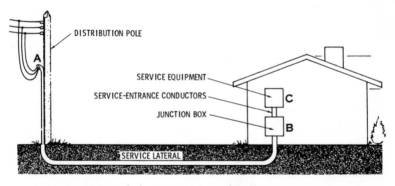

Fig. 100-4. Illustrating the service lateral extending from point **A** to point **B**.
The service entrance is from **B** to point **C**.

Service Equipment—The necessary equipment usually consisting of a circuit breaker or fuses and a switch located on the inside or outside of the building or structure, or *an otherwise defined area.* It is intended to constitute the means of disconnecting the electrical supply entering the building or structure as shown in Fig. 100-5. The change in wording of the 1971 NEC, *or an otherwise defined area,* to me changes the aspect of the location. It was always felt before that it should be on the inside or outside of the building at the closest point of entrance. It

23

now appears that the authority having jurisdiction will have the authorization to make some decisions as to location and from the wording, it might be a disconnecting means on the service pole as illustrated in Fig. 100-3. Consult your electrical inspector.

Service Lateral—These include the underground service conductors, including any risers up the pole at the street main or transformer structure. They are considered as service laterals until they enter a junction box in the building. If such a box is not used, they will cease to be service laterals at the point of entrance into the building, at which they become service-entrance conductors. If the service-entrance equipment is located on the outside of the building, there may possibly be no service-entrance conductors; they could all be termed **service laterals** (see Fig. 100-4).

Service Raceway—This is any raceway, conduit, or tubing enclosing the service-entrance conductors. Where a service mast is used, the conduit to the metering circuit, the raceway (for connection to the metering if several should be required), and the connections from the raceway to the service equipment are all considered the service raceway.

Special Permission—*The written consent of the authority enforcing this Code.* This means that permission, in writing, must be granted by the enforcing authority for any special type of electrical installation. The parts of the Code that are covered will state *by special permission.*

Isolating Switch—An isolating switch is not required to have an interrupting rating, since it is not intended to be opened under load. It must be rated at the capacity of the normal operating rate and is intended to isolate the equipment from the power source while the equipment is being tested or repaired. It is recommended that this switch be plainly marked DO NOT OPEN UNDER LOAD.

Motor Circuit Switch—This switch must be rated in horse-power and must be capable of being opened under the maximum overload current of the motor.

Ventilated—*Provided with a means to permit circulation of air sufficient to remove an excess of heat, fumes or vapors.*

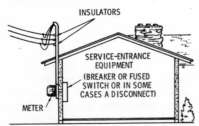

Fig. 100-5. Showing the service entrance equipment that will serve as the electrical disconnect supply.

Volatile Flammable Liquid—*A flammable liquid having a flash point below 100°F. or whose temperature is above its flash point.* In the past, there has been misunderstanding of what constituted a volatile flammable liquid—the definition is now spelled out. Under the NFPA Codes, the flash points are listed for various liquids, but please note the part about temperature in the definition. A liquid that has a flash point of 100 degrees or more under normal conditions would come under the volatile flammable liquid classification if heated higher than 100 degrees.

Voltage (of a circuit)—*Voltage is the greatest root-mean-square (effective) difference of potential between any two conductors of the circuit concerned. On various systems such as 3-phase 4 wire, single phase 3 wire and 3 wire direct current, there may be various circuits of various voltages.* In AC, we are confronted with *maximum* voltage, *effective* voltage, and *average* voltage. The maximum voltage is the peak voltage of the sine wave; the *rms* voltage is 0.707 of the peak voltage (1.414 times the *rms* voltage is the peak voltage); and the average voltage is 0.636 of the peak voltage. We deal with the effective, or *rms,* voltage in AC circuits generally. This is the voltage normally read on a voltmeter.

Bear in mind that there are numerous other definitions in the NEC. It is felt that explanations or enlargements of certain definitions will be valuable in the proper usage of these definitions. The definitions that do not appear here are felt to be self-explanatory. All of the definitions in **Article 100** should be read to gain a thorough understanding of the NEC.

ARTICLE 110—GENERAL

This Article is by-passed in the study of the Code more often than any other article. It is short, but it is actually the foundation upon which the Code is written, as it contains provisions that are used throughout the entire Code.

110-1. Scope—This is the general foundation upon which other Articles and Sections depend, and are applicable generally to the installations of electric wiring and equipment.

110-2. Approval—*The conductors and equipment required or permitted by this Code shall be acceptable only when approved. See definition of* **Approved** *under* **Article 100**.

110-3. Mandatory and Advisory Rules—In the Code, one will find both mandatory and advisory rules. The mandatory rules are characterized by the word *shall.* This means that the rules are a must and should be strictly followed. Advisory rules are characterized by *should,* and means that these rules do not have to be strictly adhered to, but it is recommended to do so. You will find that where the word *should* appears that it is considered good practice to follow the recommended procedure.

110-4. Examination of Equipment—See NEC.

110-5. Voltages—The voltages referred to in the Code are the supply voltages, regardless of their source. The supply may be a battery, generator, transformer, rectifier, or a thermopile. When considering AC voltages, the voltage is the *rms* voltage as explained in the Definitions. There are really three general classifications of voltages in the Code—0 to 50 volts; 50 to 600 volts; and voltages that exceed 600 volts. Each is dealt with in separate parts of the Code. If wires having different voltages are run in the same raceway, there are specific rules to be followed.

110-6. Conductor Gages—In dealing with wire sizes, the Code always refers to the American Wire Gage (AWG). At one time, this was known as the B&S Gage.

110-7. Conductors—In dealing with conductors, copper is the implied material used; any other material, such as aluminum, will be so indicated and the sizes should be changed to meet the current-carrying capacity allowed. Later you will find tables listing the current-carrying capacities of both copper and aluminum conductors.

110-8. Wiring Methods—Only recognized and suitable wiring methods are included in the Code. Basically, Chapter 3 covers approved wiring methods, which will be supplemented by Chapters 5, 6, 7, and 8 that cover specific conditions and occupancies. For instance, the question of whether plastic or flexible tubing is permitted often arises. The tubing referred to comes in rolls, such as flexible water pipe. Rigid nonmetallic conduit **(Article 347)** is the only type in the plastics category that is approved at the present time.

110-9. Interrupting Capacity—Interrupting capacity is far different from the rating of the amperes that is required by a load. We are faced with what are known as **fault currents.** A fault current is the amount of current that might develop under a dead-short condition. At one time, this was not much of a problem, but with increased electrical use and larger generating and distribution capacities, the problem of fault currents has increased. As you read the Code, you will find that this is taken more into consideration now than in the past, and will no doubt become an increasingly important factor. If a piece of equipment is rated at X number of amperes, this does not necessarily mean that it can be disconnected under load or faults without damage. Equipment is rated in carrying capacity as well as interrupting capacity.

110-10. Circuit Impedance and Other Characteristics—The fault currents are limited only by the capacity of the electrical supply, the impedance of the supplying circuits, and the wiring. As an example, the fault current will be much larger in circuits supplied from a large-capacity transformer supplying a heavily loaded city block than the fault current from a transformer serving a 5-HP irrigation pump in a rural area. The impedance of the supply to the 5-HP motor will be high in comparison to the impedance of the supply to the city block.

110-11. Deteriorating Agencies—Environmental factors, such as wetness, dampness, fumes, vapors, gases, liquids, temperatures, or any other deteriorating effect, must also be noted; conductors and equipment used shall be approved for the specific conditions of operation. The inspection authority is often faced with the responsibility of deciding in which category the installation belongs; it most certainly is beyond the scope of the Code to define and specify for every possible condition that will have to be met. The NFPA National Fire Codes will be of great value in this respect.

Protection shall be given to equipment, such as control equipment, utilization equipment, and busways during construction, if this equipment is approved for dry locations only. It shall not be permanently damaged by weather during the building construction.

110-12. Mechanical Execution of Work—Materials are not the only items to be watched; workmanship is also important. The Code specifically states that: *Electrical equipment shall be installed in a neat and workmanlike manner.* Not only is this necessary for safety, but an electrician is recognized by the work that he performs.

110-13. Mounting of Equipment—Mounting of equipment is an item directly related to workmanship. Wooden plugs driven into holes in masonry, plaster, concrete, etc., will shrink and rot, thereby allowing the equipment to become loose. Therefore, only approved methods of mounting and special anchoring devices may be used.

110-14. Electrical Connections—*Because of different characteristics of copper and aluminum, devices such as pressure terminal and pressure splicing connectors and soldering lugs shall be suitable for the material of the conductor and shall be properly installed and used. Conductors of dissimilar metals shall not be intermixed in a terminal or splicing connector where physical contact occurs between dissimilar conductors (such as copper and aluminum, copper and copper-clad aluminum, or aluminum and copper-clad aluminum), unless the device is suitable for the purpose and conditions of use. Materials such as solder, fluxes, inhibitors, and compounds, where employed, shall be suitable for the use and shall be of a type which will not adversely affect the conductors, installation or equipment.*

Attention must be called to the copper-clad aluminum, which is, a comparatively new item with the 1971 NEC. At this writing, not enough is published on terminations and splices, so caution must be used. The above new part of the NEC will give us a clue.

  (a) Terminals. Connections to terminals shall ensure a good electrical and mechanical contact without injury to the conductors; connection shall be by approved pressure connectors, solder lugs, or splices to flexible wires. The exception to the regulation is that No. 8 or smaller solid conductors, and No. 10 or smaller stranded conductors can be connected by means of clamps or screws with terminal plates having upturned lugs (Fig 110-1). Terminals for more than one conductor must be of the approved type for this purpose. Thus, if you should have two No. 8 solid conductors, do not try to put the conductors under the same screw unless approved terminals are provided. When permitted to place a wire under a terminal screw, wrap it in such a direction that when you tighten the screw the wire will not be squeezed out from under the head of the screw.

  (b) Splices. Splices in wires are permissible in the proper places. When making a splice, the wires must be clean and a good electrical and mechanical connection must be made. The wires may then be soldered, provided a suitable solder and flux is used. The soldering temperature should be carefully controlled since a cold solder joint is of no value; also, if the wires become too hot, the heat will damage the insulation. Remember that soldering is not permitted on conductors used for grounding. Approved connectors may also be used for splices, making sure the wires are clean and free from corrosion. After splicing, insulation at least equivalent to that on the wire must be applied to the splice. In general, this applies to all splices, but on high-voltage splicing, the specifications supplied with the high-voltage cables should be followed.

This has a great deal of importance. Many electrical connections fail because they are improperly made. A good part of our troubles have been due to electrolysis between different metals, that is the more noble metal depleting the less noble metal. Also, the oxidization of aluminum conductors and this oxidization occurs practically instantly and creates a layer having a very high resistance.

Another problem is the coefficient of expansion of different metals, creeping, and the difference in deformation of different metals. A copper-clad aluminum has appeared on the market. This has been approved, but precautions must be taken in its usage, especially with copper or plain aluminum. Be certain that you use connectors approved for use with this new product.

Inhibitors for use with aluminum are very important. Do not rely on the inhibitor alone, but thoroughly brush the aluminum conductor to remove the oxide film and then immediately apply the inhibitor to prevent the reoccurrence of the oxide film.

110-16. Working Space about Electrical Equipment (600 volts or less) —*Sufficient access and working space shall be provided and maintained about all electrical equipment to permit ready and safe operation and maintenance of such equipment.*

(a) **Working Clearances.** Most Tables that appear in the NEC are not covered in this book, but you are to refer to the NEC for these Tables, however it seems that **Table 110-16(a)** should appear here;

Table 110-16(a). Working Clearances

Voltage to Ground		Minimum clear distance	
	Condition: 1	2	3
0-150	2½ ft.	2½ ft.	3 ft.
151-600	2½ ft.	3½ ft.	4 ft.

Where the "Conditions" are as follows:

(1) *Exposed live part on one side and no live or grounded parts on the other side of the working space or exposed live parts on both sides effectively guarded by suitable wood or other insulating materials. Insulated wire or insulated bus bars operating at not more than 300 volts shall not be considered live parts.*

From this we might look at such a panel that will, from time to time, have to be worked on, as coming under *Condition No. 1.* and give a minimum of 2½ ft. clearance. This will apply to bus bars and conductors as well.

(2) *Exposed parts on one side and grounded parts on the other side.* In part *No. 1.* the panel was used as an example, but since the panel is usually contained in a metal enclosure, we must also look at part *No. 2.* where we find that this part might be the part which we must use under certain conditions.

(3) *Exposed live parts on both sides of the work space (not guarded as provided in Condition 1) with the operator between.*

This might be an electrical closet, where panels are on two walls, then 3 and 4 ft. conditions will prevail.

Exception No. 1. See the NEC.

29

Exception No. 2. This gives the inspection authority the right to make exceptions for smaller spaces, where in his judgement it seems appropriate.

Prior to the above conditions, a very important part appears, and I quote:

In addition to the dimensions shown in **Table 110-16(a)** *the work space shall be at least 30 inches wide in front of the electrical equipment. Distances are to be measured from the live parts if such are exposed or from the enclosure front or opening when such parts are enclosed. Concrete, brick, or tile walls shall be considered as grounded.*

This **Section** also contains parts **(b), (c), (d), (e)** and **(f),** for the coverage of which you are refered to the NEC. Also **Article 710** for voltages over 600 volts.

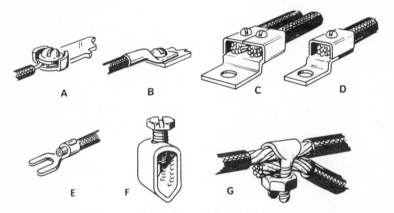

Fig. 110-1. Various types of approved pressure connectors. **(A)** Terminal plate; **(B)** Soldered lug; **(C)** Double pressure-type lug; **(D)** Single pressure-type lug; **(E)** Open-end crimp-type lug; **(F)** Pressure-type connector; **(G)** Split-bolt clamp.

110-17. Guarding of Live Parts—This section applies to parts supplied with 600 volts or less.

(a) This covers the guarding or protecting of live parts of electrical equipment that are operated at 50 volts or more, so as to prevent accidental contact with them. Approved cabinets or enclosures shall be used, according to the requirements in other portions of the Code. The following are the means by which this shall be accomplished:

(1) *By location in a room, vault, or similar enclosure which is accessible only to qualified persons.* It is recommended

that the reader turn back to **Article 100** and review the definition of qualified persons.

(2) *By suitable permanent, substantial partitions or screens so arranged that only qualified persons will have access to the space within reach of the live parts. Any openings in such partitions or screens shall be so sized and located that persons are not likely to come into accidental contact with the live parts or to bring conducting objects into contact with them.* Again, qualified persons are mentioned, and their safety is thought of in making the equipment accessible without obstruction, and giving attention to the contact of conducting materials such as conduit or pipes.

(3) By locating the equipment on a suitable balcony, gallery, or platform that is high enough or so designed to keep unqualified persons out.

(4) Installing the live electrical parts at least 8 feet above the floor.

(b) Many times electrical equipment is located in a work area where the activity around it might damage the equipment. In such a case, the enclosures or guards shall be of such strength as to prevent any damage to the electrical equipment.

(c) Warning signs shall be posted at entrances to rooms or other guarded locations, giving warning that only qualified personnel are permitted to enter. Although not specifically covered here, posting of dangers that might exist in any situation is always good safety practice.

110-18. Arcing Parts—Making and breaking of contacts usually cause sparking or arcing. Also, the white-hot filament of a light bulb broken while in operation takes a little time to cool. Any parts that normally cause arcing or sparking are to be enclosed unless they are isolated or separated from combustible material. Light bulbs were mentioned, but additional information will be given in the Articles covering hazardous areas, along with the specific requirements for switches, outlets, and other devices in hazardous locations.

110-19. Light and Power from Railway Conductors—The conductors for light and power from railway conductors that have a ground return are to be used only in connection with the operation of the railway and its lighting system, and in buildings that are specifically used in connection with the electrical railway.

110-20. Insulation Resistance—It is highly essential that when wiring systems are installed that they be free from shorts and grounds other than grounds as provided in **Article 250.** A little care in the installation and a little attention to testing the insulation resistance will pay off.

110-21. Marking—See NEC.

110-22. Identification—*Each disconnecting means required by this Code for motors and appliances, and each service, feeder or branch circuit at the point where it originates, shall be legibly marked to indicate its purpose unless located and arranged so the purpose is evident. The markings shall be of sufficient durability to withstand the environment involved.*

The 1971 preprint included a suggestion for torquing tables. This was not put into the 1971 NEC, but gives the guide-lines for torquing values, which appeal to me, so they appear here as taken from the NFPA 1971 NEC preprint.

The following table shall be used as a guide for all electrical connections of No. 8 AWG wire size and larger, and all bolted or Allen-screwed connections:

Torquing Values

Wire Connections:	Tightening Torque in Pound-Feet		
Wire Size	Screw Driver	Split Bolt	Other
18-16 AWG	1.67	6.25	4.2
14-8	1.67	6.25	6.25
6-4	3	12.5	8.0
3-1	4.2	21	10.4
0-2/0	4.2	21	10.4
3/0-200MCM		37.5	17
250-350MCM		50	21
400		62.5	21
500		62.5	25
600-750		75	25
800-1000		83.25	33
1250-2000MCM		83.25	42

Screws: Screw Size Inches Across Hex Flats	Torque—Pound-Feet
1/8	4.2
5/32	8.3
3/16	15
7/32	23.25
1/4	42

Torquing Value (Cont'd)

Bolts: Size Nonlubricated	Duronze	Standard Steel	Aluminum	High-Strength Steel
3/8	20	15	16	16
1/2	40	25	35	40
5/8	70	50	50	70
3/4	100	90	70	100
Lubricated				
3/8	15	10	13	13
1/2	30	20	25	30
5/8	50	40	40	50
3/4	85	70	60	80

Chapter 2. Wiring Design and Protection

ARTICLE 200—USE AND IDENTIFICATION OF GROUNDING CONDUCTORS

200-1. Scope—The definitions of grounded and grounding conductors were covered under **Definitions in Article 100.** They will not be repeated here, but it is suggested that these two definitions be studied again to be certain that they are thoroughly understood before proceeding.

200-2. General—This Article deals with all interior wiring which shall use one grounded conductor that is continuously identified throughout the entire system. There must, however, be some exceptions to this regulation. These exceptions include certain 3-phase systems, DC circuits, and 2-wire circuits with a potential to ground of over 300 volts. Where an AC system exceeds 150 volts to ground, but does not exceed 300 volts to ground, it is recommended (but not required) that it have a grounded conductor. Electric-crane circuits operating over combustible fibers and electric-furnace circuits need not be grounded. Circuits of less than 50 volts need not be grounded where they are supplied by a system of not over 150 volts to ground, but they must be grounded if they are supplied from an ungrounded system or if they are required to supply outdoor overhead wires.

Circuits within a flammable anesthetics location shall not be grounded and must be supplied by isolation transformers. There are a few other exceptions that do not require continuous identification of the grounded conductor; these will be considered later in the text. The preceding exceptions will be found in **Sections 200-5, 250-3, 250-5, 250-7, 503-13 and 517-63** of the NEC.

200-3. Connection to Grounded System—If there is a grounded conductor in the interior wiring system, it shall not be electrically connected to a supply system that does not have a corresponding conductor grounded. This condition could be dangerous and could cause many varied difficulties that most certainly would not be considered as safe wiring procedures. Electrically connected means that the connections are capable of carrying current. Electromagnetic induction, such as the windings on an isolating transformer, would not be considered electrically connected. Connections capable of carrying current and electromagnetic induction must be separated in one's mind. Later, the text will deal with isolation transformers and give further clarification of how and what parts of the wiring system must be grounded.

200-4. Circuits Derived from Autotransformers—Autotransformers are transformers whose windings are common to both primary and secondary. There shall be no autotransformer connected to a system unless there is an identified grounded conductor solidly connected to a similar identified grounded conductor of the supply system.

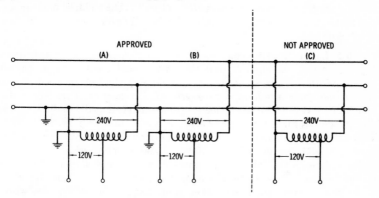

Fig. 200-1. Autotransformer connections.

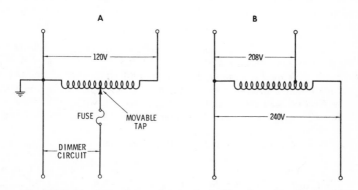

Fig. 200-2. An autotransformer dimmer circuit (A) and a voltage booster (B).

Fig. 200-1 shows three autotransformer connections. Fig. 200-1A and B are both approved connections. Fig. 200-1C is not approved, since there is no common ground between the supply and the output of the auto-transformer. Fig. 200-2A represents an autotransformer dimmer circuit and is approved by the NEC.

35

Exception. An autotransformer may be used to extend or add an individual branch circuit in an existing installation for an equipment load without the connection to a similar identified grounded conductor when transforming from a nominal 208-volt to a nominal 240-volt supply or similar from 240 volts to 208 volts.

See Fig. 200-2B. This new exception was added in 1971, to allow autotransformers for use as booster transformers from 208 volts to 240 volts, or reducers from 240 volts to 208 volts. The neutral or grounded conductor that is ordinarily required when autotransformers are used, is not required in this case.

200-5. Unidentified Circuits—*Two wire branch circuits of two or more conductors may be tapped from the ungrounded conductors of circuits having identified grounded neutrals. Switching devices in each tapped circuit shall have a pole in each ungrounded conductor.* This means that switching devices shall be placed in each ungrounded conductor. The 1965 Code has made a change. *These poles shall manually switch together where the switching devices serve as the disconnecting means required by* **Section 422-23. Section 422-23** refers to *Disconnection of Stationary Appliances.* Attention is called to the part—*These poles shall manually switch together*—this is new in the Code. In the past, breakers that tripped together due to overload, and breakers with tied handles or handles within 1/16-inch apart were sufficient. Now they must be capable of being manually switched together. The reasoning behind this is that someone not familiar with the installation might switch one side off and innocently presume the circuit to be dead when it would not be. A little thought will show the sound reasoning behind this change.

The exception to the preceding is covered in **Section 430-84** for *Motor Controllers,* **Section 424-20** for *Heating Equipment* and **Section 426-21** for *Deicing Equipment.* **Section 430-84** states that if the switching device is not a disconnecting type, it need not open all of the poles. Also in **Section 424-20**, it states that thermostats without an ON and OFF position are not required to open all ungrounded conductors.

In polyphase circuits, there need be no identified grounded conductor where voltages are expected to exceed 150 volts to ground. However, if there is a grounded conductor, it shall be identified. This stipulation will be further discussed under **Section 250-5.** Any other unidentified ungrounded systems may be used, such as the one shown in Fig. 200-3, but requires special permission. See the definition of *Special Permission* under **Article 100.**

200-6. Means of Identification of Grounded Conductors—Insulated conductors of No. 6 or smaller wire, when used as identified grounded conductors, shall have a white or natural gray colored insulation. If the

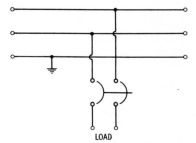

Fig. 200-3. A 3-phase line which does not require an identified grounded conductor.

insulated conductors are larger than No. 6, they shall be identified by a white or natural gray colored insulation, or by a distinctive marking (white) at the terminals while they are being installed. Type MI cable has bare conductors, so identification of the grounded conductors shall be marked generally by sleeving during the installation; the sleeving shall be white or natural gray, as indicated in Fig. 200-4.

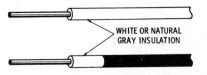

Fig. 200-4. Method of identifying grounded conductors.

#6 OR SMALLER WIRE SHALL HAVE
WHITE OR NATURAL GRAY INSULATION

WIRE LARGER THAN #6 MAY HAVE
WHITE TAPE OR PAINT TO INDICATE
GROUNDED CONDUCTORS

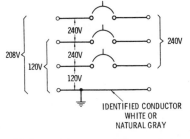

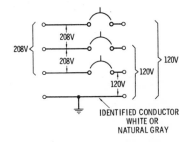

(A) 4-wire delta system with a neutral.

(B) Grounded 4-wire wye system.

Fig. 200-5. Voltage relationship on grounded 4-wire systems.

On a 4-wire delta-connected secondary (Fig. 200-5A), one phase (commonly called the **wild leg)** has a voltage equal to 1.732 times the

37

voltage to neutral of either of the other phase legs. Whenever this wild leg is grounded to supply lighting and similar loads, the wild leg must be orange or tagged otherwise effectively identified. Fig. 200-5B shows the voltage relationships on a grounded 4-wire wye system.

200-7. Identified Conductor in Grounded Circuits Only—White or neutral gray is to be used only for identified grounded conductors. There are a few exceptions made necessary by the use of cords and cables, such as types AC, NM, and UF. These cables must always carry a white or neutral gray conductor. If a cable with an identified conductor is used on a multiwire circuit, in a circuit connected to the two *hot* legs of a 3-wire circuit (as in Fig. 200-6), or if 3-wire cable is used on a 3-phase system, the white or natural gray conductor shall be unidentified at its terminals.

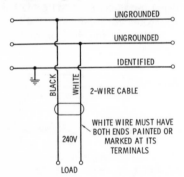

Fig. 200-6. A 2-wire cable connected to the two hot wires of a 3-wire circuit.

When two or three wires are used for a single-pole or three-way switch, the cable need not be unidentified, providing the wire feeding the switch is white or natural gray and is connected to the black wire at the source. The black wire will be connected from the switch to the load as shown in Fig. 200-7.

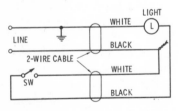 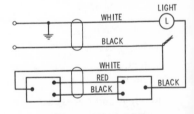

(A) Single-pole switch and light.   (B) 3-way switch and light.

Fig. 200-7. Method of connecting a common light and switch.

When a flexible cord is permitted for connecting a portable or stationary appliance and the cord used has a white or natural gray conductor or other means permitted in **Section 430-13,** this conductor may be used even though it is not connected to a receptacle which has a grounded circuit.

200-8. Connections to Screw-Shells—When connections are made to a screw-shell lampholder, the identified conductor shall be connected to the screw-shall as shown in Fig. 200-8.

200-9. Means of Identification of Terminals—Any terminal to which a grounded conductor is to be connected shall be plated with nickel or zinc, or be substantially white in color, to indicate that a white or natural gray conductor is to be attached to that terminal.

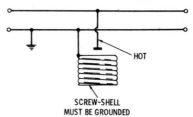

Fig. 200-8. Illustrating the grounding of

a screw-shell base.

HOT

SCREW-SHELL
MUST BE GROUNDED

200-10. Identification of Terminals

(a) *Device Terminals.* Devices that have terminals for the attachment of conductors and intended for connection to more than one side of a circuit shall have the terminals marked for identification except as follows;

Exception No. 1 states that where it is clearly evident that the terminal is to be connected to the grounded side, the markings may be omitted.

Exception No. 2 states that a single-pole device, such as switches where only one side of the line is connected, may have the terminal markings omitted.

Exception No. 3 states that on panelboards and devices for lighting, where the current does not exceed 30 amperes, require no marking except as indicated in **(b)** below.

(b) **Plugs and Receptacles.** *Two-wire polarized receptacles for attachment plugs and polarized attachment plugs shall have the terminal intended for connection to the grounded conductor marked for identification.*

Exception No. 1 states that the ordinary attachment plug, such as we are familiar with on lamps, toasters, etc., is not required to have the terminals identified.

Exception No. 2 states that three-wire and four-wire receptacles and attachment plugs, other than the grounding type, and which fall in the limits as set forth in **Section 210-21(b)** (that is, between 15 and 50 amperes, but on which one terminal may be used for a grounding conductor or a grounded circuit conductor), shall have the terminal marked to show other than a white or green finish. They shall be marked with a **G, GR,** or **Grd,** etc.

(c) **Screw Shells.** On any device with a screw shell, the identified terminal shall be connected to the shell. An example of this may be seen in Fig. 200-8. This is true of all devices having screw shells, with the exception of screw-shell fuseholders.

(d) **Screw-Shell Devices with Leads.** This part covers items commonly known as pig-tail sockets; the lead that connects to the shell must be identified with a white or natural gray lead. The same will be true of lighting fixtures that have the leads attached.

(e) **Fixed Appliances.** See NEC.

(f) **Portable Appliances.** See NEC.

ARTICLE 210—BRANCH CIRCUITS

210-1. Scope—Branch circuits are defined and explained in **Article 100.** This Article (210) will apply to branch circuits supplying lighting or appliance loads, or combinations of such loads. Motor branch circuits will be covered under **Article 430.**

210-2. Specific Purpose Branch Circuits—There are a number of exceptions or supplemental provisions of this Article on branch circuits. The listings of many of these exceptions are given in the Code book under **Section 210-2.**

210-3. Classifications—In general, branch circuits will be recognized by the maximum permitted rating or setting of the overcurrent device on the branch circuit. Otherwise, they will be classified as 15, 20, 30, 40, and 50 amperes. If conductors have to be derated, due to the number of conductors in a raceway, voltage drop, or any other reason, the overcurrent rating of the protective device shall determine the classification of the branch circuit. As an illustration, if there is a 15-ampere protective device in a circuit wired with No. 12 conductors, this will be a 15-ampere branch circuit; you cannot make a 20-ampere branch circuit out of it merely because it uses No. 12 conductors. In all probability, the No. 12 wire was installed to handle a voltage drop which was too great, or, if installed in a raceway, it is possible that derating was required because of the fill. Derating will be thoroughly covered in **Article 310.**

A. General Provisions

210-4. Multiwire Branch Circuits—The defintion of a multiwire branch circuit was covered in **Article 100.** So that multiwire circuits will be thoroughly understood and the terminology used properly, diagrams are included to explain them more fully. On a **delta** connected 4-wire system, only two ungrounded conductors and the neutral will be considered as the multiwire branch circuit. Fig. 210-1 shows a multiwire branch circuit from a 4-wire **delta** system; note that the ungrounded conductors extend

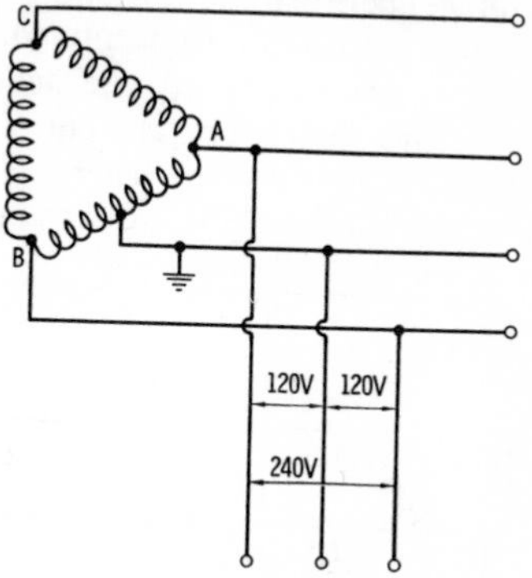

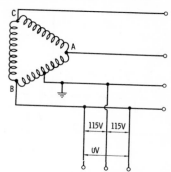

Fig. 210-1. One type of multiwire circuit from a 4-wire delta system.

from phases **A** and **B.** Phases **A** and **B** and the neutral satisfy the condition of a multiwire branch circuit since there are 120 volts from **A** to the neutral, 120 volts from **B** to the neutral, and 240 volts from **A** to **B.** There is an equal potential difference between each phase wire and the neutral, and a difference of potential between the two phase wires.

Fig. 210-2. This is not a multiwire circuit from a 4-wire delta system.

Fig. 210-2 does not satisfy the multiwire branch circuit conditions, because both ungrounded phases are connected to the same phase, so there is no difference of potential between the phase wires. Fig. 210-3 does not satisfy the definition of a multiwire branch circuit; there is a voltage between the phase wires, but the same potential difference does

41

not exist between each phase wire and the neutral. On the **wye** system shown in Fig. 210-4, the three phase conductors and the neutral satisfy the requirements for a multiwire branch circuit. Any two phase wires and the neutral satisfy the conditions; therefore, this is a multiwire branch circuit.

Fig. 210-5, which is a 3-wire, 120/240-volt single-phase circuit, is also a multiwire circuit. Fig. 210-6 does not satisfy the requirements of a multiwire branch circuit, because there is no potential difference (zero voltage) between the two ungrounded phase conductors. Multiwire branch circuits are often misinterpreted; when the conditions of multiwire branch circuits are misapplied, the neutral may be forced to carry a heavy current, and this heavy current will result in heating and damage to the conductor insulation. There is no illustration of a 277/480-volt **wye** system, but the same would apply as with the 120/208-volt **wye** system.

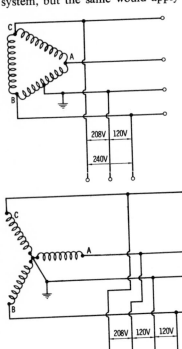

Fig. 210-3. This is not a multiwire circuit from a 4-wire delta system.

Fig. 210-4. A multiwire circuit from a 4-wire wye system.

Fig. 210-5. A 3-wire, 120/240-volt, multiwire circuit.

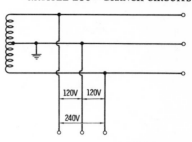

Fig. 210-6. This is not a multiwire circuit.

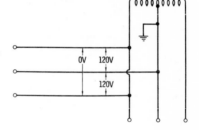

210-5. Color Code For Branch Circuits—See NEC.

(a) Grounded Conductor. When a branch circuit has a grounded conductor, and this grounded conductor may be a neutral or one phase of a Delta supply which is grounded, the grounded conductor shall have insulation (continuous) that is white or natural gray color. See Fig. 210-6A.

Where there is a raceway, box, gutter, or any other type enclosure, with conductors from more than one system and neutrals or grounded conductors are involved, one system shall use a white or natural gray color for its neutral—a second system shall use the other color and more systems with neutrals will use a white conductor with a colored stripe for the neutral. Thus, each system neutral may be easily identified. This colored stripe *should not* be green, since green always indicates equipment grounding conductors. The code states—*or other suitable and different means of identification.* This part will be up to the authority having jurisdiction to accept or reject the other means of identification.

Exception. The grounded conductor of Type MI Cable shall be identified by distinctive marking at the terminals during the process of installation.

(b) Grounding Conductor. If a conductor is used as a *grounding conductor*, it may be green, green with one or more yellow

43

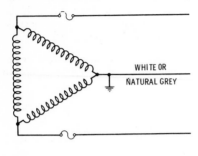

Fig. 210-6A. Showing a grounded conductor in a branch circuit.

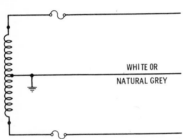

stripes, or bare. Green, green with yellow stripes, or bare are used only as grounding conductors. There is an exception to the bare conductor under services, and with SE Cable.

When equipment is internally wired, green conductors may be used for current carrying conductors, but we must stop where the lead wires from a branch-circuit attach to the equipment. Green, green with yellow stripes, and in most cases bare, shall never be used as the grounded conductor.

(c) **Ungrounded Conductor.** This is color coding and is extremely important. If requirements are followed, it will be easy to identify the different phases, assist in load balancing, and aid in trouble-shooting. Where conductors are installed in raceways, as aluminum sheathed cable, as open wiring, or as concealed knob-and-tube wiring, the conductors of multiwire branch circuits connected to the same phase and same system should conform to the following color code:

Three-wire circuits: one black, one white, and one red.
Four-wire circuits: one black, one white, one red, and one blue.
Five-wire circuits: one black, one white, one red, one blue, and one yellow.

Where more than one multiwire branch circuit is carried in the same raceway, the ungrounded conductors of the additional circuits may be other than those specified above. Fig. 210-7 illustrates the color-code regulations. The grounded conductors were covered previously.

Should such as 120/208 volt and 277/480 volt circuits be used in the same building, it would be wise to color-code the 277/480 volt system differently, such as brown, orange, and purple.

210-6. Voltage—

(a) The Code states that branch circuits having a 15-ampere or less rating, and used to supply lighting fixtures, standard receptacles, and lampholders shall not exceed 150 volts to ground. (See Fig. 210-8). This is the general rule; however, there are some exceptions.

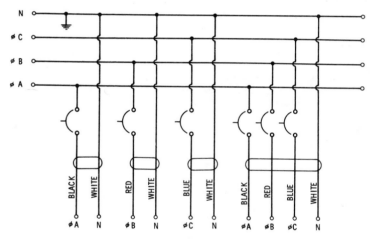

Fig. 210-7. Color-code regulations.

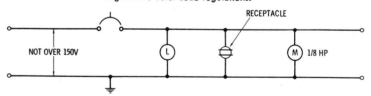

Fig. 210-8. A standard circuit having a 15-ampere or less rating.

Exception No. 1. In industrial establishments where competent individuals will service the lighting fixtures, the voltage may be as high as 300 volts to ground, provided;

45

(1) *Supply only lighting fixtures which are equipped with mogul base screw-shell lampholders or with lampholders of other types approved for the application.* The other types approved for the application would include UL Listed fixtures of the fluorescent type.

(2) The fixture must be mounted not less than 8 feet from the floor.

(3) The fixture shall not be equipped with a switch which is a part of the fixture.

Should the installation not meet any of these conditions, it should not be approved.

Exception No. 2 permits voltages not exceeding 300 volts to ground in industrial establishments, office buildings, schools, stores, public and commercial areas of other buildings, such as hotels or transportation terminals. However, the following conditions must exist:

(1) Ballasts are supplied for discharge lighting.
(2) Ballasts must be mounted in permanently installed fixtures.
(3) The manual switch shall not be an integral part of the fixture.
(4) If screw-shell-type lampholders are used for electric-discharge lamps, they must be installed not less than 8 feet from the floor.

This exception will permit the use of 277/480-volt service, and will also permit lamps to be connected across 208 volts on a 129/208-volt **wye** system with a grounded neutral; there would still be less than 150 volts to ground.

Exception No. 3 states that infrared industrial heating appliances **(Section 422-11)** may be used if the lamps are rated at 300 watts or less. They may be connected in series, provided that the lampholder voltage rating is not less than that of the circuit voltage.

Exception No. 4 covers the special provisions concerning **Section 110-19.**

Exception No. 5 is a new addition to the 1965 Code and covers branch circuits for permanent installations of electric-discharge lamps used for the illumination of highways, bridges, athletic fields, and parking lots, where they are installed at a height of 22 feet or more, or on other structures, such as tunnels, at a height of 18 feet or more. When the above conditions are met, voltages up to 500 volts between conductors may be used, providing that all of the applicable provisions of **Section 730-7(a)** covering lighting equipment on poles are met.

(b) **Voltage Between Conductors –Dwellings.** Voltage shall not exceed 150 volts between conductors for dwellings when supplying screw-shell lampholders, receptacles, or appliances, unless they are permanently connected appliances, portable or stationary appliances of 1380 watts or more, or portable motor-operated appliances of 1/4-HP or greater ratings. The question may arise concerning the use of a multiwire branch circuit and a split receptacle. There would only be 120 volts to ground between the two conductors supplying each half of the receptacle. Caution should be taken when 208 or 240 volts exist between conductors used in a residence, to make certain that the appliance has a proper grounding conductor or is approved for use without a grounding conductor.

(c) *Voltage Between Conductors–Nondwelling Occupancies. In nondwelling occupancies other than industrial establishments referred to in Exception No. 1 of* **Section 210-6(a)** *the voltage between conductors of branch circuits that supply screw-shell lampholders of the medium size shall not exceed 150 volts.*

(c) **Voltage Drop.** This is a new part added to the 1965 Code. The conductors for branch circuits shall be so sized that the voltage drop to the farthest outlet used for power, heating, lighting, or combinations of any of these, shall not exceed 3 percent. The maximum allowable voltage drop for combinations of feeder and branch circuits shall not exceed 5 percent. Special noting of this is necessary since it is the first time that branch circuits have been taken into consideration when calculating voltage drop.

210-7. Grounding–Type Receptacles and Protection—Grounding-type receptacles and cord connectors with grounding contacts shall be effectively grounded. This shall be accomplished by means of a grounding conductor or metallic raceways in lieu thereof, which shall be connected to the grounding screw of the receptacle or other approved means. **Section 250-91(b)** will cover the acceptable means of grounding.

An exception has been inserted to take care of additions to existing systems that do not have a grounded raceway or a grounding conductor. The grounding-type receptacle may be connected to a cold-water pipe near the receptacle. See Fig. 210-9. The Code specifically states *a grounded cold-water pipe;* make certain that the pipe is grounded before using it under this exception.

A new **Article 305, Temporary Wiring,** appears in the 1971 NEC and in this Section a requirement which will become effective January 1, 1974, will require *ground-fault circuit protection* on all 15- and 20-amp receptacles for construction sites.

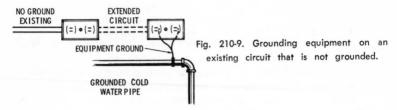

Fig. 210-9. Grounding equipment on an existing circuit that is not grounded.

210-8. Heavy-Duty Lampholders—See NEC.

B. Specific Requirements

210-19. Conductors—*Circuit conductors shall conform to the following:*

(a) Ampacity. The current carrying rating (ampacity) of the branch-circuit conductors shall not be less than the rating of the branch circuit, and shall not be less than the maximum load that it is required to carry. Even if a circuit uses No. 12 wire, this does not necessarily mean that it will have a 20-ampere rating—there may be a reason for derating the capacity. This will be covered in **Article 310.**

(b) Minimum Size. The minimum size for conductors used in branch circuits shall not be less than No. 8 for ranges rated at 8-3/4 kw or more, nor smaller than No. 14 for other loads. The neutral, in many cases, may be derated to 70 percent. If cable is used and the neutral is smaller than the ungrounded conductors, the cable shall be so marked.

(c) Exceptions:

Exception No. 1. See NEC.

Exception No. 2. Tap conductors may be of less capacity than the rating of the branch circuit, provided that the taps have a capacity of not less than that required to serve the load. In no case shall they be smaller than 20-ampere capacity when tapped to a 50-ampere branch circuit, and no less than 15-ampere capacity when tapped to a branch circuit that is rated less than 50 amperes.

(1) Individual lampholders or fixtures shall have taps extending not more than 18 inches beyond any portion of the lampholder or fixture.

(2) Individual outlets shall have taps not over 18 inches long.

(3) *Infrared lamp industrial heating appliances.*

(4) *Nonheating leads of snow and deicing cables and mats.*

Exception No. 3. See NEC.

Exception No. 4. Outlet devices may have less current-carrying capacity than the branch-circuit rating but must meet the requirements of **Section 210-21.**

Exception No. 5. Tap conductors may supply electric ranges, wall-mounted electric ovens, and counter-mounted cooking units from a 50-ampere branch circuit, providing that:

(1) The conductors are of ample size to carry the load to which they are connected.
(2) They shall not have less than a 20-ampere rating.
(3) The connections shall be no longer than necessary to serve the appliance. It will up to the inspection authority to determine what is *no longer than necessary.*

210-20. Overcurrent Protection—*The rating or setting of overcurrent devices shall conform to the following:*

(a) **Rating.** Overcurrent protection rating shall not be over that specified in **Section 240-5.**

Exception. Tap conductors and fixture wires were covered in the *Exceptions* in **Section 210-19(c).**

(b) **Single Appliance.** Where a circuit supplies a single appliance of 10-amperes or more rating, the overcurrent protection shall not exceed 150 percent of the appliance rating.

(c) **Continuous Loads.** A definition of *Continuous Load* is given in **Article 100.** Where any loads other than motor loads might constitute continuous loads, see **Section 210-23(b), Section 220-2,** and **Section 240-2.**

210-21. Outlet Devices—In no case are outlet devices to have a lower rating than the load that is intended, and must conform to the following:

(a) **Lampholders.** A lampholder connected to a branch circuit rated at over 20 amperes shall be of the heavy-duty type.

(b) **Receptacles.** In the 1962 Code revisions, the requirements were that all receptacles on 15- and 20-ampere branch circuits be equipped with grounding provisions. The installation was to be in conformance with **Section 210-7.** With this came some interpretations which were not uniform. In the 1965 Code book, this has been clarified to the point that it should be very understandable.

Grounding-type receptacles shall be used as replacements for existing nongrounding types and shall be connected to a grounding conductor installed in accordance with **Section 250-57.** *Exception. If it is impractical to reach a source of ground, a nongrounding-type of receptacle shall be used.*

The installation of a grounded-type receptacle does not mean that all appliances connected to this outlet are required to be of the grounded type. The requirements for the grounding of portables is covered in **Article 250.** Also see the Table in **Section 210-21** of the NEC.

On circuits where two or more outlets are connected, the Table shown in **Section 210-21** of the Code shall apply. In the event that different voltages or frequencies are installed on the same premises, receptacles shall be designed so that the attachment plugs cannot be used interchangeably.

Grounding receptacles rated at 15 or 20 amperes installed in circuits with less than 150 volts between conductors shall be approved for use only on potentials less than 150 volts. Grounding receptacles rated at 15 amperes and installed in circuits of 151 to 300 volts between conductors shall be approved for potentials of not less than 151 volts. See **Section 240-17(b)** of the NEC.

Receptacles on circuits of 15 or 20 amperes serving two or more outlets shall not supply loads on portable or stationary appliances of over 80 percent of the receptacle rating. Thus, a 15-ampere receptacle on a 15- or 20-ampere receptacle on a 20-ampere circuit will be limited to 12 amperes and a 20-ampere circuit will be limited to 16 amperes. *Grounding type receptacles which are of a type that reject nongrounding type attachment plugs or which are of the locking type may be used for specific purposes or in special locations. A single receptacle installed on an individual branch circuit shall have a rating of not less than the rating of the branch circuit.*

Receptacles required in **Sections 517-61(d)** *and* **517-62(e)** *are considered as meeting the requirements of this Section. These are receptacles for operating rooms of hospitals and are new with the 1971 NEC.*

Receptacles rated at 20 amperes connected to 20-ampere branch circuits serving two or more outlets shall not supply a total load in excess of 16 amperes for portable or stationary appliances.

(c) Range-receptacle capacities shall comply with the demand factors given for the various range loads in **Table 220-5,** which covers the demand factors for different sizes of ranges. The demand factor is based on the fact that it is very unlikely that a range will ever utilize the full rated capacity.

210-22. Receptacle Outlets Required—The number of receptacle outlets required in a dwelling has caused considerable confusion. The fact

50

remains that more and varied types of appliances appear on the market every day, and these must be considered in adequate wiring. The following rules govern the number of outlets in a dwelling:

(a) General. Receptacle outlets are considered as a place where portable cords may be attached. *A cord connector that is supported by a permanently connected cord pendant is considered a receptacle outlet.*

(b) Dwelling Type Occupancies. Every kitchen, family room, dining room, breakfast room, living room, parlor, library, den, sun room, recreation room, and bedroom shall have outlets installed so that no point at floor line in any wall is more than six feet, measured horizontally, from an outlet. This includes *any wall space two feet wide or greater and wall space occupied by sliding panels in exterior walls.* The receptacle outlets, in so far as practical, shall be equally spaced. Floor outlets close to the wall will be acceptable in the fulfillment of the above requirement. See Fig. 210-10.

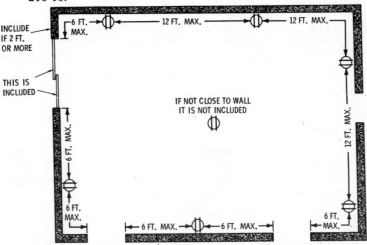

Fig. 210-10. Proper wall receptacle outlet spacing for residential housing.

A clarification of intent has been made in the 1965 Code, which states: *Outlets in other sections of the dwelling for special appliances such as laundry equipment, shall be placed within 6 feet of the intended location of the appliance.* Special appliances might also include freezers and air conditioners.

Countertops in kitchen and dining areas are various widths and are often cut up by sinks, ranges, range tops, refrigeration,

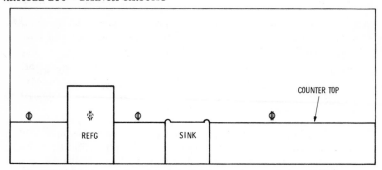

Fig. 210-10A. Proper wall receptacle outlet spacing for countertops in kitchen or dining areas.

etc. Where this is the case, any portion of the countertop space that is wider than 12 inches shall have a small appliance receptacle installed. See Fig. 210-10A. Any receptacle covered by stationary appliances, such as a refrigerator, shall not be counted.

The wall space afforded by fixed room dividers, such as free-standing bar-type counters, shall be included in the 6-foot measurement.

At least one receptacle outlet shall be installed for the laundry. At least one wall receptacle outlet shall be installed in the bathroom adacent to the basin location. This is for the electrical appliances used in the bathroom, such as, razors, toothbrushes, vibrators, etc.

Exception No. 1. In apartments or multifamily dwellings where laundry facilities are furnished in a common location on the premises and are available to all occupants, there is no need for the laundry receptacle in each dwelling occupancy.

Exception No. 2. In other than one-family dwellings, where laundry facilities are not provided and are prohibited in the individual occupancies, the laundry receptacle is not required.

Exception No. 3. Hotels, motels, or motor hotels with dwelling units are not required to have a laundry receptacle.

(c) Hotels, motels, and similar occupancies have been interpreted as coming under this category. Receptacles in these occupancies are to be installed the same as in **(b)**. Since many hotels and motels have beds, dressers, and other furniture permanently attached to the walls, receptacles under the Exception may be located conveniently for the permanent fixture layout.

(d) Ground-fault current protection is making great strides as a safety feature. With the use of outdoor tools and appliances increasing steadily for home use, and with the accidents that occur from improper use and maintenance of this equipment, all 120-volt, 15- and 20-ampere receptacles installed outdoors in residential occupancies, will be required to have ground-fault current protection, after January 1, 1973.

Such ground-fault circuit protection may be provided for other circuits, locations, and occupancies, and where used will provide additional protection against line-to-ground shock hazard.

(e) Show Windows. Screw-shell lampholders have been used for many years as an extension cord for floodlighting etc., by using adapters. The 1971 NEC requires at least one receptacle for each 12 linear feet or major fraction thereof. This should eliminate the unsavory practices mentioned above.

210-23. Maximum Load—*The maximum load shall conform to the following:*

(a) Appliances Consisting of Motors and Other Loads. If an appliance consists of motor load only, **Article 430** will apply. Branch-circuit calculations for appliances (other than portable) which use a motor larger than 1/8 HP plus additional loads such as heating elements, lighting, etc., make it necessary to figure the motor load at 125 percent, with the additional loads added to this figure. For example: A dishwasher uses a 1/3-HP motor which draws 7.2 amperes. This would be figured at 125 percent, or 9 amperes. In addition, there is a heating element that draws 840 watts at 120 volts, or 7 amperes. The figure used in calculating the branch circuit would be 9 amperes + 7 amperes, or 16 amperes. In **Section 210-21(b),** a 20-ampere branch circuit that serves two or more outlets should supply no more than 16 amperes. From this it may readily be seen that an outlet to supply the above dishwasher should be on a 20-ampere circuit of its own.

Circuits supplying only air-conditioning and/or refrigeration equipment, is now covered in **Article 440** instead of **Article 430.**

(b) Other Loads. To make sure that the total load never exceeds the rating of the branch circuit, it is recommended that a safety factor be used. Should the load be of a continuous nature, such as store lighting, the load shall not exceed 80 percent of the branch-circuit rating. Inductive-type loads, such as ballasts, autotransformers, or transformers, shall never be figured on the wattage of such loads. It is required that the total amperage ratings be used instead. This is necessary due to the fact that the power factor is involved and the rating of a branch circuit is based on amperes and not on watts.

Exception No. 1. When all of the assembly is rated for continuous operation, including the overcurrent protective devices, at 100 percent of its rating, then the total load may be equal to the branch-circuit rating.

Exception No. 2. Under *Note 8* accompanying **Tables 310-12** through **310-15,** there are derating factors which must be used when current-carrying conductors in a raceway exceed three. When these derating factors apply, it will not be necessary to use the derating factor of 80 percent for continuous loads which was covered in **(b)** of this Section.

Exception No. 3. In **Article 220** there are some explanatory notes following **Table 220-5.** *Note 5* is to be used in the calculation of range loads, and will be fully covered in **Article 220.**

Note. Attention is called to the fact that there were a number of changes made in the 1965 Code on the preceding **Section 210-23.** It is therefore advisable to become thoroughly familiar with the new section as now written.

210-24. Permissible Loads—Individual branch circuits may supply any loads, but where a branch circuit supplies two or more outlets, the following will apply:

(a) **15- and 20-Ampere Branch Circuits.** Lighting units and/or appliances shall not exceed 80 percent of the branch-circuit rating. If a fixed appliance is supplied by a branch circuit that also supplies lighting or portable or stationary appliances, the fixed appliance shall not exceed 50 percent of the branch-circuit rating. Examples of this would be a disposal, built-in dishwasher, furnace, etc., that might be supplied from a circuit that also supplies lighting or outlets other than where portable or stationary appliances might be connected. In referring to disposals and dishwashers that are built-in, it would be well to note that they should not connect to an appliance branch circuit. They may be connected to a lighting branch circuit, providing that the load drawn is not in excess of the 50 percent of the branch-circuit rating. *Small appliance branch circuits shall supply only the loads stipulated in* **Section 220-3(b).**

(b) **30-Ampere Branch Circuits.** On 30-ampere branch circuits, the rating of any motor-driven portable or stationary appliance shall not exceed 24 amperes. The 125 percent factor should be considered in the calculations of the load. Where fixed lighting units in other than dwellings are used, they are to be equipped with heavy-duty lampholders.

(c) **40-Ampere Branch Circuits.** This category includes fixed or stationary cooking appliance, electric water heaters, or clothes dryers. In other than dwelling occupancies, it might also include fixed lighting fixtures with heavy-duty lampholders or infra-red heating units. An electric range may be a fixed appliance or a stationary appliance—this would depend upon whether it was built-in or not, or whether it was permanently connected to the branch circuit or plugged in. It is recommended that a minimum of 40 amperes be used to supply clothes dryers as too many will not meet the requirements of a 30-ampere branch circuit.

(d) **50-Ampere Branch Circuits.** It is noted that in this category the term *fixed* includes cord connections that might be approved elsewhere in the Code. For example, this would include an electric range that is plugged in.

210-25. Table of Requirements—Table 210-25 gives the branch-circuit requirements. It should be noted that conductors are marked *minimum size*. This is necessary due to the fact that voltage drop or the derating factors may require the use of larger conductor sizes. Also, this is the copper conductor size. If aluminum conductors are used, it will be necessary to take this into consideration. This Table contains a great deal of useful material and should be studied carefully.

ARTICLE 215—FEEDERS

215-1. Scope—*This Article deals with installation requirements for, and, the size of the conductors in the feeders needed to supply power to branch circuits and, the loads as calculated under* **Article 220.**

A definition for feeders was given in **Article 100.** In larger buildings where it is impractical to supply all of the branch circuits from the service-entrance equipment, it is necessary to install overcurrent protection to the supply feeders leading to branch-circuit panels. The branch circuits can be supplied and protected by the overcurrent protection as required for each particular branch circuit. Fig. 215-1 illustrates a feeder circuit.

215-2. Conductor Sizes—In calculating feeder sizes, they shall have a current rating no less than the feeder load as calculated under **Section 220-4.** The voltage drop of the feeders and the branch circuits must also be taken into consideration and the feeder conductors sized, not only for the load, but for the voltage drop and any derating that may be required elsewhere in the Code. The minimum size allowed for feeders is No. 10 when they consist of a 2-wire feeder supplying two or more 2-wire branch circuits, a 3-wire feeder supplying more than two 2-wire branch circuits, or two or more 3-wire branch circuits

If a feeder supplies the total current supplied by the service-entrance conductors, the feeder from a No. 6 or smaller service-entrance conductor shall be at least the same size as the service-entrance conductors. Should a feeder circuit be required to carry more than the calculated load, the conductor size shall be increased to a current-carrying capacity large enough to take care of the load demand placed upon them. **Section 215-3** is very important and should be carefully considered and taken into account when figuring the size of feeders that will be required. **Examples No. 1 thru 7** in **Chapter 9** of the Code show how to calculate feeder sizes. **Section 220** of this text also gives additional examples so that a comparison may be made.

215-3. Voltage Drop—The voltage drop for branch circuits is covered under **Section 210-6(c).** The following is very similar and will be repeated here because of the importance. In calculating feeder conductor sizes under **Section 220-4,** the voltage drop must also be taken into consideration. For feeders, the voltage drop shall not exceed 3 percent for power, heating, or lighting, or any combination thereof. The voltage drop for the feeder and branch circuit combined shall not exceed 5 percent overall. The formula for voltage drop is as follows:

$$V_d = \frac{2L \times 12 \times I}{CM}$$

where

V_d is the voltage drop
L is the length of the circuit in feet, one way
I is the current in amperes
CM is the area of the conductors in circular mils

To arrive at the voltage drop in percent, the voltage supplied to the circuit is divided into the voltage drop.

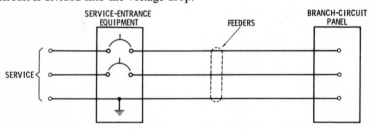

Fig. 215-1. A typical feeder circuit.

215-4. Overcurrent Protection—*Feeders shall be protected against overcurrent in accordance with the provisions of* **Article 240.** Complete details of overcurrent protection will be covered later in the text.

215-5. Common Neutral Feeder—A common neutral feeder may be used for two or three sets of 3-wire feeders or two sets of 4- or 5-wire feeders, providing that the neutral is large enough to take care of the unbalanced current that it may be required to carry, and that, when these are enclosed in a metal raceway, that all conductors are in the same raceway. This is necessary to counteract induction that might be set up, which will cause heating and possibly unbalance. Caution should be taken when current-carrying conductors and the neutral are brought into a large panel. The conductors should be run side by side (parallel) whenever possible since a voltage unbalance might be caused by induction. Running the conductors side by side tends to cancel out the induction. This explanation does not appear in the Code, but is of vital importance.

215-6. Diagram of Feeders—The enforcing authority may require diagrams showing feeder details, and they should show the area in square feet, load (before applying demand factors), demand factors selected, computed load (after applying the demand factors), and the size of the conductors. Any wiring job of any size should have the feeder diagram supplied to the owner since it is a great assistance in determining where the feeders go and what they serve. It is also mandatory that they be marked as required under the 1955 Code for easy future reference. See **Section 110-21.**

215-7. Installation Requirements—If grounding conductors are required in branch circuits fed from feeders to a branch-circuit panel, there shall be a grounding means provided to which the grounding conductors may be attached. Also, in service-entrance equipment, the grounding bus must be grounded to the enclosure. In feeders panels, the grounding bus shall not be grounded to the enclosures. This often brings up the question of where to attach the grounding conductor when it is required. The grounding conductor shall not be connected to the neutral bus of a feeder panel, but shall be connected to a separate grounding bus for the grounding conductors, or to the enclosure by approved lugs. Do not confuse a "grounded" conductor and a "grounding" conductor.

If the feeder panel is supplied by a metallic raceway which serves as a grounding conductor, the grounding conductors are attached to the enclosure and not the neutral bus, since the neutral bus is isolated from the enclosure. If there is a grounding conductor but no metallic raceway, it is attached to the enclosure as are the grounding conductors that leave the feeder panel. The latter part is not in the Code under this Section, but is very appropriate at this time.

215-8. Ground-Fault Personnel Protection—*Feeders supplying power to 15- and 20-ampere receptacle branch circuits may be protected by a ground-fault circuit-interrupter approved for the purpose in lieu of the provisions of* **Section 210-22(d).**

This would cover more circuits with a ground-fault circuit interrupter. Expect to see greater use of GFI's.

ARTICLE 220—BRANCH CIRCUIT AND FEEDER CALCULATIONS

220-1. Scope—In this Article, the basic calculations for feeders, branch circuits, loads, and the method of determining the number of branch circuits will be discussed. This Article might well be called "Fundamentals of Design," because it contains the minimum requirements for a particular design or application. This does not mean that in designing a wiring system one should not take into consideration whether or not the minimum will be sufficient or whether allowances for future expansion should be provided for. This, of course, is very hard to anticipate with much accuracy, but definitely should be considered. A good and proper design always provides for at least the immediate future requirements that can be foreseen.

220-2. Calculation of Branch Circuit Loads—This Section is to be used in the computation of branch circuits. In the calculation of loads for stores and similar occupancies, the minimums specified in this article shall be increased by 25 percent.

> *Exception No. 1.* When the complete assembly, including the overcurrent protection for branch circuits and feeder circuits, is approved at 100 percent of its rating, there will be no need of increasing the rating for the minimum unit loads.

> *Exception No.2.* When calculating the derating of conductor capacity because of more than three current-carrying conductors being placed in a raceway *(Note 8* of **Tables 310-12** through **310-**15), it will not be necessary to increase the unit loads by 25 percent.

(a) **General Lighting Load.**

(1) **In Listed Occupancies.** The calculations for loads in various occupancies are based on watts per square foot. This is a minimum basis and consideration should be given to the ever increasing trend toward higher levels of illumination. Each installation should be examined and not figured entirely on the watts per square foot basis, but on the anticipated figure demands upon the system.

In figuring the watts per square foot, the outside dimensions of the building are to be used. They do not include the area of open porches and attached garages with dwelling occupancies. If there is an unused basement, it should be assumed that it will be finished later, thus it should be included in the calculations so that the capacity of the wiring system will be adequate to serve at a later date. Conduit or EMT should be installed in concrete basement walls during construction since the cost will be much lower than at the time of finishing the basement.

The unit values given are based on 100 percent factor for the minimum requirements, so any low power factors should be taken into account in the calculations. If high power factor discharge lighting is not used, allowance should be made for the increased amperage due to the lower power factor.

(2) In Other Occupancies. In other than occupancies listed in **Table 220-2(a),** a load of not less than that specified in **Section 220-2(b)** is to be used.

(b) Other Loads. Any lighting other than general illumination, and for appliances other than motors, a minimum unit load per outlet is given in the table listed under this Section of the Code.

(c) Exceptions. *The minimum loads as outlined in* **Section 220-2(b)** *shall be modified as follows:*

Exception No. 1. Ranges. Household ranges are not subject to this regulation but their minimum loads may be determined by using **Table 220-5.**

Exception No. 2. Show-Window Lighting. For show-window lighting, a minimum of 200 watts for each linear foot measured horizontally along the base of the window shall be used. If the window is to be lighted by discharge lighting, allowance for additional amperage due to power factor must be made.

Exception No. 3. Multioutlet Assemblies. Each 5 feet or fraction thereof of either separate or continuous multioutlet assemblies shall be considered to be not less than 1-1/2 amperes capacity. Where a number of appliances will be used, each foot will be considered as being 1-1/2 amperes capacity. These requirements shall not apply to either dwellings or guest rooms in hotels. A location where 1 foot might be considered as 1-1/2 ampere capacity, could be an appliance sales floor where a number of appliances might be connected for demonstration. Another location might be in a school lab where a number of experiments using electrical apparatus would be used at the same time.

Exception No. 4. See NEC.

(d) Existing Installations. In making additional installations to existing electrical systems they shall conform to the following:

(1) Dwelling Occupancies. Sections 220-2(a or b) apply to new circuits or extensions to existing electrical systems in dwellings. They may be figured on the watts-per-square foot basis or the amperes-per-outlet basis. This will apply to a portion of the existing dwelling that has not been previously wired, or to any addition that exceeds 500 square feet in area. In this case, the addition would be figured on the watts-per-square foot basis and **Table 220-2(a)** will be used.

It is necessary that the existing electrical system be checked to make certain that the circuit or circuits being added have sufficient current-carrying capacity to take care of the additional load.

(2) Other Than Dwelling Occupancies. When adding new circuits or extensions of circuits to an existing occupancy, either watts-per-square foot or amperes-per-outlet may be used as covered in **Sections 220-2(a and b).**

220-3. Branch Circuits Required—*Branch circuits shall be installed as follows:*

(a) Lighting and Appliance Circuits. Information in **Section 220-2** is to be used in figuring branch circuits for lighting, appliances, and motor-operated appliances, unless there is a specific coverage in **Section 220-3(b).** The number of circuits may be more than required but shall be no less than the computed load and carrying capacity of the circuits as computed by the watts-per-square foot method for the type of occupancy. In figuring the number of branch circuits required, **Section 210-23** must be observed (recall that motors of over 1/8 HP, when on a circuit with other types of loads, shall be figured at 125 percent of the motor's full-load current). Where circuits have continuous loads, they are not to be loaded over 80 percent of the circuit rating. Inductive loads, such as transformers, autotransformers, ballasts, etc., are to be figured on an ampere basis instead of a watts basis.

When figuring the load on a watts-per-square foot basis, the load should be distributed evenly between the various circuits according to their capacity. In figuring dwelling occupancies, it is recommended that there be no less than one circuit for general illumination per 500 square feet, plus receptacle circuits figured at 1-1/2 amperes per receptacle. General-purpose outlets and lighting outlets are both included in the 3 watt-per-square foot figure used for dwellings. The recommendation just covered

60

would figure more than 3 watts per square foot. Attention is called to the fact that in the spacing of outlets for guest rooms in hotels, motels, and similar occupancies **(Section 210-22)**, they are to be spaced the same as required for dwelling occupancies.

(b) **Receptacle Circuits, Dwelling Occupancies.** This part covers what is commonly termed the appliance circuits of a dwelling and is for the use of small appliances, including refrigeration equipment, most of which are of the heating type. To take care of this load there shall be, in addition to the circuits as required in **Section 220-3(a)**, a minimum of two 20-ampere branch circuits to serve the outlets in the kitchen, pantry, family room, dining room, and breakfast rooms of dwellings. There must be at least two 20-ampere circuits serving the kitchen, even though these two circuits also serve one or more of the other rooms mentioned. It can be readily seen that only two circuits in the kitchen is rarely enough for today's modern homes. A receptacle used solely for an electric clock may be on the lighting circuit. A three-wire 115/230-volt branch circuit would be the equivalent of two 115-volt receptacle branch circuits. On this type of circuit, the split-type receptacle would be used which would aid in balancing the load; each receptacle would be the equivalent of two circuits.

(c) **Other Circuits.** Any loads that are for a specific purpose will be covered in other Sections of the Code pertaining to the specific load involved. This includes loads not specifically covered by **a** or **b** of this Section.

220-4. Calculation of Feeder Loads—*The computed load of a feeder shall not be less than the sum of all branch circuit loads supplied by the feeder, as determined by* **Section 220-2**, *subject to the following provisions.*

Exception: When the calculated load for a multi-family dwelling under this Section without electric cooking exceeds that calculated under **Section 220-9** *for the identical load plus electric cooking (based on 8KW per unit), the lesser of the two loads may be used.*

This was added to correct inequities resulting from a strict interpretation of **Section 220-9.**

The Code mentions that small appliance circuits shall be in the family room. There has been a great deal of confusion as to just what constitutes a family room. With this in mind, I personally submitted a proposal for the 1971 NEC to add recreation room, as I saw no difference.

The following is the panel's comment, following a rejection of the proposal, however, this comment has clarified the intent as far as I am concerned: (Proposal No. 58, Page 25, 1971 Preprint.) *Panel Comment —It is to be understood that "family room" as used in this Article includes "recreation rooms", "game rooms" and the like. The intent of this requirement is to assure that there will be adequate capacity for the small appliance loads if such loads are to be used in these locations.*

(a) Continuous and Noncontinuous Loads. *When a feeder supplies continuous loads or any combination of continuous and noncontinuous load the rating of the overcurrent devices shall not be less than the noncontinuous load plus 125% of the continuous load.*

Exception: When the assembly including the overcurrent devices protecting the feeder(s) are approved for operation at 100% of their ratings, the ampacity of the feeder may equal the sum of the continuous load plus the noncontinuous load.

1. *This will eliminate the confusion as to increases to the unit load of* **Table 220-2(a).**
2. *Recognizes that overcurrent devices are not normally rated for continuous duty at full load.*
3. *Allows the use of overcurrent devices which are rated for continuous duty at full load.*
4. *Separate the derating of conductors as a requirement from the derating of overcurrent devices as a requirement.*

(b) General Lighting. The demand factors listed in **Table 220-4(b)** cover that portion of the total branch circuit loads that are computed for lighting loads. These demand factors are only for the purpose of determining feeders to supply lighting loads and are not for the purpose of figuring the number of branch circuits. The number of branch circuits have been covered in the preceding part and will also be covered in examples in Chapter 9 of the Code as well as following parts of this coverage of **Article 220.** Particular attention should be given **Section 220-4** (**h** and **i**).

Each installation should be specifically analyzed, since the demand factors listed in this section of the Code are based only on the minimum requirements of load conditions and for 100 percent power-factor conditions. There will be conditions of less than unity power factor and conditions where these demand factors would be wrong. With the trend to higher illumination intensities, and the increased use of fixed and portable appliances, the loads imposed on the system are very likely to be greater than the minimums. Also, electric discharge lighting should be of the high power factor type—if not, additional provisions should be made for the low power factor involved.

(c) Show-Window Lighting. Show-window lighting is a separate load from that calculated on the watts-per-square foot basis. This lighting is to be figured at a minimum of 200 watts per linear foot.

(d) Motors. Feeder loads for motors will be covered in **Article 430.**

(e) Feeder Neutral Load. Neutral feeder load must be considered wherever a neutral is used in conjunction with one or more ungrounded conductors. On a single-phase feeder using one ungrounded conductor and a neutral, the neutral will carry the same amount of current as the ungrounded conductor. A two-wire feeder is rare, so in considering the neutral feeder current, we will assume that there is a neutral and two or more ungrounded phase conductors. If there are two ungrounded conductors that are connected to the same phase, and a neutral, the neutral would be required to carry the total current from both phase wires, which would not be accepted practice.

The neutral feeder load shall be the maximum unbalance of the load determined by **Section 220-4.** *The maximum unbalanced load shall be the maximum connected load between the neutral and any one ungrounded conductor; except:*

(1) On 5-wire two-phase systems, the neutral shall carry 140 percent of the unbalanced load.

(2) On feeders that supply electric ranges, wall-mounted ovens, counter-mounted cooling tops, etc., the maximum unbalanced load shall be considered to be 70 percent of the load on the ungrounded conductor. Therefore, the neutral supplying these may be 70 percent as large as the ungrounded conductors, providing that the neutral is no smaller than No. 10. The capacity of the ungrounded conductors is figured by the use of **Table 220-5.**

(3) *For 3-wire DC or single-phase AC, 4-wire 3-phase, and 5-wire 2-phase systems, a further demand factor of 70% may be applied to that portion of the unbalanced load in excess of 200 amperes. There shall be no reduction of the neutral capacity for that portion of the load which consists of electric discharge lighting.* See Fig. 220-1.

The question is often asked why a neutral that serves discharge lighting cannot be derated. This is because of a third harmonic frequency produced by the discharge lighting and its ballast. This third harmonic may load the

63

neutral to the maximum or higher allowable current. Fig. 220-2 shows the effect of the third harmonic on a three-phase system, how the harmonics are in phase and will thus be added together.

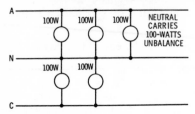

Fig. 220-1. A single-phase, 3-wire unbalanced circuit.

As an example in figuring the neutral feed load, a 4-wire, 3-phase, wye system of 120/208 volts will be used. Assume the following loads:

Discharge lighting	150 amperes per phase
Electric ranges	200 amperes per phase
Other loads, including incandescent lighting, motor (3φ), and misc.	295 amperes per phase
Total	645 amperes per phase

The neutral current is calculated as follows:

Ranges, 200 amperes @ 70%	140 amperes
Other loads	295 amperes
	435 amperes
200 amperes @ 100%	200 amperes
235 amperes @ 70%	164.5 amperes
	364.5 amperes
Discharge lighting	150 amperes
Total calculated neutral current	514.5 amperes

In the above case, it may be seen that the phase currents are 645 amperes per phase while the neutral current may be derated to 514.5 amperes. The above figures are based on demand-factor ratings.

As another example, assume a fifty-unit apartment house using a 4-wire, 3-phase, 120/208-volt, wye system, with fifty 3-wire electric ranges and a gross area of 1000 square feet per apartment.

General lighting, 50 × 3 × 1000	150,000 watts
Small-appliance loads, 50 × 2 × 1500	150,000 watts
	300,000 watts
3000 watts @ 100%	3,000 watts
117,000 watts @ 35%	40,950 watts
300,000 − 120,000 watts @ 35%	45,000 watts
Minimum feeder capacitor for general lighting and appliances	88,950 watts

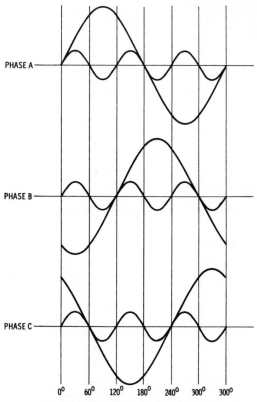

0°   60°   120°   180°   240°   300°   300°

Fig. 220-2. The effect of a third harmonic.

For the fifty ranges, this will put sixteen ranges on one phase and seventeen ranges on each of the other two phases. From **Table 220-5,** the indicated demand will be as follows: There will be a maximum demand of 17 + 17 ranges on any phase, or 34 ranges connected at the same time. According to **Table 220-5,** however, this will be 15,000 + 34,000 watts, or 49,000 watts.

From **Table 220-5**.. 49,000 watts
General lighting and small-appliance loads......................... 88,950 watts
Total........................ 137,950 watts

Maximum feeder demand:

$$\frac{137,950}{1.73 \times 208} = 384 \text{ amperes}$$

65

To size the neutral:

General lighting and small appliances.................................. 88,950 watts

Electric ranges, 49,000 @ 70%... 34,300 watts

Total.................123,250 watts

Total neutral current:

$$\frac{123,250}{1.73 \times 208} = 342 \text{ amperes}$$

So:

200 amperes @ 100%...200 amperes

142 amperes @ 70%.. 99.4 amperes

Total.................299.4 amperes

After figuring the phase load and neutral load in amperes, use the wire size necessary to carry that amount of current. In most cases, you will find that a conductor capable of carrying the exact number of amperes required will not be available, so use the next larger size.

(f) Fixed Electrical Space Heating. With two exceptions, the computed load on a feeder that serves fixed electrical space heating shall be equal to the total of the electrical space heating load on all of the branch circuits. There is no demand factor.

Exception No. 1. The inspection authority enforcing the code may grant special permission to issue a demand factor for electrical space heating where they have duty-cycling or where all units will not be operating at the same time. The feeders are required to be of sufficient current-carrying capacity to carry the load as so determined.

Exception No. 2. **Section 220-4(f)** does not apply when calculating feeder sizes for one-family dwellings as permitted in **Section 220-7**, which again refers back to **Section 220-4(l)**. This will permit you to eliminate the smaller of the two loads when one consists of air conditioning and the other electric space heating. The air conditioning is used in the summer and the heating in the winter, so they should never be in use at the same time.

Section 220-7 not only will apply to a **Single-Family Dwelling,** but also an individual apartment of a multi-family dwelling, and **Section 220-9** for **Multi-Family Dwellings.**

(g) Noncoincident Load. When adding the branch circuit loads, the smaller of two loads may be omitted if it is not likely that they will be in use at the same time.

(h) Small Appliances. In other than dwelling occupancies, where not more than 1-1/2 amperes per outlet is figured, the computed branch-circuit load may be included in the general lighting load and be subject to the demand factors listed in **Section 220-4(a).**

Dwelling Occupancies

The following requirements in **Section 220-4(h-k)** apply to dwelling-type occupancies, such as residences, multifamily dwellings, hotels, motels, and similar occupancies, and are supplemental to **Section 220-4(a-g).**

(i) 1. Small Appliances. The requirements for small-appliance receptacle outlets in single-family dwellings, multifamily dwellings with individual apartments having cooking facilities, and in hotels or motels having serving-pantry facilities or other cooking facilities, shall be a minimum of not less than two appliance circuits, as required under **Section 220-(b).** The calculated load for each circuit shall be no less than 1500 watts. These loads may be included with the general lighting load which makes it subject to the demand factors as set forth in **Section 220-4(b).**

2. Laundry Circuit. *A feeder load of not less than 1500 watts shall be included for each 2-wire laundry circuit installed as required by* **Section 220-3(c).** *This load may be included with the general lighting load and subject to the demand factors in* **Section 220-4(b).**

(j) Electric Ranges. In calculating feeder loads for electric ranges or other cooking appliances in dwelling occupancies, any that are rated over 1-3/4 KW shall be calculated according to **Table 220-5** in the NEC. The *Notes* following **Table 220-5** are a part of the *Table* and are very important in the calculation of feeder and branch-circuit loads.

Due to the increased wattages being used in modern electric ranges, it is recommended that the maximum demands for any range of less than 8-3/4 KW rating be figured using *Column A* in **Table 220-5.**

Three-phase, 4-wire wye systems are often used. When calculating the current in such systems, it is necessary to use a demand of twice the maximum number of ranges that will be connected between any two phase wires. An example of this was shown under **Section 220-4(d).**

(k) Fixed Electrical Appliances (Other than Ranges, Clothes Dryers, Air Conditioning Equipment or Space Heating Equipment). In single or multifamily dwellings where four or more fixed electrical appliances (other than electric ranges, clothes dryers, air conditioning equipment, or space heating equipment) are connected to the *same feeder,* a demand factor of 75 percent may be used. The reason that the electric ranges, etc., are omitted from this

75 percent demand factor is because they have specified demand factors that are applicable to them alone.

(l) Space Heating and Air Cooling. In dwelling occupancies having both space-heating and air-cooling equipment, the larger of the two loads is used in the calculations and the smaller omitted, providing that the likelihood of both being used at the same time is remote. Air conditioning is an inductive-type load, so in the calculations the amperes drawn by this equipment are used, as this takes into account the power factor.

(m) Farm Buildings. This is a new part of the 1965 Code. It has been felt for a number of years that a demand factor could be used on farm buildings (other than dwellings). After many tests were made, **Table 220-4(m)** was set up as the minimum capacity for computations:

(n) Farm Services.

(1) Individual farm buildings (excluding dwellings) shall have the service equipment and service-entrance conductors figured according to **Table 220-4(m)** for computing the minimum capacities required.

(2) A great many farmsteads now have a service pole from which individual buildings are fed. The minimum capacity of service conductors and service equipment, if any, at this main point of delivery to farms (including dwellings) shall be determined in accordance with the following:

100 percent of the largest demand computed in accordance with **Table 220-4(m).**

75 percent of the second largest demand computed in accordance with **Table 220-4(m).**

65 percent of the third largest demand computed in accordance with **Table 220-4(m).**

50 percent of the demands of remaining loads computed in accordance with **Table 220-4(m).**

Note 1: Consider as a single computed demand the total of the computed demands of all buildings or loads having the same function.

Note 2: The demand of the farm dwelling, if included in the demands of this formula, should be computed in accordance with *Note 1* of **Table 220-4(m).**

Note 1 refers to a farm that has the service drop for the entire farm run to the dwelling, with the other farm buildings supplied from the panel in the dwelling.

68

Note 2 refers to a farm served by a meter pole from which the service drops fan out to serve the other buildings, which may or may not include the dwelling or dwellings.

An example of each Note follows:

For a farm served by a single service drop:

Load No. 1. Single-family dwelling:

The dwelling has a floor area of 1500 sq. ft. exclusive of an unoccupied basement, an unfinished attic, and open porches. It has a 12-KW range.

Computed Load (see **Section 220-4**)

General lighting load:
1500 sq. ft. at 3 watts per sq. ft. ....4500 watts

Small-Appliance Load (two 2-wire, 20-ampere circuits)

Computed load:

General lighting	4500 watts
Small-appliance load	3000 watts
Total without range	7500 watts
3000 watts at 100%	3000 watts
7500 − 3000 = 4500 watts at 35%	1575 watts
Net computed load (without range)	4575 watts
Range load (see **Table 220-5**)	8000 watts
Net computed load (with range)	12,575 watts

Load No. 1 total for 115/230-volt, 3-wire system feeders
(12,575 ÷ 230) ....55 amperes

Load No. 2 (Feed grinder and auger)
5-HP, single-phase, 230-volt motor ....28 amperes
1-HP, single-phase, 230-volt motor .... 8 amperes
Load No. 2 total ....36 amperes

Load No. 3 (Milk barn)
Computed load:
Lighting ....2000 watts
Waterheater ....2500 watts
Total...............4500 watts

4500 watts ÷ 230 volts ....20 amperes
2-HP milker ....12 amperes
1-HP cooler .... 8 amperes
Air conditioner ....15 amperes
Load No. 3 total...............55 amperes

Load No. 4 (Chicken house)

Brooder ....3000 watts
Lighting ....450 watts
Total load...............$\overline{3450}$ watts

Load No. 4 total (3450 watts ÷ 230 volts) ....15 amperes

In the computations, the largest motor is 5-HP rated at 28 amperes. This will have to be taken at 125 percent of the load which will be 35 amperes.

The computed load is as follows:

Load No. 1 .... 55 amperes
Load No. 2 (Plus extra for 5-HP motor) .... 43 amperes
Load No. 3 .... 55 amperes
Load No. 4 .... 15 amperes
Total...............$\overline{168}$ amperes
First 60 amperes at 100% .... 60 amperes
Next 60 amperes at 50% .... 30 amperes
Remainder of 48 amperes at 25% .... 12 amperes
Computed Load using **Table 220-4 (1)** ....$\overline{102}$ amperes

Thus, the service supplying the farm will be figured on the basis of 102 amperes instead of the 168 amperes total.

The computed load where there is a farm service pole, and all four loads are served by separate service drops would be figured as follows:

Largest demand, 55 amps at 100% .... 55 amperes
2nd largest demand, 55 amperes at 75% .... 42 amperes
3rd largest demand 43 amperes at 65% .... 28 amperes
Balance .... 15 amperes
Total...............$\overline{140}$ amperes

Under this condition, the load would be computed at 140 amperes instead of 168 amperes total.

Table 220-6(a) is a table of feeder demand factors for commercial electric cooking equipment, including dishwashers, booster heaters, water heaters, and other kitchen eguipment. See **Table 220-6(a)** in NEC.

Table 220-6(b) is a table of demand factors for household electric clothes dryers. It should be noted that this Table is for household dryers only, as no mention is made of commercial dryers. Also, note that there is no reduced demand factor until the 5th dryer is added. When using more than one dryer, it is understood that these demand factors will be used in the computation of dryer loads such as might be found in apartment houses. See **Table 220-6(b)** in NEC.

(o) Electrical Clothes Dryers. When wiring is installed, the clothes dryer is practically never available, so that the feeder circuit which shall feed it may be sized properly. With this in mind, the NEC added the following: *When feeder capacity and circuits are installed for one or more electric clothes dryers, a feeder load of 5,000 watts or the nameplate rating of the appliance, whichever is larger, shall be included for each dryer, subject to the demand factors of* **Table 220-6(b)**.

Many inspectors have insisted on No. 8 copper or the equivalent for dryers, as most dryers pull approximately 30 amperes. Nameplate rating and a branch circuit should not be loaded to exceed 80% of its capacity.

220-7. Optional Calculation for Single-Family Dwelling or Individual Apartment of Multifamily Dwellings—When a one-family residence is serviced by a 115/230 volt, 3-wire, 100-ampere or larger service, and supplied by one feeder or one set of service-entrance conductors, either **Table 220-7** or **Section 220-4** may be used, whichever is most applicable.

220-8. Optional Calculation for Additional Loads in Existing One-Family Dwelling Occupancy—This takes into consideration the load calculations for existing one-family dwellings which are currently being served by 115/230 volts or 120/208 volts, 3-wire, and which currently have a 60-ampere service. See Table in **Section 220-8**.

220-9. Optional Calculation for Multifamily Dwellings—
(a) This is for multifamily dwellings equipped with:
   (1) Electric cooking.
   (2) Electric spacing heating.
   (3) Air conditioning.
   (4) No more than one feeder to each individual dwelling unit.
This method may be used in lieu of the method in **Section 220-4**. Any house loads are to be calculated in accordance with the applicable sections of **Article 220**. These calculations shall be added to those as determined by this section.
   (b) *The connected load to which the demand factor applies shall include:*
      (1) *1500 watts for each 2-wire 20 ampere appliance circuit required by* **Section 220-3(b)** *and 1500 watts for each 2-wire 20 ampere laundry circuit installed in accordance with* **Section 220-3(b)**.
      (2) *Lighting and portable appliances at 3 watts per sq. ft.*
      (3) *All fixed or stationary appliances including ranges, wall-mounted ovens, counter-mounted cooking units, and laundry dryers at nameplate rated load (Kva for motors and other low power-factor loads).*

(4) *Water heaters at nameplate rated load, using only the maximum possible at one time in the case of a water heater with interlocked elements.*

(5) *The larger load of all space heating units or all air conditioning units as per* **Section 220-4(l).**

(c) *The required demand load for each feeder and for service entrance conductors shall not be less than the connected load of the space heater or air conditioning, whichever is greater.*

The best possible explanation appears in the 1971 NEC (Proposal No. 68, Page 29, 1971 Reprint). *Supporting Comment: It has come to our attention that certain very large area electrically heated apartments with minimum-sized major appliances could have an unusually high ratio of space heating to other connected load. We recommend that the service-entrance capacity be not less than the connected space heating or air conditioning, whichever is greater.*

ARTICLE 230—SERVICES

A. General Requirements

230-1. Scope—This Article is a complete coverage of service conductors and equipment for the control and protection of all services. In **Article 100** covering definitions, these were the conductors and equipment from the source of power through the service-entrance equipment. The source might be distribution lines, transformers, or generators.

A thorough knowledge of this Article is very important since a good service is the keystone of the entire installation. Services may be overhead or underground. A review of **Article 100** and the definitions pertaining to services is essential. The following is a list of definitions pertaining to services which appear in **Article 100.**

(1) Services.
(2) Service cable.
(3) Service conductors.
(4) Service drop.
(5) Service-entrance conductors (overhead system).
(6) Service-entrance conductors (underground system).
(7) Service equipment.
(8) Service lateral.
(9) Service raceway.

Although it is not a Code requirement, the local utility company should always be consulted as to the location for the service entrance. See **Sections 110-15, 230-45,** and **230-70 (b).**

230-2. Number of Services to a Building or Other Premises Served—Fundamentally, there is to be only one set of services to a building or premises. However, there are some exceptions to this rule, as follows:

Exception No. 1. Fire Pumps. Separate services may be required for fire pumps. This would indicate an instance where a fire pump is being served from a separate transformer. It would accomplish nothing if the fire pump and the other service came from one transformer.

Exception No. 2. Emergency Lighting. A separate service may be installed for emergency lighting and power. One would be a standby in the event of failure of the other service. An example of this might be a hospital where two separate services are installed, each being served from a different distribution feeder. In the event that one source failed, the other service might be fed from an emergency standby generator.

Exception No. 3. Multiple-Occupancy Buildings.

(a) By special permission (in writing), more than one service may be run to a building if there is no space available for service equipment that is accessible to all occupants.

(b) Multiple-occupancy buildings may have two or more separate sets of service-entrance conductors tapped to one service drop or service lateral (Figs. 230-1 and 2). Two or more sets of service-entrance conductors may be tapped from a single set of main service conductors.

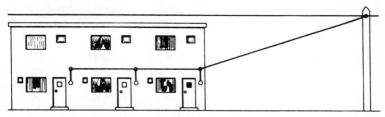

Fig. 230-1. One service drop feeding three service-entrance conductors.

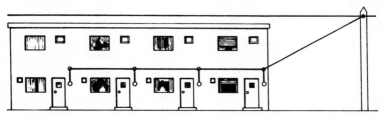

Fig. 230-2. One service drop feeding four service-entrance conductors.

DEFINITION: *Sub-sets of service-entrance conductors are taps from main service conductors run to service equipment.*

Exception No. 4. Capacity Requirements. By special permission or where capacity requirements are in excess of 3,000 amperes, two or more services may be installed.

When we get into large ampacity services, it is felt that it is better to run two or more services than merely one service for the entire capacity requirement. Note *by special permission.* This is permitted, as shown in Fig. 230-3.

Exception No. 5. Buildings of Large Areas. For buildings covering large areas, it may be necessary to have more than one service. This exception is not as prevalent as it was at one time, due to the increases in voltages, and the use of transformer vaults and dry types of transformers.

Exception No. 6. Different Characteristics or Classes of Use. Following are some of the reasons why additional services may be required:

    (1) Different voltages.
    (2) Different frequencies.
    (3) Different phases.
    (4) Different classes of use, such as:
        (a) Lighting rate.
        (b) Power rate.
    (5) Controlled water-heater service.

Exception No. 7. Separate Enclosures. Where two to six service disconnecting means in separate enclosures supply separate loads from one service drop or lateral, one set of service-entrance conductors may supply each or several such service enclosures.

The above may be best explained by quoting the 1971 preprint: *Supporting Comment—To permit a separate set of service-entrance conductors to supply each of two to six grouped disconnecting means where each disconnecting means supplies a separate load. It was never intended that the several sets of service-entrance conductors had to be connected in parallel. The proposed Exception is intended to eliminate the possibility of a group of unecessary taps and connections and clarifies the original intent of CMP 3.*

230-3. Supply to a Building from Another—Service conductors, which are defined as: The supply conductors which extend from the street mains or from transformers to the service equipment of the premises supplied. Service conductors that supply each building or structure shall never be allowed to be run through one building to another unless the buildings are under single occupancy or management. You are then referred to **Section 230-45,** which explains when conductors are considered to be outside a building. One should, even when under the same occupancy or management, be careful in permitting conductors to be run through the buildings. See Figs. 230-4, and 230-5.

Fig. 230-3. A parallel service entrance.

B. Insulation and Size of Service Conductors

230-4. Insulation of Service Conductors—Service conductors shall have insulation capable of withstanding exposure to atmospheric conditions and preventing detrimental leakages of current to adjacent conductors or to ground. For Service Drops, see **Section 230-22.**

230-5. Sizes of Service Conductors—The size of service conductors is to conform to the following:

(1) Have adequate current-carrying capacity.
(2) Temperature rise in the conductor shall not be detrimental to the insulation of the conductor.
(3) Shall have adequate mechanical strength.

The minimum sizes for service conductors are given in the following references:

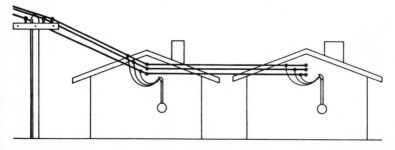

Fig. 230-4. The service entrance for two buildings under the same ownership.

75

Section **230-23** for service drops.

,Section **230-40** for service-entrance conductors.

Section **230-30** for underground-service conductors.

Section **220-4(n)** for farmstead service conductors.

C. Service Drops

230-21. Number of Drops—There is to be only one service drop to a building. Refer back to **Section 230-2**.

230-22. Service Drop Conductors—

(a) Where multiple-conductor cables are used for service drops, the conductors shall be covered with a rubber or thermoplastic type of insulation, with the exception that a bare grounded conductor may be used when the maximum voltage to ground does not exceed 300 volts.

(b) When open individual conductors are used for service drops, all conductors shall be insulated. Service-drop conductors with extruded coverings are to have the same ampacities as listed in **Tables 310-13** and **310-15**.

230-23. Minimum Size of Service Drop Conductors—The first requirement shall always be that service-drop conductors shall be of sufficient size to carry the load. They shall not be smaller than No. 8 copper or the equivalent, except for limited loads as covered in **Section 230-41**. Exception permits service-entrance conductor to be as small as No. 12, providing that they only furnish a single circuit, such as a small polyphase motor, controlled water heaters, or similar loads, and providing they are hard-drawn copper or equivalent.

Overhead conductors to a building or other structure from another building or other structure (such as a pole) on which a meter or disconnecting means is installed shall be considered as a service drop and installed accordingly.

Figs. 100-3 and 230-5 show the service drops when the structure is a pole. The same condition could be a building with the meter on the building and/or a disconnecting means and other buildings or structures from said meter and/or disconnecting means. The grounded conductor of **Service Drops** shall be sized as per **Section 250-23(b)**.

230-24. Clearance of Service Drops—This Section pertains to services that are not readily accessible, do not exceed 600 volts, and must conform to the following:

(a) **Clearance Over Roof.** The basic requirement is that all services shall have a clearance of 8 feet over the highest points of the roof or roofs over which they pass, but the following exceptions may also apply:

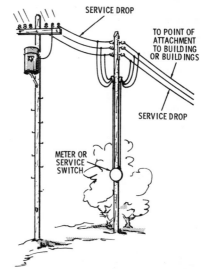

Fig. 230-5. A metering pole.

Exception No. 1. This applies to services that do not exceed 300 volts between conductors. Formerly, services over roofs that were not readily accessible were permitted to have a clearance of not less than 3 feet. This was a very debatable question as to what was not readily accessible. The 1965 Code has clarified this—*where*

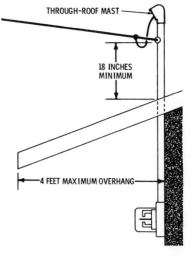

Fig. 230-6. A service-drop mast mounted through the roof.

the voltage between conductors does not exceed 300 and the roof has a slope of not less than 4 inches in 12 inches the clearance may be not less than 3 feet.

Exception No. 2. Another exception has been added which clarifies the attachment of services to approved masts. *Service drop conductors of 300 volts or less which do not pass over other than a maximum of 4 feet of the overhang portion of the roof for the purpose of terminating at a (through-the-roof) service raceway or approved support may be maintained at a minimum of 18 inches from any portion of the roof over which it passes.* This exception does not mention the slope of the overhang, but does clear up the height of the point of attachment to the mast. An illustration (Fig. 230-6) shows where this exception is applicable.

(b) Clearance from Ground. This pertains to voltages not to exceed 600 volts and covers clearances of Service Drops. See Fig. 230-8.

10 feet—above finished grade, sidewalks or from any platform or projection from which they may be reached.

12 feet—over residential driveways and commercial areas such as parking lots and drive-in establishments not subject to truck traffic.

15 feet—over commercial areas, parking lots, agricultural or other areas subject to truck traffic.

18 feet—over public streets, alleys, roads and driveways on other than residential property.

(c) Clearance from Building Openings. Again this is for services not exceeding 600 volts. (For clearances of conductors of over 600 volts, see the *National Electrical Safety Code,* available from the Superintendent of Documents, Government Printing Office, Washington, D.C.). There is to be a clearance of not less than 36 inches from windows, doors, porches, fire escapes, or similar locations. Conductors above windows are considered out of reach.

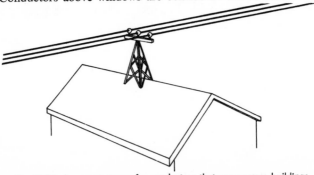

Fig. 230-7. A support tower for conductors that span across buildings.

230-25. Supports over Buildings — Supports shall be used, where practical, for supporting conductors that pass over buildings. They shall be of substantial construction. Where conductors pass over buildings, and the 8-foot or 3-foot clearances (as may be required) cannot be properly maintained, supports shall be constructed to give the proper clearance, as illustrated in Fig. 230-7.

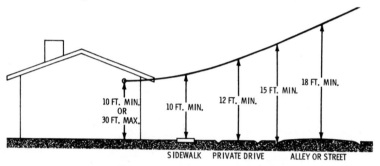

Fig. 230-8. Minimum service-drop clearance.

230-26. Point of Attachment—*The point of attachment of a drop to a building or other structure shall be not less than 10 feet above finished grade and shall be at a height to permit the minimum clearance requirements of* **Section 230-24.**

When sufficient attachment height for service drops cannot be obtained due to the construction of the building, a mast type of riser (Fig. 230-9) may be used providing it is capable of withstanding the strain that might be imposed upon it. In considering the strain that might be imposed, the prevailing weather conditions should be considered. Each locality will no doubt have specifications which should be met.

230-27. Means of Attachment—In attaching multiple-conductor cables to buildings or other structures, only approved devices shall be used. In the attachment of open conductors, only approved, noncombustible, nonabsorptive types of fittings shall be used.

D. Underground Services

230-30. Insulation—*Service lateral conductors shall be insulated for the applied voltage.*

Exception: A grounded conductor may be:

(1) *Bare copper used in a raceway.*
(2) *Bare copper for direct burial where bare copper is judged to be suitable for the solid conditions.*
(3) *Bare copper for direct burial without regard to soil conditions*

79

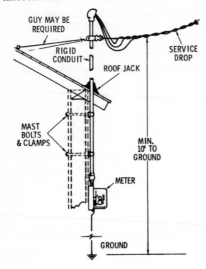

GUY MAY BE REQUIRED

RIGID CONDUIT

ROOF JACK

SERVICE DROP

MAST BOLTS & CLAMPS

MIN. 10' TO GROUND

METER

GROUND

Fig. 230-9. Mast installation for proper service-drop height.

where part of an approved cable assembly with a moisture-and-fungus-resistant outer covering.

(4) *Aluminum without individual insulation or covering used in a raceway or for direct burial when:*

(a) *Part of an approved cable assembly with a moisture-and-fungus-resistant outer covering, and when:*

(b) *The normal voltage to ground of any conductor is not over 300 volts.*

Take note of the bare copper for direct burial, but also take note of the fact that the soil conditions must be judged suitable and this judging is up to the authority having jurisdiction, as provided in **Section 90-7.**

230-32. Protection Against Damage—

(a) **In the Ground.** *Underground service conductors shall be protected against physical damage by being installed:*

(1) *in duct;*

(2) *in rigid metal conduit or electrical metallic tubing made of a material suitable for the condition, or provided with corrosion protection suitable for the condition;*

(3) *in rigid nonmetallic conduit if installed in accordance with* **Sections 347-2 and 347-3;**

(4) *By direct burial in the earth. Conductors buried directly in the earth, whether single conductors or as a multi-conductor* *cable, shall be of a type approved for the purpose. Where necessary to prevent physical damage to the conductors from rocks, slate, etc., or from vehicular traffic, etc., direct burial conductors shall be provided with supplementary protection, such as sand, and suitable running boards, suitable sleeves, or other approved means. Conductors under a building shall be in a raceway that is extended to the outer perimeter of the building.*

In **Sections 310-1(b) 310-5** and **310-6** there is additional coverage for direct burial conductors or cables, and the requirements are given. The sand will protect the insulation from damage by weight or frost heave, where rocky soil is encountered and many inspectors have required this for some time past.

(5) *Other approved means.*

(b) **On Poles.** Approved cable, pipe, or other approved means shall be used to give mechanical protection to underground service conductors which are carried up a pole. The minimum protection for this purpose is to a height of 8 feet. Where conductors are carried farther up the pole (as they would be in most cases), they should be protected from damage caused by lineman hooks. This is another case for the inspection authority to decide.

(c) **Where Entering Building.** It is required that where underground service conductors enter a building, they must have mechanical protection, such as:

(1) Rigid or flexible conduit.
(2) Electric metallic tubing.
(3) Auxiliary gutters.
(4) The metal tape of an approved service cable.
(5) Other approved means.

This mechanical protection shall extend to the service-entrance equipment unless the service switch is installed on a switchboard.

230-33. Raceway Seal—Raceways or ducts on an underground service shall be sealed at the point of entrance into the building with suitable compound to prevent the entrance of gases or moisture. Also, any unused or spare ducts shall also be sealed.

230-34. Grounding Raceways and Cable Sheaths—This coverage is lengthy and detailed, so it appears in **Section 230-63**.

230-35. Termination at Service Equipment—See **Section 230-42 (Exception No. 3)** and **Section 230-53**.

E. Service-Entrance Conductors

230-40. Insulation of Service-Entrance Conductors—

(a) *Service-entrance conductors entering buildings or other structures shall be insulated. Where only on the exterior of buildings or other structures the conductors shall be insulated or covered:*

Exception: A grounded conductor may be:

    (1) *Bare copper used in a raceway.*

    (2) *Bare copper for direct burial where bare copper is judged to be suitable for the soil conditions.*

    (3) *Bare copper for direct burial without regard to soil conditions where part of an approved cable assembly with a moisture-and-fungus-resistant outer coating.*

    (4) *Aluminum without individual insulation or covering used in a raceway or for direct burial when:*

        (a) *Part of an approved cable assembly with a moisture-and-fungus-resistant outer covering and when:*

        (b) *The nominal voltage to ground of any conductor is not over 300 volts.*

It would be well to note the similarity of this **Section** and **Section 230-30,** and the same notation will apply here.

(b) Any individual conductors on the exterior of the building or structure, and which enter the building or structure, shall be insulated or covered.

230-41. Size of Service-Entrance Conductors, Overhead System and Underground System—This section also applies to **Section 230-31**.

The first requirement, as always, is that the conductors be of sufficient ampacity to carry the required load. The determination of the size required was covered thoroughly in **Article 220,** and the ampacities given in **Tables 310-12** through **310-15.** The requirement is that the minimum size of service-entrance conductors be no smaller than No. 6, except:

Exception No. 1. Any single-family residence which has an initial load of 10 KW or more, as computed in accordance with **Section 220-4,** is required to have a service of no less than 100-ampere 3-wire capacity. There is a further recommendation that a minimum of 100-ampere 3-wire service be provided for all individual residences. The cost of this size of service at the time of original installation will be much less than it would be if it were necessary to rewire to this size of service at a future date.

If the initial installation has five or more 2-wire branch circuits, the service-entrance conductors shall have an ampacity of not less than 100 amperes. From this **Exception No. 1,** one may readily see that, for single-family dwellings, the minimum size service just naturally shall be 100 amperes in most any conceivable case.

Exception No. 2. Installations that have no more than two 2-wire branch circuits may have the minimum size of service-entrance conductors reduced to No. 8.

Exception No. 3. The service-entrance conductors may be reduced to no less than size No. 8 by special permission where due to limitations of the supply source or load requirements.

Exception No. 4. For loads of only one branch circuit in which the conductors are no smaller than No. 12, and where this single branch serves a limited load such as a controlled water heater or a small polyphase motor, the service-entrance conductors may be reduced to No. 12.

Exception No. 5. The grounded (neutral) conductor shall have an ampacity in conformity with **Section 220-4(e)**, *and shall not be less than the minimum size required by* **Section 250-23(b)**.

When referring to **Section 250-23(b),** note that the 1971 NEC added an *Exception: The grounded conductor need not be larger than the largest ungrounded service conductor.*

230-42. Service-Entrance Conductors without Splice—*Service-entrance conductors shall be without splice execpt as follows:*

Exception No. 1. Clamped or bolted connections in a meter enclosure are permitted.

Exception No. 2. Taps to main service conductors are permitted as provided in **Section 230-2** *Exception No. 3(b) or to individual sets of service equipment as provided in* **Section 230-70(g)**.

Exception No. 3. Where an underground service conductor enters a build-

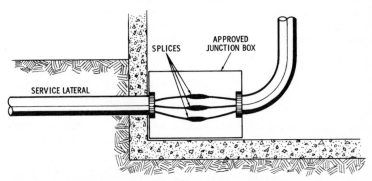

Fig. 230-10. A splice in an underground service.

83

ing, a splice may be made in an approved enclosure for connecting to approved service raceway or cable. (See Fig. 230-10.)

Exception No. 4. On existing installations, a connection will be permitted where service conductors are extended from a service drop to an outside meter and returned to connect to the service-entrance conductors of an existing installation.

230-43. Other Conductors in Service Raceway—See NEC.

F. Installation of Service-Entrance Conductors

230-44. Wiring Method—*Service Entrance conductors extending along the exterior, or entering buildings or other structures may be installed as follows:*

(a) *As separate conductors in cables approved for the purpose, cablebus or enclosed in rigid conduit.*

(b) *For circuits not exceeding 600 volts the conductors may be installed in electrical metallic tubing, wireways, auxiliary gutters, busways or as a cablebus installed for services in accordance with* **Article 365.**

Service-entrance conductors should not be run within the hollow spaces of frame buildings unless provided with over-current protection at their outer end. This is often interpreted to mean only SE cable, but this is not the case, as it could also mean conduit. Again, this comes back to the inspection authority as to what might be safe practice.

230-45. Conductor Considered Outside Building—Service-entrance conductors in conduits or ducts that are enclosed in two inches of concrete, brick, or under a concrete floor, or encased in a concrete wall are considered as being outside the building.

230-46. Mechanical Protection—Where individual open conductors or other than approved cables, such as SE cable, are installed, they shall not be installed less than 8 feet from the ground or where they might be exposed to any physical damage. Where approved SE cable is installed and is likely to become exposed to physical damage in any exposed places, such as driveways, or in any other location in which they might be exposed to physical damage, they shall be protected by conduit, electrical metallic tubing, or other approved means. The other approved means is the responsibility of the enforcing authority.

230-47. Individual Open Conductors Exposed to Weather—There are three conditions under which open conductors that are exposed to the weather shall be supported. In each case they shall be supported by approved insulators, racks, brackets, or other means which shall keep them at least 2 inches away from the surface wired over. They shall also be at least 8 feet above the ground. The three conditions are:

(1) Supports placed are not to exceed 9 feet apart, and the insulators placed so that the conductors are at least 6 inches apart.

(2) Supports placed are not to exceed 15 feet apart, provided that the insulating supports maintain at least a 12-inch separation between conductors.

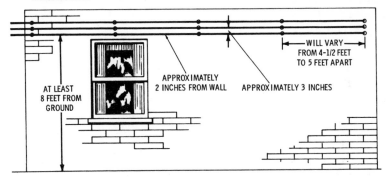

WILL VARY FROM 4-1/2 FEET TO 5 FEET APART

APPROXIMATELY 2 INCHES FROM WALL

APPROXIMATELY 3 INCHES

AT LEAST 8 FEET FROM GROUND

Fig. 230-11. Service conductors run on an outside wall.

(3) When the voltage is 300 volts or less between the conductors, they may have a separation of not less than 3 inches and the supports shall be no more than 4½ feet apart. The approved method of installing conductors is shown in Fig. 230-11.

230-48. Individual Open Conductors Not Exposed to Weather—When individual conductors that are not exposed to weather must be supported on buildings or other structures, they are to be supported by glass or porcelain insulators not more than 4½ feet apart. They are to be separated from the wall by not less than 1 inch and the minimum spacing between conductors shall not exceed 2½ inches.

230-49. Individual Conductors Entering Buildings—Where individual conductors enter buildings, they are required to pass inward and upward through noncombustible and nonabsorptive insulating tubes, or through roof bushings. The Code calls for a drip loop. However, one should consider **Section 250-51,** which requires the service head to be above the service drop to prevent the entrance of moisture.

230-50. Service Cables—

(a) **Approved Service-Entrance Cable.** This gives the necessary information for installing approved service-entrance cable. Support SE cable by straps or other approved means:

(1) Within 12 inches of the service-head, goose-neck or connection to a raceway or enclosure.

(2) Otherwise support the cable at intervals not to exceed 4½ feet.

(b) Other Cables. If the cables are not approved for mounting in contact with the building, they are to be mounted on insulators at intervals not to exceed 15 feet and must have a minimum clearance of 2 inches from the surface on which they are mounted.

230-51. Connections at Service Head.—

(a) *Service raceways shall be equipped with a raintight service head.*

(b) *Service cables, unless continuous from pole to service equipment or meter, shall be either:*

(1) *equipped with a raintight service head or*

(2) *formed in a gooseneck, taped and painted or taped with a self-sealing weather-resistant thermoplastic.*

(c) To prevent water from entering the conductor, which has caused some troubles due to siphoning between the conductor and its insulation, *service heads and goosenecks in service-entrance cables shall be located below the point of attachment of the service-drop conductors to the building or other structure.*

There are as usual exceptions to this which might be required if it is impractical to meet the above requirements. Where necessary to locate the service head below the service-drop conductors, this service head may be located at a point not to exceed 24 inches from the termination of the service-drop conductors. There should also be a mechanical connector at the lowest point to prevent siphoning of water by the service-entrance conductors, as shown in Fig. 230-13.

(d) *Service cables shall be held securely in place by connection to service-drop conductors below the gooseneck or by a fitting approved for the purpose.*

(e) *Service heads shall have conductors of opposite polarity brought out through separately bushed holes.* See Fig. 230-12.

(f) *Drip loops shall be formed on individual conductors. To prevent the entrance of moisture, service-entrance conductors shall be connected to the service-drop conductors either:*

(1) *below the level of the service head, or*

(2) *below the level of the termination of the service-entrance sheath.*

(g) *Service-drop conductors and service-entrance conductors shall be so arranged that water will not enter service raceway or equipment.*

230-52. Raceways to Drain—This section was updated with the 1971 NEC to include nonmetallic conduit. Where exposed to the weather, raceways enclosing service-entrance conductors shall be raintight and arranged to drain. Where embedded in masonry, raceways shall be arranged to drain.

86

230-53. **Termination at Service Equipment**—This was rewritten in the 1971 NEC to include all types of cables and raceways. *Any service raceway or cable shall terminate at the inner end in a box, cabinet, or equivalent fitting that effectively encloses all live metal parts.*

Exception: Where the service disconnecting means is mounted on a switchboard having exposed bus-bars on the back, a raceway may terminate at a bushing.

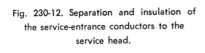
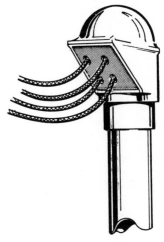

Fig. 230-12. Separation and insulation of the service-entrance conductors to the service head.

230-54. Grounding Service Raceways and Cable Armor—This is covered in **Section 230-63.**

G. Service Equipment

230-60. Hazardous Locations—The service-equipment requirements that apply to hazadrous locations will be covered in **Chapter 5, Article 500 to 517.**

230-61. Service Equipment Grouped—When a building is supplied by more than one set of service laterals that are mounted to the same side of the building, the service equipment shall be grouped together. The service equipment shall be marked showing what it serves.

To be compatable with **Article 700,** a paragraph was added to the Code which states that *when two or more disconnecting means for fire pumps or for emergency service are installed, they shall be installed sufficiently remote from the regular 1 to 6 service disconnecting means, so as to minimize the possibility of their being opened as regular disconnects and thus simultaneously open the emergency service.*

H. Grounding and Guarding

230-62. Guarding—*Live parts of service equipment shall be enclosed so that they will not be exposed to accidental contact, unless mounted on a switchboard, a panelboard or controller accessible to qualified persons only and located in a room or enclosure free from easily ignitible material.* Often, service equipment might be located out-of-doors, in schools, etc., where innocent persons might come in contact with the live electrical parts. In the case of breaker panels, the fronts are screwed on, but the doors of fuse panels are easily opened. In these cases, locks should be provided to make them inaccessible.

230-63. Grounding and Bonding—The following three paragraphs covers the grounding of service equipment:

(a) **Equipment. Article 250** covers the manner in which service equipment is to be grounded, **unless:**

    (1) the voltage does not exceed 150 volts to ground and such enclosures are (2) isolated from conducting surfaces, and (3) unexposed to contact by persons or materials that may also be in contact with other conducting surfaces.

Although Fig. 230-14 is actually a part of **Article 250**, it is shown here to familiarize one with proper grounding of service equipment.

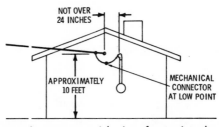

Fig. 230-13. A connection to prevent siphoning of water into the service-drop head.

(b) **Raceways and Cable Armor.** All service raceways, cable armor, and the metallic sheath of service cables shall be grounded (Fig. 230-15). Conduit from an underground supply shall be considered effectively grounded where it is bonded to an underground lead-sheathed cable system.

(c) **Flexible Conduit.** It is sometimes necessary to use a piece of flexible conduit in a service-entrance raceway. Whenever this becomes necessary, the flexible conduit shall be bonded by a conductor and approved clamps (copper strapping is not approved for this purpose). These bonding conductors are to be sized according to **Table 250-94(a).** The flexible conduit in itself is not considered as an adequate ground in service-equipment raceways.

This is the reason that it must be bonded. The clamps and bonding conductors shall not be subject to physical damage. Should the flexible conduit terminate at the service-entrance cabinet, the flexible conduit shall be bonded to the cabinet. (See Fig. 230-16).

Bonding, as discussed here, should not be confused with equipment grounding. Such grounding is made at a point after the service-entrance equipment, in which case metallic raceways may be used without bonding, except in special conditions. It is often difficult to secure proper bonding at service-entrance equipment with flexible conduit that might be used. Therefore, the precautions discussed are necessary because the over-

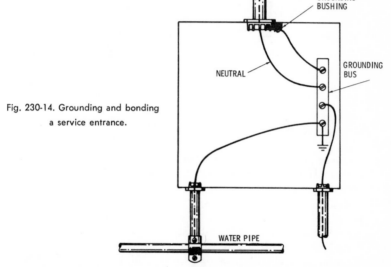

Fig. 230-14. Grounding and bonding a service entrance.

current protection is in the service-entrance equipment and not ahead of the service entrance. If the neutral should open, the raceway might carry the neutral current if the bonding were absent or not properly made. Neutral current through the raceway could cause heating with the possibility of a resulting fire.

J. Disconnecting Means

230-70. General—

(a) Disconnection from Service Conductors. *Means shall be provided for disconnecting all conductors in the building or other structure from the service entrance conductors.*

(b) Location. *The disconnecting means shall be located at a readily accessible point nearest to the entrance of the conductors, either*

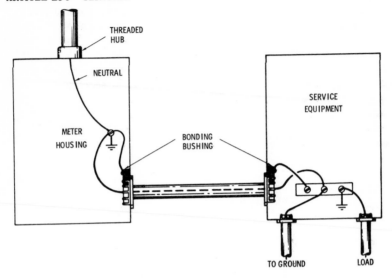

Fig. 230-15. Grounding and bonding a typical service entrance.

inside or outside the building or other structure. Sufficient access and working space shall be provided about the disconnecting means.

The preceding is plainly stated, but the term *point nearest to the entrance* is quite broad in its meaning. Many inspection authorities set a maximum for this distance, such as 15 feet. The Code cannot be explicit about this because many things can influence this distance. It must therefore be left up to the inspection authority.

Readily accessible was defined in **Article 100.** The term *disconnecting means* is just what it implies; it is a means of disconnecting the interior wiring in the event of trouble, and it must be readily accessible so that one will not have to go into a closet, go down into the basement, behind the stairs, etc. If it should become necessary to disconnect the service-entrance equipment from the service-entrance conductors, it might be an emergency and this action should not be hampered by any obstacles. In the event that the logical location should be considered to be too far from the point of entrance, it is usually possible to install a disconnecting means with overcurrent protection on the outside of the building. In this case, the conductors from this point become feeders and are to be treated as such.

In a multiple occupancy building, each occupant shall have access to his disconnecting means. A multiple occupancy building having individual occupancy above the second floor shall have service equipment grouped in a common accessible place, the disconnecting means consisting of not more than six switches or six circuit breakers. Multiple occupancy buildings that do not have individual occupancy above the second floor may have service conductors run to each occupancy in accordance with Section 230-2, Exception No. 3 and each such service may have not more than six switches or circuit breakers.

(c) Approval. *The disconnecting means shall be of a type approved for service equipment and for prevailing conditions.*

Thus, if a disconnect is installed on the outside, a raintight or weatherproof piece of equipment must be used, while indoors in a general location the ordinary type of equipment is satisfactory. In a hazardous location, the equipment must be approved for that type of service.

(d) Types Permitted. *The disconnecting means for ungrounded conductors shall consist of either:*

(1) A manually-operated switch, a manually-operated circuit-breaker, or other suitable operating means. All must be positively identified and marked for mechanical operation by hand.

(2) An electrically-operated switch or circuit breaker may be used provided that it is capable of being opened by hand in the event of a power failure, and provided that the open and closed positions are readily marked and properly indicated to the operator. All ungrounded conductors are to be simultaneously opened.

(e) Externally Operable. *An enclosed service disconnecting means shall be externally operable without exposing the operator to contact with live parts.*

Exception: An electrically operated switch or circuit breaker need not be capable of being externally operable by hand to the closed position.

When a single circuit or group of circuits are separately metered, as in apartment-house installations, it is recommended that the devices (disconnecting means) be installed in a convenient location to control each separately-metered installation. These devices (main disconnects) are to be enclosed and the switch or circuit breaker be externally operable.

In this type of installation, a maximum of six main disconnects

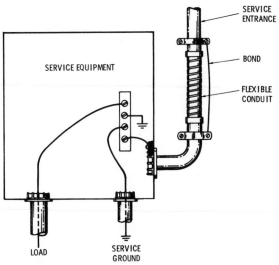

SERVICE
ENTRANCE

BOND

FLEXIBLE
CONDUIT

SERVICE EQUIPMENT

LOAD

SERVICE
GROUND

Fig. 230-16. Bonding flexible conduit in a service entrance.

shall be maintained or a main disconnect must be installed to take care of all the circuits. In the installation, it should be remembered that the main disconnects shall be accessible to the occupants of the apartments. This is a condition that causes much concern, although it need not if all the requirements that must be met are considered. Fig. 230-17 illustrates a typical example of such a condition. This installation may use a wiring trough or gutter, or a combination meter installation and trough or gutter. The illustration shown will, of course, not meet all installation requirements, but is an example of the intent in this matter. The one point to bear in mind is that there are to be no more than six main disconnects in service-entrance equipment. It would be suggested that when this type of installation is anticipated, the authorities be consulted and the installation worked out before the work is done.

(f) Indicating. *The disconnecting means shall plainly indicate whether it is in the open or closed position.*

(g) Switch and Circuit Breaker. The disconnecting means may consist of not more than six switches or six circuit breakers, either in a common enclosure or a group of separate enclosures that are located together. This operation is commonly referred to as the **six operations** to comply with rules for service-entrance equipment. Two- or three-pole switches or circuit breakers are counted as one unit—the point to remember is that they shall control

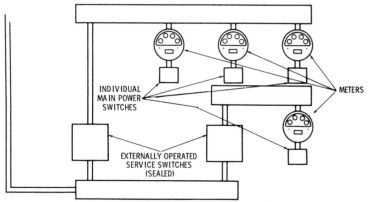

Fig. 230-17. Typical service disconnect switches.

multiwire circuits. This does in no manner mean that a two- or three-pole switch or circuit breaker can have each pole connected to the same phase—all of the conditions of the multiwire circuit must be met.

Fig. 230-18. A two-pole circuit-breaker switch which cannot be used as a service disconnect.

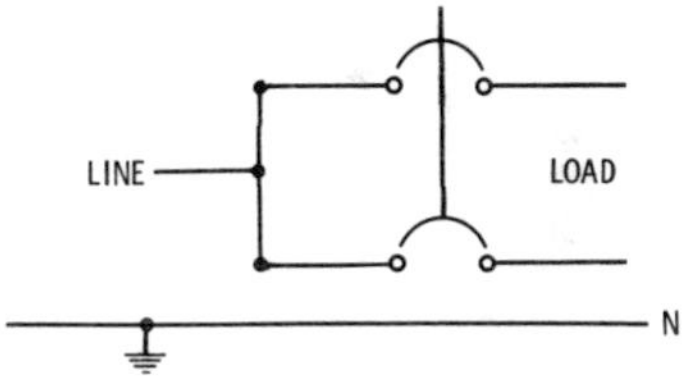

The operation of a two- or three-pole switch or circuit breaker is counted as one operation in the preceding conditions. They must be equipped with either tie handles or a master handle so as to make it practical to disconnect all conductors of the service with no more than six operations of the hand. Refer to **Section 200-5 (a).**

Fig. 230-18 illustrates what is meant by hooking up a **two-pole** circuit breaker to the same phase. This **does not** comply with the requirements and is not permitted. Fig. 230-19 shows eighteen circuit breakers in one panel which conforms to the rule since they are tied together in groups of three. Each circuit breaker of each group ties to a different phase conductor. The **prior refer-** ence to **Section 200-5** covers the color coding shown in **this** illustration. Each disconnecting means, whether there or 1 or 6, shall be permanently marked to indicate which is the service disconnect(s).

(h) Simultaneous Openings. The disconnecting means is required to disconnect all ungrounded conductors simultaneously. See Fig. 230-20.

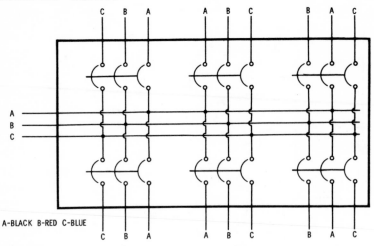

Fig. 230-19. Illustrating eighteen circuit breakers tied together in groups of three.

(i) Disconnection of Grounded Conductor. The disconnecting means may be so designed that it also opens the grounded conductor simultaneously with the ungrounded conductors. Where the disconnect does not accomplish this, there shall be other means provided in the service cabinet for disconnecting the grounded conductor from the interior wiring. This is usually accomplished by pressure-type connectors for the grounded conductor. The service-entrance ground shall always be attached to the service side of the disconnecting means. This is required so that there will be ground on the service, even though the grounded conductors on the interior wiring have been disconnected.

230-71. Rating of Service Equipment—

(a) *The service equipment shall have a rating not less than the load to be carried determined in accordance with* **Article 220.** *The service disconnecting means shall have a rating not less than 60 amperes except:*

Exception No. 1. Any single-family residence which has an initial load of 10 KW or more, as computed in accordance with **Article 220,** is required to have a service of not less than 100-amperes 3-wire capacity. The cost of this size of service at the time of original installation will be much less than it would be if it were necessary to install this size service at a future date.

If the initial installation has five or more 2-wire branch cir-

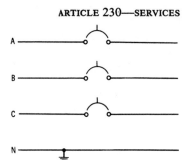

Fig. 230-20. Multiwire circuits not supplying polyphase motors.

cuits, then the service-entrance equipment shall have an ampacity of not less than 100 amperes, 3-wire. This portion must not be confused, but shall be coordinated with *Exception No. 1* of **Section 230-41.** One is talking about the service-entrance conductors and the other about the service-entrance equipment, but they both come out 100 amperes 3-wire.

Exception No. 2. There are cases where the minimum of 50 or 60 amperes would not be practical, such as a traffic light or lighted sign. Therefore, a minimum of a 30-ampere service is permitted if there are no more than two 2-wire branch circuits and if the load drawn is less than 30 amperes.

(b) Where more than one switch or circuit breaker is used as a disconnecting means in accordance with **Section 230-70(g),** the combined ratings of the switches or circuit breaker that are used shall be no less than what would be required had only one switch or circuit breaker been used.

230-72. Connections to Terminals—Soldered connections are never to be used for connecting service conductors to service equipment. The conductors shall be connected by means of pressure connectors, clamps, or other means approved for the purpose.

230-73. Equipment Connected to the Supply Side of Service Disconnect—*Equipment shall not be connected to the supply side of the disconnecting means.*

Exception No. 1. Service fuses.

Exception No. 2. Fuses and disconnecting means or circuit breakers, in meter pedestals, connected in series with the ungrounded service conductors and located away from the building supplied.

Exception No. 3. Meters nominally rated not in excess of 600 volts, provided all metal housings and service enclosures are grounded in accordance with **Article 250.**

Exception No. 4. Instrument transformers (current and potential), high-ampedance shunts, surge-protection capacitors, time switches and lightning arresters.

Exception No. 5. Taps used only to supply time switches, circuits for emergency systems, fire pump equipment, fire and sprinkler alarms if provided with service equipment and installed in accordance with requirements for service-entrance conductors. See Fig. 230-21 and 230-22.

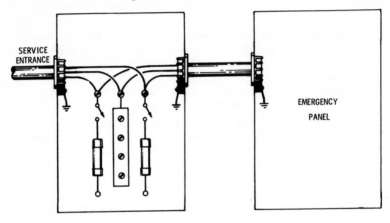

Fig. 230-21. Unapproved means of connecting an emergency panel.

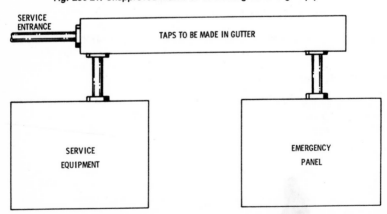

Fig. 230-22. Approved means of connecting an emergency panel.

230-74. Safeguarding Emergency Supply—Article 700 is to be followed in the installation of emergency systems. When an emergency supply is provided to feed conductors that are supplied from a service disconnecting means, it shall be so arranged that all of the ungrounded conductors from the usual supply are opened before the connection to the emergency supply is made.

230-75. Multiple Occupancy—Each occupant in a multiple occupancy shall have access to his disconnecting means at all times. Where a multiple occupancy has individual occupancy above the second floor, the disconnecting means shall consist of not more than six switches or six circuit breakers. The disconnecting means shall also be located in a common accessible place.

Where the multiple-occupancy building does not have individual occupancy above the second floor, service conductors may be run to each individual occupancy, as per **Section 230-2, Exception 3.** Each occupancy shall have no more than six switches or six circuit breakers serving as the disconnecting means; otherwise, a main disconnect shall be provided for each occupancy. Refer to **Sections 230-70 (b), 230-45,** and **110-15.** There are so many and varied applications of this section that it is impossible to cover them all.

230-76. More than One Building or Other Structure—

(a) **Disconnect Required for Each.** Where the property consists of one or more buildings or structures under single management, each building or structure shall have a readily accessible disconnecting means which opens all ungrounded conductors. This disconnecting means may be in, on, or adjacent to the building or structure. See Fig. 230-23.

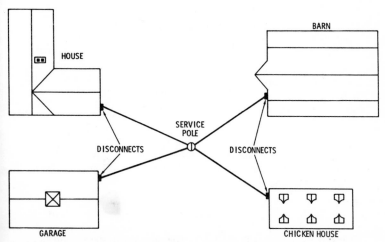

Fig. 230-23. A group of farm buildings showing a service drop to each building.

ARTICLE 230—SERVICES

(b) Suitable for Service Equipment. The disconnecting means, mentioned in **(a)** above, shall be suitable for service entrance equipment.

On residential property where there are garages and out-buildings, the disconnecting means may consist of a snap switch, a set of 3-way switches, or 4-way snap switches that are suitable for use on branch circuits.

K. Overcurrent Protection

230-90. Where Required—*Each ungrounded service-entrance conductor shall have overcurrent protection.*

(a) Ungrounded Conductor. This overcurrent protection shall be in series with the conductor, and shall not have a rating higher than the allowable ampacity of the conductor. There are some exceptions.

An example of the above would be that a 100-ampere service should have No. 3 RH conductors or larger, and a 300-ampere service would have 350 MCM RH or larger conductors. Any derating that might be applicable in **Article 310** must always be considered.

Exception No. 1. Motor starting currents will have to be dealt with separately, and the ratings must be in conformity with **Sections 430-52, 430-62,** or **430-63.** Although not stated in this Section of the Code, you should always take into consideration what might be added in the future and, if possible, make allowances for this at the time of installation.

Exception No. 2. Where nonadjustable circuit breakers do not conform to the ampacity of the conductor, the next larger size may be used provided that it is 800 amperes or less. If the breaker is adjustable, it shall not be set at a rating of more than 125 percent of the ampacity of the conductor. When fuses are used, if there is not a standard size to fit the ampacity of the conductor, the next larger size may be used provided that it is 800 amperes or less.

Exception No. 3. Not more than six circuit breakers or six sets of fuses may serve as the overcurrent device. Here, one must remember that a single-pole, a two-pole, or a three-pole breaker may count as one.

Exception No. 4. This governs multiple-occupancy buildings;
    (1) Each occupant shall have access to his overcurrent protective devices.
    (2) Where there is individual occupancy above the second floor,

98

the service equipment shall be grouped in a common readily accessible place.

(3) The overcurrent protection shall consist of not more than six circuit breakers or six sets of fuses (see *Exception 3*).

(4) Where there is no indicidual occupancy above the second floor, service conductors may be run to each occupancy, as covered in **Section 230-75.**

Exception No. 5. Fire Pumps. Where the service to the fire pump room is judged to be outside of buildings, these provisions shall not apply. Service equipment for fire pump services shall be selected or set to carry locked-rotor current for the motor(s) indefinitely (See NFPA No. 20—1970, Standard for Centrifugal Fire Pumps.)

This exception was added to the 1971 NEC to clarify what some members of the NFPA Committee consider to be the original intent of **Sections 230-90** and **230-94.**

(b) **Not in Grounded Conductor.** There is to be no overcurrent device in the grounded service conductor. The exception to this is that the circuit breaker shall simultaneously open all conductors of the circuit. A little explanation of this might be in order. Should the grounded conductor overcurrent device open by itself and the ungrounded conductor overcurrent devices not open, an unbalanced voltage condition would exist that might cause damage to equipment. See Fig. 230-24.

(c) **More Than One Building.** Please refer back to **Section 230-76.** Where more than one building or structure is under single management, the ungrounded conductors serving each building or structure shall have overcurrent devices of the proper size to protect them. These may be located in the building served or in another building or structure, but in all cases they are to be

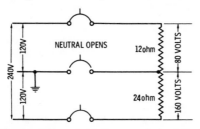

Fig. 230-24. A breaker in the neutral. The neutral circuit breaker must open simultaneously with the breaker contacts in the phase wires.

readily accessible to the occupants of the building being served. A case in point would be a farmstead with a residence and a guest house. Should the overcurrent device be located in the residence, it would not be considered as being accessible to the guest house.

230-91. Location—See NEC.

230-92. Location of Branch-Circuit Overcurrent Devices—If the service overcurrent protection is not accessible, the design shall be such that the branch-circuit devices will operate in case of an overload and will be accessible for servicing. Since the branch-circuit devices will have a smaller rating than the inaccessible service overcurrent protection device, there will be less likelihood that it will trip.

230-93. Protection of Specific Circuits—To prevent tampering, it might become necessary to provide a locked or sealed automatic overcurrent device to serve some specific load, such as a water heater. Such a locked or sealed device must be in an accessible location.

230-94. Relative Location of Overcurrent Device and Other Service Equipment—*The overcurrent device shall protect all circuits and devices except as follows:*

(a) *The service switch may be placed on the supply side.*

(b) As permitted under **Section 230-73**, the following may be installed on the supply side of the service disconnecting means:

    (1) Potential coils of meters or other high-impedance circuits.

    (2) Lightning arresters.

    (3) Surge-protection capacitors. (These are required to have overcurrent protection.)

    (4) Instrument transformers.

(c) Where supplied with separate overcurrent protection, such circuits as emergency circuits and time switches may be connected to the supply side of the service overcurrent protection. In fact, emergency systems must be ahead of the service disconnecting means as covered in **Article 700** and in **NFPA 101** by reference.

(d) Circuits for fire alarms and other protective signaling equipment, as well as fire-pump equipment, may be connected ahead of the service overcurrent protection provided that they have their own overcurrent protection.

(e) See NEC.

(f) *Where service equipment is operated electrically, the control circuit may be connected ahead of the service equipment if suitable over-current protection and disconnecting means are provided.*

230-95. Ground-Fault Protection of Equipment—*Ground-fault protection of equipment shall be provided for grounded electrical services* *of more than 150 volts to ground, but not exceeding 600 volts phase-to-phase for any service disconnecting means rated 1,000 amperes or more. The ground-fault protection may consist of over-current devices or combination of overcurrent devices and current transformers or other equivalent protective equipment which shall operate to cause the service disconnecting means to open all ungrounded conductors of the faulted circuit within one second at fault current values of 1,200 amperes or more.*

When a switch and fuse combination is used, the fuses employed shall be capable of interrupting any current higher than the interrupting capaccity of the switch during a time when the ground-fault protective system will not cause the switch to open.

It is recognized that ground-fault protection is desirable for service disconnecting means rated less than 1000 amperes on grounded systems having more than 150 volts to ground, not exceeding 600 volts phase-to-phase.

This added protective equipment at the service equipment will make it necessary to review the over-all wiring system for proper selective overcurrent protection coordination. Additional installations of ground-fault protective equipment will be needed on feeders and branch circuits where maximum continuity of electrical service is necessary.

The fault currents that are available, plus the damaging effects of ground-faults, have made it necessary to do something about injury to personnel and damage to equipment.

230-96. Working Space—*Sufficient working space shall be provided in the vicinity of the service overcurrent devices to permit safe operation, replacements, inspection, and repairs. In no case shall this be less than specified in* **Section 110-16.**

230-98. Available Short-Circuit current—*Service equipment and its overcurrent protective devices shall have short-circuit current rating equal to or not less than the available short-circuit current at its supply terminal.*

The electrical trade is often not aware of the tremendous increases in available fault current over what it used to be. Larger transformers or lower impedance transformers, has increased fault currents available to all types of occupancies. Residential services are particularly vulnerable, as there is usually no engineering done on these services. Circuit breakers most commonly used in residential service equipment are tested for 5,000 amperes but types suitable for 10,000 amperes are available. All inspection authorities as well as wiremen, engineers, etc., should take a long look at this Section and govern the installation accordingly.

101

L. Services Exceeding 600 Volts

All of the material immediately preceding pertained to services of 600 volts or less. This portion pertains to services of over 600 volts. Also see **Article 710** for voltages over 600 volts.

230-100. Scope—*Circuits with 600 volts or more will be governed by the preceding Sections of* **Article 230,** *where applicable, and by the following Sections which are modifications or additions to the preceding Sections.*

Secondary conductors, not the primary conductors, are the service conductors to the building proper in the following cases:

(1) Where step-down transformers are located outdoors.
(2) Where step-down transformers are located in a separate building from the one served.
(3) Where step-down transformers are located in the building served and in a transformer vault conforming to the requirements of **Article 450,** *and under the sole control of the supply company.*

In all other cases, the primary conductors are the service conductors.

In no case will the provisions of this Article apply to equipment not directly connected to service conductors, and consequently will not apply to equipment in vaults under the sole control of the supply company.

This section is of great importance in the interpretation of the Code. Where a primary is installed by the electrical contractor for the customer's use, even though the supply company accepts the maintenance of same after installation, the primary will come under the Code and is subject to inspection by the inspection authority. If the supply company owns, installs, and has sole control over the primary, it will not come under the Code.

230-101. Service-Entrance Conductors—

(a) **Conductor Size.** *Service conductors shall be not smaller than No. 6 unless in cable. Conductors in cable shall be not smaller than No. 8.*

(b) **Wiring Methods.** *Service-entrance conductors shall be installed by means of one of the following wiring methods:*

(1) In rigid metal conduit.

(2) In rigid nonmetallic conduit where encased in not less than 2 inches of concrete. When encasing in concrete, a few of my personal observations might be inserted. The concrete should be poured thin enough to thoroughly encase the conduits, the conduits should have spacers that will permit ¾″

aggregate to pass and in order to thoroughly encase the conduit, a 7″ slump is very appropriate. Should the conduits, especially duct-banks tend to float, they should be well staked down to stop flotation.

(3) As multi-conductor cable approved for the purpose.

(4) As open conductors where supported on insulators approved for the purpose and where accessible only to qualified persons or where effectively guarded against accidental contact.

(5) In cablebus.

Where surface contamination cannot be prevented and high surface resistivity cannot be maintained, metallic shielding shall be used at over 3 kv. See **Table 710-5** *for shielding of solid dielectric-insulated conductors.*

(c) Open Work. See NEC.

(d) Supports. In the event of short circuits, extra strain is placed on the supports due to magnetic fields. The supports, including the insulators, shall have sufficient strength to withstand this extra strain.

(e) Guarding. *Open wires shall be guarded where accessible to unqualified persons.*

(f) Service Cable. Potheads or other suitable means shall be used to protect the conductors where they emerge from a metal sheath or raceway. This protection shall be for moisture and physical damage.

(g) Draining Raceways. Unless raceways have conductors that are specifically approved for that use, they shall be arranged to drain where they are:

  (1) Embedded in masonry.
  (2) Exposed to the weather.
  (3) In wet locations.

(h) Over 15,000 Volts. Here, you are referred to **Sections 450-41** to **450-48.** Conductors are required to enter either a metal enclosure for the switchgear or a transformer vault.

(i) Conductor Considered Outside Building. Conductors in a duct or conduit which is encased in 2 inches or more of concrete are treated as being outside of the building.

230-102. Warning Signs—*High-voltage signs shall be posted where unauthorized persons might come in contact with live parts.*

Under **Section 230-70,** it was required that all ungrounded conductors be opened simultaneously. A circuit breaker or the alternates covered in **Section 230-106** will answer the purpose. A new part has been added to this section: *The disconnecting means shall be capable of being closed on a fault within the maximum interrupting rating of the overcurrent protection.* These faults will become more and more prevalent as capacities increase and must be dealt with.

230-103. Disconnecting Means—See NEC.

230-104. Isolating Switches—It is essential for safety that when a disconnecting means is opened on higher voltages, some sort of isolation be provided to ensure the extra safety precautions that are needed. These are as follows:

(a) See NEC.

(b) When fuses are capable of being used as a disconnecting switch **(Section 230-106),** *they may serve as the isolating switch when they completely disconnect the oil circuit breaker and all service equipment from the source of supply.*

(c) See NEC. Take note of the grounding, as mentioned. It serves as a precaution should a switch accidentally become energized. Also with shielded-type high-voltage cables of any great length, the cable and the shield become a fair sized capacitor, and the grounding bleeds the charge away, thus preventing what might be a painful shock.

230-105. Equipment in Secondaries—See NEC.

230-106. Overcurrent Protection. There have been substantial changes made in this Section of the Code. Therefore, this section of the NEC should be carefully reviewed and the changes noted.

230-107.—Lightning Arresters—See NEC.

ARTICLE 240—OVERCURRENT PROTECTION

A. Installation

240-1. Scope—*This Article provides the general requirements for the application of overcurrent protective devices.* Other articles contain more specific requirements, as explained in **Section 240-3.**

240-2. Purpose of Overcurrent Protection—Conductors have specific current-carrying capacities (ampacity) for different sizes of conductors, for different insulations, and for different ambient-temperature conditions.

The purpose of overcurrent protection is to protect the insulation of the conductors from damage caused by the current reaching too high a value.

240-3. Protection of Equipment—Equipment shall be protected by overcurrent devices. The table in this Section of the NEC covers the equipment that is to be protected.

240-5. Overcurrent Protection—It is the intent that conductors shall be protected according to their ampacities. These are given in **Table 310-12** through **310-15** in the NEC. Accompanying the tables of ampacities are Notes governing deratings that are required under various conditions. In figuring the ampacities of the conductors, these deratings shall be taken into consideration. The following exceptions apply:

Exception No. 1. Ratings of Nonadjustable Overcurrent Protection of 800 Amperes or Less. If the standard current ratings of fuses or nonadjustable circuit breakers do not conform to the ampacity of the conductors being used, it is permissible to use the next larger standard rating when below 800 amperes. This applies only where the rating is 800 amperes or less.

Exception No. 2. Fixture Wires and Cords. A 20-ampere overcurrent protection is considered as being adequate protection for fixture wires or flexible cords in sizes No. 16 or No. 18, or for tinsel cord, except on elevators, dumbwaiters, etc., as covered in **Section 620-61.** Fixture-wire taps that comply with **Section 210-19 (c-2)** are permitted to be protected by 30; 40; and 50-ampere branch circuits.

Flexible cords for specific appliances will be considered to be protected as follows:

20-ampere circuits, No. 18 cord or larger.
30-ampere circuits, cords of 10 amperes capacity or more.
40-ampere circuits, cord of 20 amperes capacity or over.
50-ampere circuits, cords of 20 amperes capacity or more.

Exception No. 3. Motor Circuits. Motor and motor-control circuit conductors protected in accordance with Parts **c, d, e,** *and* **f** *of* **Article 430.** *Motor-operated appliance circuit conductors protected in accordance with Parts* **b** *and* **d** *of* **Article 422.** *Air-conditioning and refrigeration equipment circuit conductors protected in accordance with Parts* **c** *and* **f** *of* **Article 440.**

Exception No. 4. Control Circuits. Where not in the same cable with communication circuits, as provided in **Section 725-7,** *conductors of control circuits other than motor-control circuits shall be considered as protected by overcurrent devices that are rated or set at not more than 300 percent of the ampacity of the remote-control conductors.*

Exception No. 5. Transformer Secondary Conductors. Conductors supplied by the secondary side of a single-phase transformer having a 2-wire (single-voltage) secondary shall be considered as protected by overcurrent protection provided on the primary (supply) side of the transformer, provided this protection is in accordance with **Section 450-3 (a) (1)** *or* **(b) (1)** *and does not exceed the value determined by multiplying the secondary conductor ampacity by the secondary-to-primary transformer voltage ratio.*

Exception No. 6. Tap Conductors. Tap conductors as permitted in **Sections 210-19 (c); 240-15,** *Exceptions Nos. 3, 5, 6 and 7;* **364-9** *and* **364-10;** *and Part D of* **Article 430.**

(b) **Standard Ratings.** *Standard ratings for fuses and non-adjustable circuit breakers are 15, 20, 25, 30, 35, 40, 45, 50, 60, 70, 80, 90, 100, 110, 125, 150, 175, 200, 225, 250, 300, 350, 400, 450, 500, 600, 700, 800, 1000, 1200, 1600, 2000, 2500, 3000, 4000, 5000, and 6000.*

Standard ratings for fuses and circuit breakers were formerly different but are now the same.

240-6. Fuses—

(a) A limitation as to voltage is placed on plug fuses and fuse holders. Please note that plug fuses and fuse holders are not to be used in circuits exceeding 125 volts between conductors except in circuits supplied from a system having a grounded neutral and with no conductor in such circuits operating at more than 150 volts to ground. This will allow plug fuses to be used on 120/240-volt single-phase systems, but will not permit them to be used on 240-volt **delta** three-phase systems where a neutral is used. They can be used on 120/208-volt wye systems with a grounded neutral.

(b) This part is new in the 1965 Code. A new fuse (type SC) has been approved for 300-volt systems. This was a necessity due to the extended use of 277/480-volt wye systems, which before required the use of a 600-volt fuse. These are a noninterchangeable type of cartridge fuse and are made to fit certain devices the size of circuit breakers. This will allow the use of either circuit breakers or fuses in the same panel.

(c) *The screw-shell of plug-type fuse holders shall be connected to the load side of the circuit.* The reason for this is that, as the fuse is unscrewed, the screw-shell will be disconnected from the hot side of the circuit so that there will be no danger of receiving a shock. A screw-shell plug-type fuse holder is illustrated in Fig. 240-1.

240-8. Thermal Devices—Thermal cutouts, thermal relays, etc., that are
not designed to open under short-circuits or grounds, shall not be used

to protect conductors against overcurrent. They may be used for motor protection as explained in **Section 430-40.** Fuses or circuit breakers having a rating that does not exceed four times the rating of the motor shall be used ahead of the thermal device. (See Fig. 240-2.)

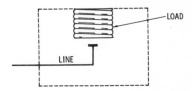

Fig. 240-1. A screw-shell fuse holder.

240-9. Feeders at Supply Stations—Conductors on a constant potential system entering or leaving a supply station (with the exception of grounded neutrals) shall be protected from excessive currents by circuit breakers or by an equivalent device of approved design. These devices shall be located as near as practical to the point where the conductors enter or leave the building. Where outgoing circuits, such as from an isolated plant, are not connected with other sources of power, the overcurrent protection may be placed on the supply side of the transformers (Fig. 240-3).

240-11. Ungrounded Conductors—

(a) *An overcurrent device (fuse or overcurrent trip unit of a circuit breaker) shall be placed in each ungrounded conductor. For motor circuits see* **Article 430.**

(b) *Circuit breakers shall open all ungrounded conductors of the circuit, except as follows:*

    Exception. Individual single-pole circuit breakers may be used for the protection of each ungrounded conductor of:

    (1) Ungrounded 2-wire circuits.
    (2) Each ungrounded conductor of 3-wire DC or single-phase circuit.

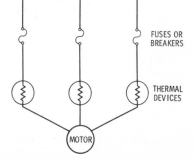

Fig. 240-2. Thermal protection for motors.

107

(3) Each ungrounded conductor of light or appliance branch circuits connected to 4-wire, three-phase systems.

(4) Five-wire, two-phase systems, provided that lighting or appliance circuits are supplied from a system having a grounded neutral, and that no conductor in such circuits operates at a voltage greater than permitted in **Section 210-6.** See Figs. 240-4 and 5.

240-12. Grounded Conductor—_No overcurrent device shall be placed in any permanently grounded conductor, except as follows:_

Exception No. 1. Where the overcurrent device simultaneously opens all conductors of the circuit. (See Fig. 240-6.)

Exception No. 2. Running protection for motors are specified in **Sections 430-36, 430-37,** and **Table 430-37.** The Note under the table

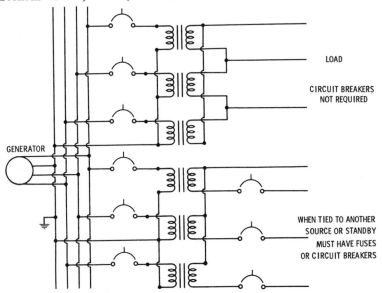

Fig. 240-3. Overcurrent protection for feeders at supply stations.

should be carefully considered. To further clarify this note, a definition of **unattended** appears for the first time in the 1965 Code. This table should be carefully studied.

When installing motor protection, such as magnetic starters, it is very important that the three overcurrent devices be used. The new definition of **unattended** has greatly cleared up the intent. Motor rewinding is costly, as well as the inconvenience of a breakdown. Certainly the cost of the third overload element is a very small item, so its use is a very good policy. Check with the local inspection authority to see what is required in your area.

240-13. Change in Size of Grounded Conductor—See NEC.

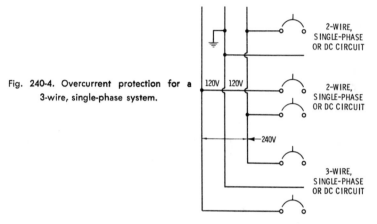

Fig. 240-4. Overcurrent protection for a 3-wire, single-phase system.

240-14. Fuses or Circuit Breakers in Parallel—*Overcurrent devices consisting of fuses and/or circuit breakers shall not be arranged or installed in parallel.*

Exception: Circuit breakers assembled in parallel which are tested and approved as a single unit.

The practice of installing fuses in multiple, which has been prevalent for many years, has been entirely eliminated. There are never to be installations of fuses in parallel. An exception permits circuit breakers in parallel, but only when they have been tested and approved as a unit.

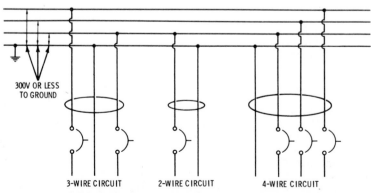

Fig. 240-5. Overcurrent protection for 4-wire grounded system.

109

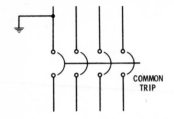

Fig. 240-6. Common-trip circuit breaker opening the neutral.

B. Location

240-15. Location in Circuit—*Overcurrent devices shall be located at the point where the conductor to be protected receives its supply, except as follows:*

Exception No. 1. Service Conductors. An overcurrent protective device for service conductors shall be an integral part of the service disconnecting means or located adjacent thereto unless located at the outer end of the service. See Figs. 240-7, 8, and 9.

Exception No. 2. See NEC.

Exception No. 3. Branch Circuits. **Sections 210-19** and **210-20** mentioned in this exception covers conductors, with **Exception No. 1** of **Section 210-19** explaining that taps are allowed to wall-mounted ovens, counter-top cooking units, and to electric ranges in households only.

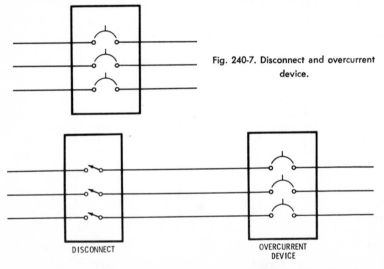

Fig. 240-7. Disconnect and overcurrent device.

DISCONNECT

OVERCURRENT DEVICE

Fig. 240-8. Separate disconnect and overcurrent device which must be adjacent.

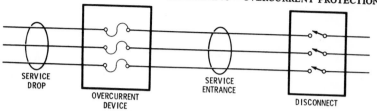

Fig. 240-9. Separate disconnect and overcurrent device which are separated because of service-entrance length.

Exception No. 4. See NEC.

Exception No. 5. Feeder taps Not Over 10 Feet Long. For conductors tapped to a feeder where all of the following conditions are met:

(a) Tap conductor is not over 10 feet long,

(b) The ampacity of the tap conductor is not less than;

    1. Combined computed loads of the combined circuits supplied by the tap conductors.

    2. The ampacity of the tap conductors is not less than the rating of the switchboard or panelboard that the tap conductors are supplying.

(c) The tap conductors stop at the switchboard or panelboard that they are supplying.

(d) The tap conductors shall be enclosed in a raceway, except at the point of attachment to the feeder and this raceway shall extend to an enclosed switchboard, panelboard or control device, or to the back of an open switchboard.

Exception No. 6. Feeder Taps Not Over 25 Feet Long. In this exception, the taps have a definite set minimum of 1/3 of the ampacity of the feeders to which they are connected. This differs from **(1)** of **Exception 5,** where the ampacity of the circuits that the taps supplied was the limiting factor, and they could supply a number of circuits without a single set of overcurrent protection. In **Exception No. 6,** they must feed a single set of overcurrent protection devices before feeding the branch circuits, as shown in Fig. 240-10.

Exception No. 7. Transformer Feeder Taps with Primary Plus Secondary Not Over 25 Feet Long. This one is a little tricky and very important. I find nothing covering the intent, but am certain that it was written to give some leeway in the placement of the overcurrent device protecting the secondary of a **Separately Derived System.** Note the heading.

111

All of the following conditions must be met:

1. The tap conductors supplying the primary of the transformer (if there are tap conductors) shall have an ampacity of at least ⅓ the ampacity of the conductors that they are tapped to, or the overcurrent device supplying the tap conductors.

2. The conductors supplied by the secondary of the transformer, to whatever they supply, shall have an ampacity that when multiplied by the ratio of the secondary-to-primary voltage, is at least one-third the ampacity of the conductors or overcurrent protection from which the primary conductors are tapped.

3. That the total length on one primary conductor plus one secondary conductor and this total length will exclude any portion of the primary supply conductor which is protected by overcurrent devices at the ampacity of the conductor and is not over 25 feet long.

4. Suitable protection from physical damage is afforded both the primary and secondary conductors.

5. The secondary conductors terminate in a single circuit breaker or set of fuses which will limit the load to that allowed in **Tables 310-12** through **Table 310-15.**

One example of this would be the primary of the transformer is supplied from a feeder panel with 100-ampere fuses and the conductors from the panel to the primary of the transformer are No. 2 THW copper, then these would not count in the total of the 25 ft. and the secondary feeder conductors to the secondary overcurrent device have sufficient ampacity in relation to the secondary overcurrent device.

240-16. Location in Premises—*Overcurrent devices shall be located where they will be:*

(a) See NEC.

(b) See NEC.

(c) *Not in the vicinity of easily ignitible material.* When an overcurrent protective device opens there will be a spark and possible particles of hot metal which could cause a fire. This explains why most inspection authorities do not permit overcurrent panels in clothes closets, and other similar locations.

(d) Occupant to Have Ready Access. This was added to the 1971 NEC to assure that occupants have ready access to the supply conductors supplying his occupancy. *Each occupant shall have ready access to all overcurrent devices protecting the conductors supplying his occupancy.*

Exception: In a multiple-occupancy building where electric service and electrical maintenance are provided by the building management and where these are under continuous building management supervision, the service overcurrent device and feeder overcurrent devices supplying more than one occupancy may be accessible to authorized management personnel only.

C. Enclosures

240-17. Enclosures for Overcurrent Devices—

(a) General. By enclosing overcurrent devices in cabinets, the exposed electrical parts are kept away from unqualified persons. See **Section 240-17(a)** of the NEC.

(b) Damp or Wet Locations. See NEC. Also see Fig. 240-11.

(c) Vertical Position. Wherever practical, the enclosures for overcurrent devices shall be mounted vertically.

(d) Rosettes. At one time, rosettes were fused. This practice is no longer permitted.

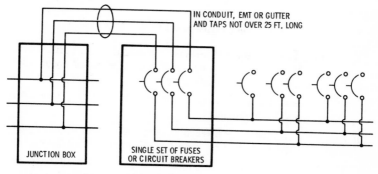

IN CONDUIT, EMT OR GUTTER
AND TAPS NOT OVER 25 FT. LONG

JUNCTION BOX

SINGLE SET OF FUSES
OR CIRCUIT BREAKERS

Fig. 240-10. Illustrating tap circuits not over 25 feet long.

240-18. Disconnection of Fuses and Thermal Cutouts Before Handling
—*Disconnecting means shall be provided on the supply side of all fuses or thermal cutouts in circuits of more than 150 volts to ground and cartridge fuses in circuits of any voltage, where accessible to other than qualified persons.* This is so that the fuses or thermal cutouts may be independently disconnected from the supply source.

Recall that plug fuses come under the 125-volt classification and the screw-shell of the holder is connected to the load side. Thus, they are not required to have a disconnecting means. Service fuses (fuses at the outer end of the service entrance) may be ahead of the disconnecting means. See **Section 230-70.** A group of motors may be served by a single disconnecting means providing that the requirements of **Section 430-112** are met.

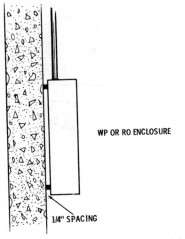

WP OR RO ENCLOSURE

1/4" SPACING

Fig. 240-11. Spacing overcurrent devices in damp locations.

240-19. Arcing or Suddenly Moving Parts—See NEC.

E. Plug Fuses and Fuseholders

240-20. Plug Fuses of the Edison-Base Type—Edison-base fuses means those having a base that is the same as the medium-based incandescent lamp. They shall conform to the following:

(a) **Classification.** Edison-base fuses shall not be rated at more than 125 volts and 0-30 amperes.

(b) **Live Parts.** *Edison base fuses and fuseholders when installed and assembled together shall have no live electrical parts exposed.*

(c) **Marking.** Plug fuses of 15-ampere rating or less shall have an hexagonal recess on top to designate that they are rated at 15 amperes or less. They shall have a mica or similar window to show whether or not the fuse has blown.

It states that *plug fuses of the Edison-base type are recognized in this Code only as a replacement item in existing installations where there has been no evidence of overfusing or tampering.* This means that all inspection authorities should condemn any new installations that use Edison-base fuses, regardless of how they are used or in what type of electrical device. The reason for this ruling is because of the dangerous practice of replacing a blown fuse with one of a higher rating than the ampacity of the conductor they are supposed to protect. This type of fuse also makes it easy to use a penny or other metal disk when a replacement fuse is not available. The proper plug fuse to be used on new installations is covered in **Section 240-22.**

Fig. 240-12. Type-S plug-fuse adapter.

240-21. Fuseholders for Plug Fuses—*Fuse holders for plug fuses of 30 amperes or less shall not be installed unless they comply with* **Section 240-22** *or are made to comply with* **Section 240-22** *by the insertion of an adapter.* Type-S fuses can be used in any Edison-base fuse holder by using an inexpensive adapter that screws in like a fuse and locks in place. This permits inserting and removing a Type-S fuse just like an ordinary fuse. This adapter is shown in Fig. 240-12.

240-22. Plug Fuses and Fuseholders of Type S—On all new installations requiring plug fuses, the Type-S plug fuse is required to be used. Although not required, a Type-S adapter should be installed in all Edison-base fuseholders in old installations to convert them to the new requirements.

(a) **Classification.** *Plug fuses and fuseholders of Type S shall be classified at not over 125 volts; 0 to 15 amperes, 16 to 20 amperes, and 21 to 30 amperes.* Note these classifications.

(b) **Use of Fuses in a Fuseholder of a Different Classification.** With reference to the above classification, the 16- to 20-ampere and the 21- to 30-ampere classifications shall not be usable in a fuseholder or adapter designed for lower amperages.

(c) **Fuseholders and Adapters.** *Fuses, fuseholders, and adapters shall be so designed that a fuse other than a Type S fuse cannot be used in a fuseholder or adapter designed for a Type S fuse.*

(d) **Tamperability.** Fuses, fuseholders, and adapters for Type-S plug fuses are to be so designed as to make tampering or bridging difficult.

(e) **Adapters to be Nonremovable.** Adapters are to be so designed that once in place they cannot be removed. Fig. 240-12 shows an S adapter with a sharp pin near the bottom which permits it to be screwed into an Edison-base fuseholder but prevents it from being unscrewed.

(g) **Plug Type.** Fuses and Fuseholders shall be of the plug type.

Edison-base and Type-S fuses are both considered as plug-type fuses.

(h) **Ampere Rating.** See NEC.

(i) **Marking.** As with Edison-base plug fuses, Type-S plug fuses shall have a hexagonal recess or top on all fuses of 0 to 15 amperes to designate that they are 15 amperes or less in rating. They shall have a mica or similar window to show whether or not the fuse has blown.

F. Cartridge Fuses and Fuseholders

240-23. Cartridge Fuses and Fuseholders—*Cartridge fuses and fuseholders shall conform to the following:*

(a) **Classification.**

(1) *0-600 ampere cartridge fuses and fuseholders shall be classified as regards current and voltage as follows:*
See NEC.

(2) *601-6000 ampere cartridge fuses and fuseholders shall be classified at 600 volts as follows:*
See NEC.

There are no 250 volt ratings over 600 amperes, but 600 volt fuses may be used for lower voltages.

A higher amperage fuse switch is often needed on a 250-volt system. Due to the fact that 600 amperes is the largest 250-volt fuse rating, a 600-volt fuse switch is used instead of paralleling 250-volt fuses. Thus, amperages up to 6000 may be handled. Caution: Never use a switch or fuse of a lower voltage rating than is required. A higher voltage rating is always permissible.

(b) **Noninterchangeable — 0-6000 Ampere Cartridge Fuseholders.** Adapters may be purchased for using lower current rated cartridge fuses in a higher current rated fuseholder. A 100-ampere rated fuse switch may be adapted to use a 60 ampere fuse, but a 60-ampere fuse switch is not to be altered to adapt a 100-ampere fuse. Current-limiting fuses, which will be covered in **Section 240-27,** are a special type of fuse and are not to be interchangeable with fuses that are not current limiting.

(c) **Marking.** See NEC.

G. Link Fuses and Fuseholders

240-24. Link Fuses and Fuseholders—See NEC.

H. Circuit Breakers

240-25. Circuit Breakers—*Circuit breakers shall conform to the following:*

(a) **Method of Operation.** Circuit breakers shall be capable of being opened and closed by hand without employing other sources of power, even though they are designed to be normally operated by electrical, pneumatic, or other sources of power.

Large circuit breakers which are opened or closed by means of electrical, pneumatic, or other power shall be capable of being closed by hand for the purpose of maintenance, and shall also be capable of being opened by hand under load without the use of any other form of power.

(b) **Injury to Operator.** See NEC.

(c) **Indicating.** Circuit breakers shall be plainly marked so as to indicate whether they are in the open or closed position.

(d) **Nontamperable.** Air circuit breakers for branch circuits shall be nontamperable so that the calibration of the trip point cannot be easily changed.

(e) **Marking.** See NEC.

H. General

240-27. Current Limiting Overcurrent Protective Device—See NEC.

240-30. Supplementary Overcurrent Protection—Any supplementary overcurrent protection that is used in connection with appliances or other utilization equipment, and is for the specific purpose of protecting individual parts or circuits of the appliance or utilization equipment, does not in any manner take the place of nor is deemed a substitute for the branch-circuit protection. Neither is it the intent that any such supplementary overcurrent protective device be subject to the accessibility required for branch-circuit protective devices.

ARTICLE 250—GROUNDING
A. General

250-1. Scope—*This Article covers general requirements for grounding and bonding of electrical installations, and specific requirements for the following:* Grounding has three fundamental purposes;

1. Limit excessive voltage from lightning, line surges and crossovers with higher voltage lines.
2. To keep conductor enclosures and non-current carrying enclosures and equipment at zero potential to ground.
3. To facilitate the opening of overcurrent devices in the event of insulation failures or faults.

This Article is divided into the following parts:

A. **General**

B. **Circuit and System Grounding**

C. **Location of Grounding Connections**

D. **Enclosure Grounding**

E. **Equipment Grounding**

F. **Methods of Grounding**

G. **Bonding**

H. **Grounding Electrodes**

J. **Grounding Conductors**

K. **Grounding Conductor Connections**

L. **Instrument Transformers, Relays, Etc.**

M. **Lightning Arresters**

250-2. Other Articles — Other Articles in the Code list additional grounding requirements for specific conductor and equipment installation other than those covered in this Article. A listing to which additional grounding requirements apply, other than those covered here, is given in **Section 250-2** of the Code.

B. Circuit and System Grounding

250-3. Direct-Current Systems — Two-wire direct-current systems shall be grounded when supplying interior wiring and operating at a voltage not exceeding 300 volts between conductors. This does not apply to industrial equipment where a ground detector is being used.

It is recommended that direct-current systems operating at more than 300 volts between conductors be grounded whenever a neutral point can be established so that the voltage to ground does not exceed 300 volts. Whenever the voltage to ground exceeds 300 volts, grounding is not recommended.

250-5. Alternating-Current Circuits and Systems to be Grounded— *AC circuits and systems shall be grounded as provided for in* **(a)**, **(b)** *or* **(C)** *below. Other circuits and systems may be grounded.*

(a) **Alternating-Current Circuits of Less than 50 Volts.** *AC circuits of less than 50 volts shall be grounded under any of the following conditions:*

1. If transformers supplying the low voltage receives its supply from a system of over 150 volts to ground. Such could be from a 277/480-volt system.
2. If the supply to the transformer is from an ungrounded system. See Fig. 250-3.
3. Where the low voltage conductors are installed as overhead conductors outside of buildings. See Fig. 250-4.

(b) **Alternating-Current Systems of 50 Volts and Over.** *AC systems supplying interior wiring systems shall be grounded under any of the following conditions:*

1. *Where the system can be so grounded that the maximum voltage to ground on the ungrounded conductors does not exceed 150 volts.*
2. *Where the system is nominally rated 277/480 volts, 3-phase, 4-wire in which the neutral is used as a circuit conductor.*

This would not include a 480/277 volt high resistance grounded system, where the mid-point of the Y is grounded through a resistor, but this connection is not used as a circuit conductor.

This is best described by Fig. 250-2E, where the mid-point of one phase of a delta supply is grounded and this mid-point is used as a neutral.

3. *Where a service conductor is uninsulated in accordance with* **Section 230-4.**

Exception: Former **Section 250-6. Furnace Circuits,** was deleted in the 1971 NEC and is now covered by this *Exception: Electric systems used exclusively to supply industrial electric furnaces for melting, refining, tempering, and the like, need not be grounded.* Ungrounded systems, if used with suitable ground detectors, will provide extra protection.

(c) **Separately Derived Systems.** Where interior wiring systems are supplied by generators not connected to the supply system, such as emergency generators, or where transformers in the supply system are used for other than supply voltage and the primary and secondary are isolated, (which also includes converter windings that have no direct connections to the supply

119

source,) grounding is required as stated in **(a)** and **(b)** above. Grounding will be as explained in **Section 250-26.**

250-7. Circuits not to be grounded. *The following circuits shall not be grounded.*

1. *Circuits for electric cranes operating over combustible fibers in Class III locations, as provided for in* **Section 503-13.**
2. *Circuits as provided in* **Article 517.** This would be anesthetics locations.

C. Location of Grounding Connections

250-21. Current Over Grounding Conductors—All grounding of wiring systems, circuits, lighting arresters, and metal raceways of all types shall be so arranged that there will be no objectionable flow of current over the grounding conductors. Any temporary flow of current which should occur while the grounding is performing its function, such as in the case of faults, is not considered objectionable.

Where an objectionable flow of current is noted, the following remedies may be used:

(1) Abandon one or more grounds.
(2) Change the location of the ground.
(3) Suitably interrupt the continuity of the conductors between the ground connections.
(4) Use other suitable means that might be approved by the Code-enforcing authority.

Objectionable current flow over the grounding conductors is not to be taken lightly. All connections of grounding conductors, locknuts, and bushings are to be made tight. Bonding may sometimes be necessary.

Ground resistance is highly important. This resistance varies greatly with different types of soil, and may be great enough to set up serious current flow. Remember that proper grounding is very important, and that with each Code revision, changes are made which eliminate some of the hazards.

250-22. Grounding Connection for Direct-Current Systems—On direct-current systems that are to be grounded, the grounding shall be done at one or more supply stations, but not at the individual services. This refers to the grounding of the supply conductors and not to the service equipment itself. The equipment is to be grounded at the service, but the neutral is to be isolated from the equipment at the service-entrance equipment.

These requirements are greatly different than those for alternating-current systems because any passage of current between the ground at the supply station and at the service-entrance equipment may cause objectionable electrolysis, which must be avoided.

250-23. Grounding Connections for Alternating-Current Systems—

(a) The reason for grounding on the supply side of the service-entrance equipment is because if the supply side is ever disconnected there will still be a ground on the supply system. In the event that the distribution system is ungrounded, there would, of course, be no ground from the primary supply. See Fig. 250-1. *See* **Section 250-24** *for two or more buildings supplied by a single service and* **Section 250-26** *for separately derived systems.*

Exception No. 1. A grounding electrode conductor shall be connected to each separately derived system as provided in **Section 250-26.**

Exception No. 2. A grounding conductor connection shall be made at each separate building where required by **Section 250-24.**

Exception No. 3. For ranges, counter-mounted cooking units, wall-mounted ovens, and clothes dryers as permitted by **Section 250-61.**

It is recommended that the grounding electrode conductor of a service of large capacity be connected within the service equipment enclosure.

As an inspector, I like to see the grounding electrode conductor connected in the service equipment enclosures of any size of service. Here it is accessible for service problems.

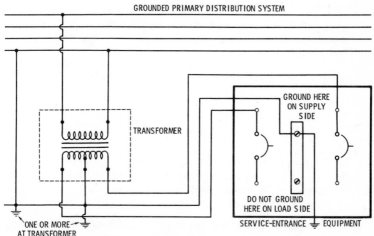

GROUNDED PRIMARY DISTRIBUTION SYSTEM

TRANSFORMER

GROUND HERE ON SUPPLY SIDE

DO NOT GROUND HERE ON LOAD SIDE

ONE OR MORE AT TRANSFORMER

SERVICE-ENTRANCE EQUIPMENT

Fig. 250-1. Grounding on the supply side of the service-entrance equipment will provide a ground on the supply if it is ever disconnected.

(b) On grounded secondary systems that are grounded at any point, the grounded conductor shall be run to each individual service, regardless of whether or not it is to be used in the interior wiring system. The grounding conductor shall be no smaller than that specified in **Table 250-94 (a).** A case in point would be a three-phase, 4-wire, Wye system supplied from a grounded Wye secondary system in which the intent is to use only the three-phase circuits and not the neutral. However, the neutral shall be run to the building and to the service-entrance equipment where it shall be grounded to a proper grounding electrode. It may be terminated at the service-entrance equipment, however. In many cases the size, as permitted in **Table 250-94(a)**, could be smaller than would be required where the neutral is to be used for some of the circuits. Should it look as if there might be a possible change in the need for the neutral at a future date, it would be wise to size it sufficiently large at the time of installation. *For service phase conductors larger than 1100 MCM the ground conductor shall not be smaller than 12½ percent of the area of the largest phase conductor.*

Exception. The grounding conductor need not be larger than the largest ungrounded service conductor.

250-24. Two or More Buildings Supplied From Single Service Equipment—This Section was changed in the 1971 Code to clarify many existing problems. *Where two or more buildings are supplied from a single service equipment:*

1. On a grounded system, a grounding electrode shall be used and connected to the supply side of the disconnecting means at each building.
2. If the system is an ungrounded system, the grounding electrode shall be connected to the enclosure of the building disconnecting means.

Exception. A grounding electrode at a separate building supplied by a feeder or branch circuit is not required where either of the following conditions are met:

1. **(a)** Only one branch circuit is supplied.
   (b) There is no noncurrent-carrying equipment used, such as enclosures for motors, tools, appliances and etc.
   (c) There is no livestock housed in the building.

2. An equipment grounding conductor is run with the feeders or branch circuit conductors and:

   (a) This equipment grounding conductor is run to;

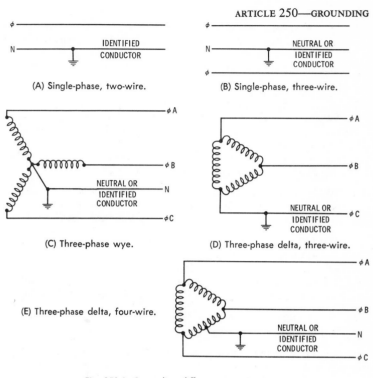

(A) Single-phase, two-wire.

(B) Single-phase, three-wire.

(C) Three-phase wye.

(D) Three-phase delta, three-wire.

(E) Three-phase delta, four-wire.

Fig. 250-2. Grounding different type circuits.

1. Water piping,
2. Building metal frames.

(b) *If the separate building has an approved grounding electrode and/or interior metallic water piping system, the equipment grounding conductor shall be bonded to the electrode and/or piping system.*

250-25. Conductor to be Grounded—Article 200 covers the use and identification of grounding conductors. Ordinarily, the identified conductor is commonly known as **the white wire,** although it will be recalled that a neutral gray color may also be used. Fig. 250-2 illustrates the different grounding circuits used.

250-26. Grounding Separately Derived Alternating-Current Systems— *A separately derived AC system that is required to be grounded by* **Section 250-5** *shall be grounded in the following manner:*

(a) *A bonding jumper sized in accordance with* **Section 250-79(c)** *for derived phase conductors shall be used to connect the*

123

system noncurrent-carrying equipment enclosures to the system circuit conductor that is to be grounded. This connection shall be made on the supply side of the separately derived system and ahead of any system disconnecting means or overcurrent device.

(b) *A grounding conductor sized in accordance with* **Section 250-94(a)** *for derived conductors shall be used to connect the circuit conductor of the system that is to be grounded to the grounding electrode as specified in* **(c)** *below. This connection shall be made on the supply side of the separately derived system and ahead of any system disconnecting means or overcurrent device.*

(c) *The grounding electrode shall be as near as practicable to and perferably in the same area as the grounding conductor connection to the system. The grounding electrode shall be:*

(1) *The nearest available effectively grounded structural metal member of the structure.*
(2) The nearest available effective grounded metal water piping.
(3) Other electrodes as specified in **Sections 250-82** and **250-83** where electrodes specified in **(1)** or **(2)** are not available.

(d) *In all other respects, grounding methods shall comply with requirements prescribed in other parts of this Code.*

As to **(c) (2)**, above, one must be careful in attaching to just any water pipe as it may be opened for repairs, moved or disbanded and a dangerous condition might develop at a future date. USE DISCRETION.

D. Enclosure Grounding

250-32. Service Conductor Enclosures—See NEC.
250-33. Other Conductor Enclosures—See NEC.

E. Equipment Grounding

250-42 and -43. Fixed Equipment—General and —Specific—See NEC.

250-44. Nonelectrical Equipment—See NEC.

250-45. Equipment Connected by Cord and Plug—See NEC.

250-46. Spacing from Lightning Rods—See NEC.

F. Methods of Grounding

250-50. Equipment Grounding Connections—*The grounding connections for metal noncurrent-carrying equipment shall be made on the supply side of the service disconnecting means or as in* **Section 250-5(c)** *if for a separately derived system.*

250-51. Effective Grounding—This Section is quite short, but may be considered a key section in **Article 250**. *The path to ground from cir-*

cuits, equipment, and conductor enclosures shall (1) be permanent and (2) shall have ample carrying capacity to conduct safely any currents liable to be imposed on it, and (3) shall have impedances sufficiently low to limit the potential above ground and to facilitate the operation of the overcurrent devices in the circuit.

Parts (1) and (2) are very important, but are self-explanatory. However, part (3) is often ignored, probably because of the word "Impedance". Impedance is AC resistance. Refer back to **Section 110-10.** Fault currents available are constantly increasing in amplitude. This refers to phase-to-phase faults, phase-to-ground faults, and to both bolted faults and arcing faults. Part (3) points out to be ever mindful of impedances in connection with grounding, and to keep these impedances as low as possible.

250-52. Location of System Ground Connection—The grounding electrode conductor of a wiring system shall also be used to ground equipment, conduit, supply side of the disconnecting means. This is so that when the disconnecting means is opened, the grounding conductor will not be opened, which would interrupt the grounding on the system. On services of high capacity, it is recommended that the grounding conductor be connected within the service-entrance equipment.

There may be occasions where attempts may be made to bring the grounding from a telephone circuit or antenna circuit into the service equipment. **This should not be permitted.** It is proper to tie them to the same grounding electrode, but they are not part of the system supply and should not be in the same enclosure.

250-53. Grounding Path to Grounding Electrode—

(a) Grounding Electrode Conductor. *A grounding electrode conductor shall be used to connect the equipment grounding conductors, the service-equipment enclosures and, when the system is grounded, the grounded conductor to the grounding electrode.* See Fig. 250-7.

(b) Main Bonding Jumper. *For a grounded system, an unspliced main bonding jumper shall be used to connect the equipment grounding conductor and the service-equipment enclosure to the grounded conductor of the system.* See Fig. 250-3.

A main bonding jumper may be a wire, bus, screw, or similar suitable conductor.

Exception: It will be recalled that, according to **Section 210-7,** in extensions to existing installations that do not have a grounding conductor in the branch circuit involved, the grounding conductor of a grounding-type receptacle may be grounded to the nearest cold-water pipe.

125

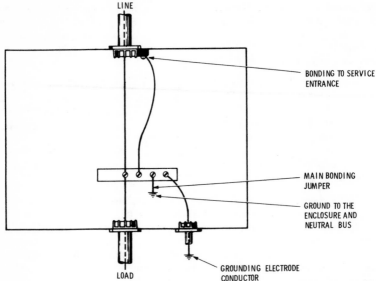

Fig. 250-3. The grounding conductor that grounds the neutral must also be used for all other grounding.

250-54. Common Grounding Electrode—This Section applies to alternating-current systems and requires that the same grounding electrode in or at the building shall be used to ground the conductor enclosure and equipment in or on that building.

Two or more electrodes that are effectively bonded together are to be treated as a single electrode in this sense.

250-55. Underground Service Cable—Where an underground service is supplied by a continuous metal-sheathed or armored cable which is bonded to the underground system, it need not be grounded at the building and may be insulated from the interior conduit. Please note that this is quite different from an overhead system in which the cable sheath or armor and/or conduit shall be grounded at the service entrance.

250-56. Short Sections of Raceway—See NEC.

250-57. Fixed Equipment—

(a) Where metal raceways or armor are connected to metal boxes, cabinets, and fittings, or to noncurrent carrying parts of fixed equipment by means of a metallic connection, locknut, or bushing, they shall be considered as grounded by such connection. This is not to imply that on service-entrance equipment, and in other areas where bonding is required, this type of connection will satisfy the conditions.

(b) Where they are not connected as provided in **(a)**, they may be grounded by means of one of the following methods:

(1) By running a grounding conductor with the circuit conductor. This grounding conductor may be bare, covered with a continuous green-colored insulation, or with a continuous green insulation with a yellow stripe.

(2) A separate grounding conductor may be installed or it may be a part of a cable assembly, such as NM, NMC, UF, etc. A bare or an insulated green conductor will be found in such a cable assembly. The grounding conductor shall be run with the phase conductor and neutral in order to maintain a low impedance.

(3) In places where a cord connection is approved (these are defined in **Section 400-3),** the grounding conductor may be a part of the cord. In this case you will usually find a green insulated conductor which is never to be used for any other purpose than as a grounding conductor.

(4) By special permission from the inspection authority, other means of grounding of fixed equipment may be used.

250-58. Equipment on Structural Metal—

(a) *Electrical equipment secured to and in contact with the grounded structural metal frame of a building,* is considered to be grounded.

Note: The grounded structure in no way means that all metal buildings are properly grounded. It will be recalled that in **Section 250-44(d),** grounding of metal buildings was recommended. Be certain that a grounded structure is really grounded.

(b) The metal car frames of elevators and similar devices are considered to be adequately grounded if attached to a metal cable running over or attached to a metal drum that is well grounded according to the grounding requirements of the Code.

250-59. Portable and/or Cord and Plug-Connected Equipment— *The noncurrent carrying metal parts of cord and plug-connected equipment required to be grounded may be grounded in any one of the following ways:*

(a) *By means of the metal enclosure of the conductors feeding such equipment, provided an approved grounding type attachment plug is used, one fixed contacting member being for the purpose of grounding the metal enclosure, and provided, further, that the*

> *metal enclosure of the conductors is attached to the attachment plug and to the equipment by connectors approved for the purpose.*

The above means that the outlet shall be of the grounded receptacle type, and that the attachment plug shall be of the type approved for grounding from a grounding-type receptacle, and that the cord shall carry a grounding conductor, one end of which is attached to the grounding terminal of the attachment plug and the other end to the frame of the portable equipment. Since it was found that it's not always possible to attach a portable appliance or equipment to a grounding-type receptacle because the grounding terminal of the attachment plug was often broken off or cut off to fit an old type of receptacle, the following exception has therefore been added:

Exception: The grounding contacting member of grounding type attachment plugs on the power supply cord of hand-held tools or hand-held appliances may be of the movable self-restoring type.

In other words, there are approved attachment plugs that have a hinged grounding prong with a spring so that it can be folded out of the way and yet will restore itself to the normal position for use on grounding-type receptacles.

(b) The grounding conductor may be run in the cable or flexible-cord assembly, provided that it terminates in an approved grounding-type attachment plug having a fixed grounding-type contact member. This grounding conductor in the cable or cord assembly may be bare, but if insulated, shall be green or green with a yellow stripe. You will notice that it says a **fixed grounding contact member**—again there is an exception. This exception is exactly as in **(a)** above—that is, the contact member may be a restoring type.

(c) See NEC.

250-60. Frames of Electric Ranges and Electric Clothes Dryers—Frames of electric ranges and electric clothes dryers shall be grounded as provided for in **Sections 250-57** and **250-59**—that is, by metal raceways or a grounding conductor. There is another alternative on 120/240-volt three-wire circuits, or 120/208-volt circuits derived from a three-phase 4-wire supply. This type of circuit may be grounded to the neutral conductor provided that the neutral or grounded circuit conductor is no smaller than No. 10 AWG copper. This applies to wall-mounted ovens and counter-top cooking units as well. This is the one instance where the neutral may be used also as the grounding conductor, providing all other conditions are met.

Where SE cable with a bare neutral is used for ranges or dryer branch circuits, it shall originate only for service equipment. If it were per-

128

mittcd to originate from feeder panels, we would have an isolated neutral bus with a bare conductor attached. With a bare conductor, it could easily touch the enclosure and defeat the protection that the isolated neutral affords.

250-61. Use of Grounding Circuit Conductor for Grounding Equipment—This Section was rewritten in the 1971 NEC, to clarify intent.

(a) Supply-Side Equipment. *A grounded circuit conductor may be used to ground noncurrent-carrying equipment on the supply side of the service disconnecting means, such as meter enclosures, service raceways, etc., and on the supply side of the main disconnecting means of separate buildings and of separately derived systems as provided in* **Section 250-24** *and* **250-26** *respectively.*

(b) Load-Side Equipment. *A grounding circuit conductor shall not be used for grounding noncurrent-carrying equipment on the load side of the service disconnecting means or the overcurrent devices for a separately derived system not having a main disconnecting means.*

Exception No. 1. The frames of ranges, wall-mounted ovens, counter-mounted cooking units, and clothes dryers under the conditions specified in **Section 250-60.**

Take note that in **Section 250-60,** a range, etc., as covered above, shall not be connected to the grounded conductor as a means of securing an equipment ground, when the circuit to same originates from a feeder panel. Only when the circuit originates from the service-entrance equipment for these particular items.

Exception No. 2. As permitted in **Section 250-24** *for separate buildings.*

Exception No. 3. By special permission as provided in **Section 250-57(b) (3).**

250-62. Multiple Circuit Connections—See NEC.

G. Bonding

250-70. General—*Bonding shall be provided where necessary to assure electrical continuity and the capacity to conduct safely any fault current likely to be imposed.*

This Section is very basic and important. Larger available fault currents demand proper means of safely handling this problem.

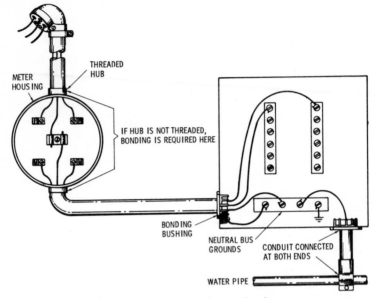

Fig. 250-4. An example of proper bonding.

250-71. Bonding at Service Equipment—This is an item that has been a part of the Code for many years, but is often overlooked. It is recommended that a careful understanding of the reason for bonding at this location be gained because of its importance. The way in which this bonding is to be done will be covered in **Section 250-72.** An example of proper bonding is shown in Fig. 250-4.

(a) See NEC.

(b) See NEC.

(c) *Any conduit or armor which forms part of the grounding conductor to the service raceway.* This is meant to include the conduit or armor that serves to protect the grounding wire to the grounding electrode. See Fig. 250-5.

250-72. Continuity at Service Equipment—The following is the procedure to be followed to assure continuity at service equipment:

(a) *Bonding equipment to grounded service conductor in manner provided in* **Section 250-113.** This is illustrated in Fig. 250-6.

(b) See NEC.

(c) See NEC.

(d) *Bonding jumpers meeting the other requirements of this article.* This requires that, in services and entrance equipment, as well as other points where there are eccentric or concentric knockouts, bonding jumpers be used around concentric or eccentric knock-outs. It is also necessary to use bonding around any flexible conduit that might be used in conjunction with service entrances. See Fig. 250–7 .

(e) Locknuts and bushings of the conventional type are **not** approved for continuity at service entrances. Devices shall be approved for the purpose—that is, bonding type of bushings, wedge nuts, etc.

250-73. Metal Armor or Tape of Service Cable—When using service cable with an uninsulated grounding conductor, the armor or metal tape

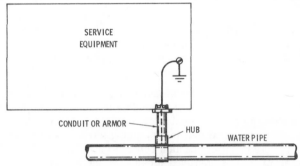

Fig. 250-5. Conduit or armor used to protect the grounding wire shall be bonded to the grounding electrode and to the service-equipment enclosure.

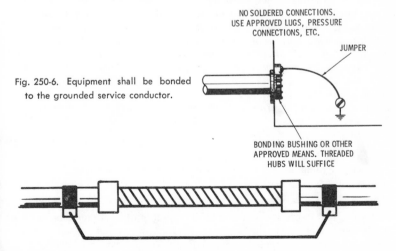

Fig. 250-6. Equipment shall be bonded to the grounded service conductor.

Fig. 250-7. Bonding must extend around any flexible conduit used in conjunction with service-entrance equipment.

shall be considered as adequately grounded if the armor or metal tape is in continuous electrical contact with the grounding conductor.

250-74. Bonding at Grounding-Type Receptacles—There has been considerable discussion on this subject and many opinions, but this is clarified in the 1965 Code. *Grounding continuity between a grounded outlet box and the grounding circuit of the receptacle shall be established by means of a bonding jumper between the outlet box and the receptacle grounding terminal.*

Exception No. 1. When the box is surface mounted, direct metal-to-metal contact between the device yoke and the box may be used to establish the grounding circuit.

Exception No. 2. Contact devices or yokes designed and approved for the purpose may be used in conjunction with the supporting screws to establish the grounding circuit between the device yoke and flush-type boxes installed in walls.

The results of the above established that a grounding jumper shall be used from grounded boxes to the grounding terminal of the receptacle in all cases, including boxes on conduit circuits and EMT circuits, unless the box is surface mounted so that the mounting screws may be tightened to make a secure grounding connection between the device yoke and the box. Of course, if a device is approved for making the proper grounding connection, the bonding will not be necessary. See Fig. 250-8.

250-75. Bonding Other Enclosures—This Section has been completely changed in the 1971 NEC to clarify intent. *Metal raceways, cable armor, cable sheath, enclosures, frames, fittings, and other metal non-current-carrying parts that are to serve as grounding conductor shall be effectively bonded where necessary to assure electrical continuity and the capacity to conduct safely any fault current likely to be imposed on them. Any nonconducting paint, enamel, or similar coating shall be removed at threads, contact points, and contact surfaces or be connected by means of fittings so designed as to make such removal unnecessary.*

The, *shall be effectively bonded where necessary—*, to me is the key of this Section. It appears to become a design and an inspection problem to pass judgment as to where to bond and where bonding will not be required.

250-76. Voltages Exceeding 250 Volts—Metal raceways and conduits enclosing conductors at more than 250 volts to ground (other than service conductors) shall have the electrical continuity assured by one of the methods outlined in **Section 250-72 (b-e)**. Recall that this Section covered continuity at service equipment. The following methods are also approved:

132

(a) *Threadless fittings, made up tight, with conduit or metal-clad cable.* Note **made up tight.**

(b) *Two locknuts, one inside and one outside of boxes and cabinets.* These locknuts are also to be made up tight. Elsewhere in the Code it is permissible to use one locknut and one bushing where it is not practical to use two locknuts and a bushing. Where the voltage exceeds 250 volts to ground, there are to be two locknuts as outlined above.

250-77. Loosely Joined Metal Raceways—*Expansion joints and telescoping sections of raceways shall be made electrically continuous by bonding jumpers or other approved means. Metal trough raceways used in connection with sound recording and reproducing, made up in sections, shall contain a grounding conductor to which each section shall be bonded.* In recording and reproducing, the bonding wire will reduce the conditions that affect the quality of recording and reproduction.

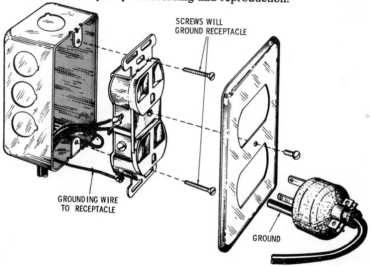

SCREWS WILL
GROUND RECEPTACLE

GROUNDING WIRE
TO RECEPTACLE

GROUND

Fig. 250-8. A grounding jumper shall be used from grounded boxes to the grounding terminal of the receptacle.

250-78. Hazardous Locations—Regardless of the voltage, the electrical continuity of raceways and boxes shall be assured by one of the methods in **Section 250-72 (b-e).** However, this does not cover the continuity in hazardous locations in entirety—the requirement for the specific type of hazardous condition involved should be looked up. These are covered in **Sections 500** to **517** inclusive. In reality, this Section **(250-78)** is rather broad and does not cover all hazardous locations.

250-79. Main and Equipment Bonding Jumpers—

(a) **Material.** *Main and equipment bonding jumpers shall be of copper or other corrosion-resistant material.* This automatically eliminates aluminum in many places. Remember that if other than copper is used, it shall be sized to an equivalent to what would be required for copper jumpers.

(b) **Attachment.** *Main and equipment bonding jumpers shall be attached in the manner specified by the applicable provisions of* **Section 250-113** *for circuits and equipment and by* **Section 250-115** *for grounding electrodes.*

Both of these Sections should be reviewed, noting that soldering is not permitted. The question of aluminum for common grounding conductors is always arising. This is taken care of in **(a)** above and to my knowledge there is no grounding clamp approved by UL for grounding with aluminum. If it were to go to a made electrode, it could not be run closer than 18″ to the earth and if to a water pipe, the water piping is subject to sweating and would cause corrosion of the aluminum. This should clarify the problems that we have had in the field.

(c) **Size-Equipment Bonding Jumper on Supply Side of Service and Main Bonding Jumper.**

See Fig. 250-7. There seems to be considerable confusion in **Tables 250-94(a), 250-94(b),** and **250-95.** By looking at the headings there should be no confusion. **Table 250-94(a)** is for: **Grounding Electrode Conductor for Grounded System, Table 250-94(b)** is for: **Grounding Electrode Conductor for Ungrounded System,** and **Table 250-95** is for: **Size of Equipment Grounding Conductors for Grounding Interior Raceway and Equipment.**

The bonding jumper shall not be smaller than the sizes given in **Table 250-94(a)** for grounding electrode conductors. Where the service-entrance phase conductors are larger than the sizes given in **Table 250-94(a),** the bonding jumper shall have an area not less than 12½ percent of the area of the largest phase conductor. Where the service-entrance conductors are paralleled in two or more raceways, the size of the bonding jumper for each raceway shall be based on the size of service conductors in each raceway. The last part of **(c)** will clarify paralleled circuits.

(d) **Size-Equipment Bonding Jumper on Load Side of Service.** The equipment bonding jumper on the load side of the service overcurrent devices shall not be smaller than the sizes listed by **Table 250-95** for equipment grounding conductors.

250-80. Bonding of Piping Systems—*All interior metallic water and gas piping which may become energized shall be bonded together and made electrically continuous. A bond having a size in conformance with* **Table 250-95** *shall be made between the bonded piping systems(s) and the grounding electrode conductor at the service disconnecting means.*

This tells us that the bonding jumper to piping system(s) between the grounding electrode and the piping, *shall be made at the service disconnecting means.* Also if the water piping is used as the grounding electrode, see Fig. 250-9 for connections to same.

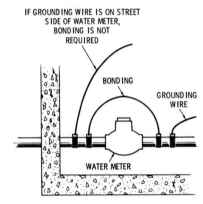

IF GROUNDING WIRE IS ON STREET SIDE OF WATER METER, BONDING IS NOT REQUIRED

BONDING

GROUNDING WIRE

Fig. 250-9. Proper bonding of a water meter.

WATER METER

LEAVE BONDING JUMPER LONG ENOUGH SO THAT IT WILL NOT HAVE TO BE REMOVED IN METER REPLACEMENT

H. Grounding Electrodes

This part of **Article 250** is the basis for the proper construction of a grounded system. Great care should be taken to thoroughly understand the contents of this part, and to adhere to the installation as required by the Code.

250-81. Water Pipe—A buried metallic underground water-supply system shall always be used as the grounding electrode wherever there are 10 feet or more of buried pipe, including any well casing that is bonded to the system. If there is a chance of the piping system being disconnected or an insulated coupling being installed, the pipe electrode shall be supplemented by one or more made electrodes bonded to the piping.

A new edition to the 1965 Code is that an interior metallic cold-water piping system shall always be bonded to the one or more grounding electrodes. Note that the electrical wiring system should be adequately grounded without depending on the outside piping system. This means that supplementing the water pipe system with made electrodes is advised. Additional safety may be gained by bonding the grounding electrode to the gas, sewer, and hot-water piping, and to metallic air ducts within the building.

250-82. Other Available Electrodes—When a water piping system which meets the requirements of the preceding Section is not available, a grounding connection may be made to the following:

(a) The metal frames of buildings that are effectively grounded.

(b) Gas pipelines, provided the following conditions are met:

(1) Permission is granted by the gas supplier.
(2) Permission is granted by the inspection authority.
(3) It is electrically continuous, with no insulated couplings.
(4) It is made up of uncoated metallic pipe.

(c) Other local metallic underground objects:

(1) Piping.
(2) Tanks.
(3) Well casings.

(d) Concrete-encased steel reinforcing bar or rod systems of underground footings or foundations has been added to the 1971 NEC as one of the available electrodes other than buried water piping. The criteria for this shall be:

1. Not less than 50 ft. in length.
2. A minimum of ⅜" bar or rod.
3. A minimum of not less than 2½ ft. below the earth surface.

The connections to these rods and/or bars shall be made by metal-fusing, if the connection is encased in concrete. This is also termed Cad-Welding, or Exo-Thermic Welding. If the connection is not in the concrete and is available for inspection, it may be made by use of clamps, etc.

Concrete makes a very good addition to the grounding system. It seems to give the effect of a larger electrode and concrete also seems to have the quality of drawing moisture. The author has recently had some very satisfactory experience with re-bar grounding to supplement water pipe grounding. You will find in **Section 250-83,** the Concrete-Encased Electrodes, made of copper, this is commonly known as the Ufer Ground in honor of Mr. Ufer who did much experimentation with its use.

250-83. Made Electrodes—If no grounding means, as outlined in the two preceeding Sections, are available, grounding may be accomplished by any one of the following means provided that it meets with the requirements in each case.

(a) **Concrete-Encased Electrodes**. *Not less than 20 feet of bare copper conductor not smaller than No. 4 encased by at least 2 inches of concrete and located within and near the bottom of a concrete foundation footing that is in direct contact with the earth.*

This method of grounding has been under test for a long time and has proven to be a very good grounding method. Not only will concrete draw moisture, but the building pressure against the earth also helps materially in securing a low resistance ground. The installation is a little tricky to keep the conductor low in the footing and still keep it in the concrete.

(b) **Plate Electrodes** may be used that have at least 2 sq. ft. of surface exposed to the soil. Iron or steel plates shall be at least ¼-inch thick while nonferrous metals shall be at least 0.06-inch thick. In referring to nonferrous metals, it will be found that the inspection authority will require metals that are noncorrosive, such as copper. Elsewhere in the Code it is stated that aluminum grounding can be no closer than 18 inches to the soil, so this automatically eliminates aluminum.

(c) **Pipe Electrodes.** Pipe or conduit may be used, but must meet the following requirements:

(1) Be at least ¾-inch trade size.
(2) Have the outer surface galvanized.
(3) Be metal coated for corrosion protection.

(d) **Rod Electrodes.** Rod electrodes shall meet the following requirements:

(1) Be at least ⅝-inch in diameter if of iron or steel.
(2) Be at least ½-inch in diameter if of approved nonferrous materials.

(e) **Installation.** Electrodes shall, in so far as practical, be driven into a permanent moisture location. They shall be driven to a depth of at least 8 feet, regardless of size, unless bedrock is encountered. They shall be of a standard commercial length and preferably in one piece. Where bedrock is encountered, they may be laid horizontally at a depth of at least 4 feet.

Each electrode shall be separated by at least 6 feet from other electrodes used for signal circuits, radio, lightning rods, and for other purposes. Although not in the Code, it is considered good practice to bond the electrodes together.

250-84. Resistance—Made electrodes shall have a resistance to ground of 25 ohms or less, wherever practicable. When the resistance is greater than 25 ohms, two or more electrodes may be connected in parallel or extended to a greater length. The Code cannot go into the mechanics of grounding, but good practice indicates that the electrode has a lower resistance when not driven close to a foundation.

Water piping usually has a ground resistance of less than 3 ohms. Metal frames of buildings often make a good ground and usually have a resistance of less than 25 ohms. As was pointed out in **Section 250-82 (a),** the metal frame of a building (when effectively grounded) may be used as the ground. Local metallic water systems and well casings also make good grounds in most cases.

Grounding, when made electrodes are used, can be greatly improved by the use of chemicals, such as magnesium sulphate, copper sulphate, or rock salt. A doughnut-type hole may be dug around the ground rod into which the chemicals are put. Another method is to bury a tile close to the rod and fill with the chemical. Rain and snow will dissolve the chemicals and allow them to penetrate the soil. See Fig. 250-10.

The Code recommends that the resistance of ground rods be tested periodically after installation. This is rarely done, however, except by utility companies who realize the importance of an adequate ground. The testing of ground resistance is a mystery to many electricians. Never attempt to use a common ohmmeter for the testing, the readings obtained are apt to be most anything due to stray AC or DC currents in the soil or due to

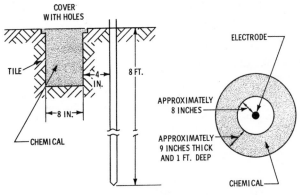

Fig. 250-10. Adding chemicals to the soil to lower its ground resistance.

DC currents set up by the electrolysis in the soil. There are many measuring devices on the market, such as the ground megger, a battery-operated ground tester that uses a vibrator to produce pulsating AC current. In recent years, the transistor-type ground tester has appeared on the market.

An example of what you might expect to get by the paralleling of ground rods might be as follows (these figures are general and should not be taken as being the results in every case): Two rods parallel, with a

5-foot spacing between, will reduce the resistance to about 65% of what one rod would be. Three rods paralleled with a 5-foot spacing between will reduce the resistance to about 42%, while four rods paralleled will reduce the resistance to about 30%.

250-86. Use of Lightning Rods—Lightning-rod conductors and made electrodes for grounding of lightning rods shall not be used in place of made electrodes for grounding wiring systems and equipment. However, they may be bonded together—in fact, the Code recommends the bonding of these electrodes to limit the difference of potential that might appear between them.

J. Grounding Conductors

250-91. Material—Materials for grounding conductors shall be as follows for system or common grounding conductors.

(a) Grounding Electrode Conductor.

(1) Copper or other corrosive-resistance materials.

(2) Solid or stranded.

(3) Insulated or bare.

(4) Without splices or joints, except in the case of bus bars.

(5) Electrical resistance per foot (linear) shall not exceed that of the allowable copper conductors that might be used for this purpose. Thus, if aluminum (in cases where permissible) is used, the conductor will have to be larger than copper would have to be for the same purpose.

(6) If aluminum is used, check **Section 250-92,** which tells us; *Aluminum grounding conductors shall not be used where in direct contact with masonry or the earth or where subject to corrosive conditions. Where used outside, aluminum grounding conductors shall not be installed within 18 inches of the earth.* Also check **Section 250-91(a),** which tells us that the **Common Electrode Conductor**—*shall be installed in one continuous length without joint or splice.*

Exception No. 1. A bus-bar may be spliced.

Exception No. 2. For a grounding electrode conductor of an ungrounded system only, rigid metal conduit pipe, and electrical metallic tubing, including such conduit, pipe and tubing with threaded or threadless joints, may be used and size in accordance with **Table 250-94(b).** *Note that this is for ungrounded systems only.*

(b) Types of Equipment Grounding Conductors. The equipment grounding conductor shall be run with the circuit and may consist of one of the following:

139

(1) A copper or corrosion-resistant conductor, either stranded or solid.
(2) Rigid metal conduit.
(3) Electrical metallic tubing.
(4) Flexible metal conduit approved for the purpose.
(5) Armour of type AC metal-clad cable.
(6) Sheath of MI cable.
(7) Sheath of ALS cable.
(8) Other raceways specifically approved for grounding purposes.

Exception No. 1. Flexible metal conduit may be used for grounding provided all of the following conditions are met:

(a) *The length does not exceed 6 ft.*

(b) *The circuit conductors contained therein are protected by over-current devices rated at 20 amperes or less.*

(c) *The conduit is terminated in fittings approved for the purpose.*

Exception No. 2. Liquidtight flexible metal conduit may be used for grounding in the 1¼ inches and smaller trade size if the length is 6 ft. or less and it is terminated in fittings approved for the purpose.

250-92. Installation—Grounding conductors shall be installed as follows:

(a) Grounding Electrode Conductor. No. 4 or larger grounding conductors may be attached to the surface—knobs or insulators are not required. Mechanical protection will be required only where the conductor is subject to severe physical damage. No. 6 grounding conductors may be run on the surface of a building if protected from physical damage and rigidly stapled to the building structure. Grounding conductors smaller than No. 6 shall be in conduit, EMT, or armor.

The metallic enclosures for the grounding conductor shall be continuous from the cabinet or equipment to the grounding electrode and shall be attached at both ends by approved methods. **Articles 346 and 348,** covering rigid metal conduit and EMT electrical metallic tubing, shall govern the installation of the enclosure for the ground conductor. A common error is often made here—if the system or common grounding conductor is smaller than No. 6, it shall **always** be in conduit, EMT, or armor. This is often confused with a conductor used for grounding equipment and enclosures only.

Due to corrosion, aluminum grounding conductors shall not be

140

placed in direct contact with masonry, earth, or other corrosive materials. Also, where aluminum grounding conductors are used, they shall not be closer than 18 inches to the earth. Please note that this does not prohibit the use of aluminum for grounding conductors, but merely places certain restrictions on it. One sadly abused use of aluminum grounding conductors is in antenna grounding. Remember also that the grounding conductor is to be without splice. If a metal raceway is used merely as a physical protection for the common grounding conductor, it is often not attached to either the enclosure or the grounding electrode. If this is the case, you are required to bond the common grounding conductor to both ends of the metal protective raceway. This will lower the impedance of the circuit, which is very necessary upon fault.

It is recommended that magnetic metal enclosures, such as steel pipe or armor, not be used where protection from physical damage can be otherwise obtained, such as the size of the conductor itself or by nonmetallic enclosures.

(b) Equipment Grounding Conductor. *An equipment grounding conductor shall be installed as follows:*

(1) *Where it consists of a raceway, cable armor, or cable sheath or where it is a wire within a raceway or cable, it shall be installed in accordance with the applicable provisions in this Code using fittings for joints and terminations approved for use with the type raceway or cable used. All connections, joints, and fittings shall be made tight by using suitable tools.*

(2) *Where it is a separate grounding conductor as provided in* **Section 210-7** *or by special permission as provided by* **Section 250-57(b) (b),** *it shall be installed in accordance with* **Section 250-92 (a)** *in regard to restrictions for aluminum and also in regard to protection from physical damage.*

Exception: Sizes smaller than No. 6 need not be enclosed in a raceway or armor where run in the hollow spaces of a wall or partition or where otherwise installed so as not to be subject to physical damage.

All of this was changed—*To indicate that the fittings as well as the cables are acceptable for use as a part of an equipment grounding conductor where properly installed and to insure that cables, fitting, and raceways will be properly installed.*

250-93. Direct Current Systems—See NEC.

250-94. Alternating Current Systems—This section, as well as **Section 250-95** and **Tables 250-94(a), 250-94(b),** and **250-95,** are often confused in the field. Refer to the NEC for interpretation as well as the accompanying summary.

Please note the words *for Grounded Systems* in the heading of **Table 250-94(a)**. Refer to **Sections 250-51** and **250-52**. From **Section 250-52:**

The grounding connection may be connected to the grounding conductor of the wiring system at any convenient point on the premise on the supply side of the disconnecting means.

It is recommended that high capacity services have the grounding conductor connected to the grounded conductor of the system within the service entrance equipment enclosure.

Section 250-53, in essence, states that the grounding conductor grounds the grounding conductor of the system, plus grounding equipment, raceways, etc. **Section 250-54** states that the one common grounding electrode grounds all of the system, the grounding conductor, and the equipment and equipment grounding conductor, whether raceways or conductors. Thus, **Table 250-94(a)** refers to grounding to the grounding electrode.

Take note of the heading of **Table 250-94(b).** This table is for *Ungrounded Systems* and must not be confused with **Table 250-94(a).**

Table 250-95 refers to equipment grounding conductors. It lists conductor sizes and conduit sizes which are permitted for equipment grounding purposes as covered in **Section 250-57.** Note that No. 16 copper and No. 14 aluminum are permitted only when part of an approved cable assembly. The Table covers currents up to 1200 amperes. A note states that for ratings above 1200 amperes, the size of the grounding conductor must be proportionally increased. The ampere rating of the overcurrent device of that portion of the system with which we are concerned is the rating that is to be used.

250-95. Size of Equipment Grounding Conductors—See NEC

250-97. Outline Lighting—Where a conductor complying with **Table 250-95** is used to ground outline lighting systems, the isolated noncurrent carrying parts of this system may be bonded together with a No. 14 conductor which is protected from physical damage.

250-98. Grounding Conductor in Common Raceway—*A grounding conductor may be installed in the same raceway with other conductors of the system to which it is connected.* It is preferable to do so as impedances will be lower.

250-99. Continuity—There shall be no automatic cutouts or switches placed in a grounding conductor unless it will disconnect all sources of supply when it opens. This is common sense, because if the grounding

142

conductor should open and the source of power not opened, the purpose for which the grounding conductor was installed would be defeated.

K. Grounding Conductor Connections

250-111. To Raceway or Cable Armor—Care shall be taken to ground raceways or cable armor on interior wiring by connecting to grounding conductors as near as possible to the source of supply. Also, the grounding conductor shall be chosen so that no raceway or cable armor is grounded by a grounding conductor smaller than that required by **Table 250-95.**

250-112. To Grounding Electrode—This Section tells us that the grounding conductor *shall* be connected to the grounding electrode in such a manner that a *permanent and effective* ground will result. Most inspectors insist that this connection be accessible wherever possible, or cad-welded or brazed.

Where water piping is used as the grounding electrode, any joints that may be disconnected for repairs or replacement shall be bonded around. The same shall be done with insulated coupling, unions, and water meters. This applies to water meters in the house or other buildings where the grounding conductor is connected to the piping on the building side of the meter. It is a common practice to connect the grounding conductor to the street side of the piping ahead of the water meter. Most inspectors prefer it this way when practical to do so. If the meter is at the curb, and there are ten feet or more of buried water piping (metallic), bonding is not required. See Fig. 250-9.

250-113. Attachment to Circuits and Equipment—*The grounding conductor, bond or bonding jumper shall be attached to circuits, conduits, cabinets, equipment and the like, which are to be grounded, by means of:*

(1) Suitable lugs.
(2) Pressure connectors.
(3) Clamps
(4) Other approved means.

Soldering is never permitted. Neither is the strap type of grounding clamp. Be certain that the device used is approved for the purpose.

250-114. Continuity and Attachment of Branch Circuit Equipment Grounding Conductors to Boxes—Whenever more than one grounding conductor enters a box, all are required to make good electrical contact with each other, and shall be so arranged that if a receptacle, fixture, or other device is removed, the continuity of the grounding will not be interrupted.

This has caused considerable concern in the field. The grounding conductor is to be attached to a screw used for no other purpose, or by approved means. Boxes are available with two or more 10-32 tapped holes for this purpose. The clamp screws on loom-wire boxes are not intended to be used as grounding screws. All grounding conductors entering the box are to be made electrically and mechanically secure, and the pigtail made from them is to serve as the grounding connection to the device being installed. Thus, if the device is removed, the continuity will not be disrupted. **Soldering is not permitted.** Pressure connectors should be used—twisting the wires together is not satisfactory, as poor contact may result. Most inspectors require that all of this be done at the time of the rough-in inspection so that he does not have to open all of the outlets to see that they have been properly made up. See Fig. 250-11.

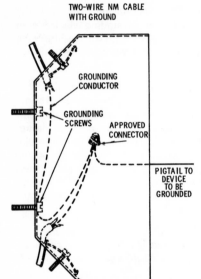

TWO-WIRE NM CABLE
WITH GROUND

GROUNDING
CONDUCTOR

GROUNDING
SCREWS

APPROVED
CONNECTOR

PIGTAIL TO
DEVICE
TO BE
GROUNDED

Fig. 250-11. Illustrating the proper method of grounding boxes and carrying the grounding conductor on to the device to be grounded.

250-115. Attachment to Electrodes—See NEC.

250-116. Ground Clamps—Soldered connections shall never be permitted. Grounding clamps shall be of metal suitable for attachment to the metal of the electrode. Thus, dissimilar metals should not be used because of possible galvanic action which may cause a poor connection with high resistance.

250-117. Protection of Attachment—Unless approved for general use without protection, ground clamps and fittings shall:

(1) Be located so that they will not be subject to damage, or
(2) Be enclosed in metal, wood, or other protective covering.

250-118. Clean Surfaces—In grounding, nonconductive surfaces, such

144

as paint, enamel, corrosion, etc., shall be removed from equipment, conduit, couplings, or fittings where grounding contact is to be made.

L. Instrument Transformers, Relays, etc.

250-121. Instrument Transformer Circuits—Current transformers (CT) and potential transformers (PT) shall have the secondary windings grounded when the primary windings are connected to more than 300 volts to ground, regardless of the primary voltage. The exception to this is when the primary is connected to 750 volts or less, and when there are no live parts or wiring exposed to other than qualified persons.

250-122. Instrument Transformer Cases—The cases of PT's and CT's shall always be grounded where accessible to other than qualified persons except where the primaries are not over 150 volts to ground, and where current transformers are used exclusively to supply meters.

250-123. Cases of Instruments, Meters and Relays—Operating Voltage 750 or Less—Instruments, meters and relays which operate with windings or working parts at 750 volts or less shall be grounded as follows:

(a) **Not on Switchboards.** All cases and other exposed metal parts of instruments, meters, and relays that are not on switchboards shall be grounded when the windings or working parts operate at 300 volts or more to ground, and when they are accessible to other than qualified persons.

(b) **On Dead Front Switchboards.** All instruments that are mounted on a switchboard that has no live parts on the front panel shall be grounded, whether direct connected or whether supplied by instrument transformers.

(c) **On Live Front Switchboards.** All instruments that are mounted on a switchboard which has live parts exposed shall not have their cases grounded, but there shall be mats of rubber or other insulating materials placed on the floor wherever the voltage to ground exceeds 150 volts.

250-124. Cases of Instruments, Meters and Relays—Operating Voltage Over 750—*Where instrument, meters and relays have current-carrying parts over 750 volts to ground, they shall be isolated by elevation or protected by suitable barriers, grounded metal or insulating covers or guards. Their cases shall not be grounded, except as follows:*

(a) Where electrostatic ground detectors are used, the internal ground segments of the instrument are connected to the instrument case and grounded. Here, the ground detector shall be isolated by elevation.

250-125. Instrument Grounding Conductor—See NEC.

145

M. Lightning Arresters

250-131. On Secondary Services, 750 Volts or Less—All connections of secondary services to lightning arresters shall be as short as possible. The grounding conductor for the lightning arrester may be:

(1) The grounded service conductor.
(2) Common grounding conductor.
(3) Service-equipment grounding conductor.

The bonding or grounding conductors shall not be smaller than No. 14 copper or equivalent corrosive-resistant material. In sizing the grounding conductor, physical damage must be considered. If the grounding conductor is exposed, the sizing should follow sizes for other grounding conductors.

No mention is made in the Code, but when installing lightning protection equipment, bends in conductors should be long and sweeping. Lightning will take the shortest path to or from ground.

250-132. On Primary Circuits—*The grounding conductor of a lightning arrester protecting a transformer which supplies a secondary distribution system may be interconnected as follows:*

(a) **Metallic Interconnection.** *A metallic interconnection may be made to the secondary neutral provided that, in addition to the direct grounding connection at the arrester:*

(1) That the secondary is grounded elsewhere to a continuous underground metallic water pipe system. In urban areas where there are at least four such secondary grounds on the neutral, and not less than four such grounds per mile, direct grounding at the transformer may be omitted and a metallic interconnection made to the secondary neutral.

(2) Where the neutral or secondary ground conductor is a part of a multigrounded neutral system, and the primary has at least four grounding connections per mile in addition to the ground at each service, the grounds may be interconnected.

(b) **Through Spark Gap.** Where the secondary or neutral ground does not meet the requirement of part (a) of this Section, but is grounded as required by **Sections 250-82** and **250-83** covering grounding electrodes, if an interconnection is made it shall be through a spark gap having a 60-cycle breakdown voltage of at least twice the primary voltage but not necessarily more than 10KV. In addition, there shall be at least one additional ground on the secondary not less than 20 feet from the lightning-arrester grounding electrode.

146

(c) **By Special Permission.** *Except as above provided, interconnection of the arrester ground and the secondary neutral may be made only by special permission.*

Article 250 is perhaps one of the most important Articles in the Code as far as safety is concerned. It is highly recommended that the reader become thoroughly familiar with its contents.

ARTICLE 280—LIGHTNING ARRESTERS

A. Industrial Stations

280-1. Where Required—In areas that are frequented by thunder storms, industrial stations are required to have lightning arresters installed to aid in protecting the equipment and service to the system supplied. Specific coverage of lightning protection of hazardous locations is covered in **Articles 500** thru **517**. However, in general, arresters are to be provided in Class I locations supplied from ungrounded overhead systems. In Class II Div. 1 and 2 locations, lightning protective devices are required where the system is subject to lightning disturbances.

280-2. Number Required—The requirement is that there be one lightning arrester in each ungrounded conductor entering or leaving the station. Where there is more than one circuit leaving the station, one set of lightning-arresters on a common bus is all that will be required.

280-3. Where Connected—See NEC.

B. Other Occupancies

280-11. Utilization Equipment--—Arresters that are installed for the protection of utilization equipment may be installed either on the inside or outside of the building containing the equipment. The arresters are required to be isolated by elevation or else made inaccessible to unqualified persons. Where the voltage exceeds 750 volts between conductors, the arresters are required to be made inaccessible to unqualified persons.

It is not a requirement of the Code, but it is recommended that in mounting arresters within a building that they be separated from combustible surfaces by asbestos board or other inflammable materials.

C. General

280-21. Location–Indoors—See NEC.

280-22. Location-Outdoors—Arresters that are mounted outdoors and contain oil, shall have adequate facilities for draining away any accumulated oil.

280-23. Connections—Size and Material—All connections to or from lightning arresters shall be by copper wire or cable, or its equivalent. These

147

wires or cables shall be no smaller than No. 6 and made as short and straight as possible, except as provided for in **Section 250-131.** Turns and bends should be kept to a bare minimum, especially sharp bends.

280-24. Installation—See NEC.

280-25. Switch for Isolating Arrester—See NEC.

280-26. Grounding—*Lightning arresters shall be grounded in the manner prescribed in* **Article 250,** *except that grounding conductors shall not be run in metallic enclosures unless bonded to both ends of such enclosures.*

Chapter 3. Wiring Methods and Materials

Basically, Chapter 3 covers voltages up to 600 volts; however, there will be references to higher voltages in places. **Article 710** covers voltages of over 600 volts and **Article 720** covers voltages of 50 volts or less.

ARTICLE 300—WIRING METHODS— GENERAL REQUIREMENTS

300-1. Scope—

(a) The provisions of Chapter 3 apply to the electrical and mechanical requirements for the various methods of installing fixed electrical conductors for:

(1) Electric light.
(2) Electric heat.
(3) Electric power.
(4) Certain signal systems.

(b) This Article applies to all wiring installations except:

(1) Remote control.
(2) Low-voltage relay switching.
(3) Low-energy power.
(4) Low-energy signal systems.
(5) Communications systems.

These are covered in **Articles 725** and **800.**

(c) It is possible (although not probable) that a continuous metallic water-piping system is not available for a grounding electrode or that a ground of permanently low resistance is not available. In such a case, it is recommended that a wiring system without metallic enclosures be used unless the occupancy or character of the building would require a metallically enclosed wiring system.

(d) Conductors which form an integral part of motors, motor controllers, and similar equipment are not covered by this Article. The wiring covered starts with the conductors entering or leaving the motor controllers and motor terminals, or the connection boxes that are a part of the motor.

300-2. Voltage Limitations—As previously mentioned, Chapter 3 applies to wiring of 600 volts or less unless specific mention is made to other voltages in other Sections or Articles of the Code. The intent is that these general wiring methods may be used for higher voltages where permitted elsewhere in the Code.

300-3. Conductors of Different Systems—

(a) Conductors for light and power systems of 600 volts or less may occupy the same enclosures. It makes no difference whether the individual circuits are AC or DC. The requirements are that the conductors shall be insulated for the maximum voltage of any one conductor within the enclosure, and that the voltage of any circuit therein is 600 volts or less. The 24-volt control from a furnace thermostat may be installed in the same circuit with the 120-volt circuit supplying the motor of the furnace, providing that the 24-volt wire is insulated and approved for the 120-volt supply, which in most cases would have 600-volt insulation.

(b) Conductors operating at 600 volts or less shall not occupy the same enclosure as conductors operating at over 600 volts.

(c) Discharge lighting with a secondary voltage of 1000 volts or less may have its conductors in the same fixture enclosure as the branch-circuit conductors, providing that the secondary conductors are insulated for the voltage involved. This takes care of the higher voltages that are encountered in discharge type of lighting fixtures.

(d) *Primary leads of electric discharge lamp ballasts, insulated for the primary voltage of the ballast, when contained within the individual wiring enclosure may occupy the same fixture as the branch-circuit conductors.* An example is a 277-volt ballast that might have primary leads rated at 300 volts. These primary leads may be in the same enclosure as the branch-circuit conductors having 600-volt insulation.

(e) Conductors used in connection with any individual motor or starter may occupy the same enclosure as the motor-circuit conductors, such as:
(1) Excitation conductors.
(2) Control conductors.
(3) Relay conductors.
(4) Ammeter conductors.

(f) Power or light conductors shall not be permitted to occupy the same enclosure as signal and radio conductors, except as permitted in the following Sections:

(1) For elevators, **Section 620-36.**

(2) For sound recording, **Section 640-6.**

(3) For remote-control, low-energy power and signal circuits, **Sections 725-16** and **725-42.**

(4) Communication systems, **Sections 800-3** and **800-21.**

300-4. Protection Against Physical Damage — Where conductors might be subject to physical damage they shall be protected by metal raceways, cabinets, running boards, etc.

300-5. Protection Against Corrosion—*Metal raceways, cable armor, boxes, cable sheathing, cabinets, metallic elbows, couplings, fittings, supports and support hardware shall be of materials suitable for the environment in which they are to be installed.*

This and the following are 1965 and 1968 Code revisions and were necessary because of corrosive action, especially where raceways were imbedded in concrete or were in direct contact with the soil.

(a) *Ferrous raceways, cable armor, boxes, cable sheathing, cabinets, metallic elbows, couplings, fittings, supports and support hardware shall be suitably protected against corrosion inside and outside (except threads at joints) by a coating of approved corrosion resistant material such as zinc, cadmium, or enamel. Where protected from corrosion solely by enamel, they shall not be used out of doors or in wet locations as described in* **(c)** *below. When boxes or cabinets have an approved system of organic coatings and are marked "Raintight" or "Outdoor Type" they may be used out of doors.*

(b) *Unless made of material judged suitable for the condition, or unless corrosion protection approved for the condition is provided, ferrous, or non-ferrous metallic raceways, cable armor, boxes, cable sheathing, cabinets, elbows, couplings, fittings, supports or support hardware shall not be installed in concrete or in direct contact with the earth, or in areas subject to severe corrosive influences.*

This part has given wide latitude to installations. Additives in concrete can cause serious corrosive action. Also, certain soil conditions can cause corrosion. The inspection authority now has a wide control over where the conduit is placed and of what material it is made. In case of doubt, the installer can always check with the inspector in charge for a ruling on his interpretation of the conditions.

(c) *In portions of dairies, laundries, canneries and other indoor wet locations, and in locations where walls are frequently washed or where there are surfaces of absorbent materials, such as damp paper or wood, the entire wiring system, including all boxes, fittings, conduits and cable used therewith, shall be mounted so*

151

that there is at least one-quarter inch air space between it and the wall or supporting surface.

Meat-packing plants, tanneries, hide cellars, casing rooms, glue houses, fertilizer rooms, salt storage, some chemical works, metal refineries, pulp mills, sugar mills, round houses, some stables, and similar locations are judged to be occupancies where severe corrosive conditions are likely to be present.

It can be seen from the above that precautions have been taken for protection from corrosive elements, including excess moisture. There may be conditions in which the best conduit might be the rigid nonmetallic type. If this type is used, the Article covering the installation of same must be adhered to. Plastic coated conduit is now available.

300-6. Raceways Exposed to Different Temperatures—

(a) Sealing. *Where portions of an interior raceway system are exposed to widely different temperatures, as in refrigerating or cold-storage plants, provisions shall be made to prevent circulation of air from a warmer to a colder section through the raceway.*

While not specifically covered, conditions will be found in which the wireman runs a service mast down an inside wall of a house to the service-entrance equipment. The temperature in the house will run possibly 75° and the mast exposed to an outside temperature of −10° to −30°. This will cause a chimney effect. The warm air will rise and be cooled, thus causing moisture to run down inside the conduit into the panel.

(b) Expansion Joints. *Expansion joints for runs of raceways shall be provided where required to compensate for thermal expansion and contraction.*

Where these joints are to be used will require common sense. In using expansion joints it is necessary to provide bonding jumpers, as required under **Section 250-77**, so as to make good electrical contact around the expansion joints.

300-7. Underground Runs—Section 230-32 explained the protection of service conductors run underground. This same Section may be interpreted to include branch circuits and feeders. See **Sections 310-1(b), 310-5, 310-6, 338-1(b)**, and **Article 339.** Some inspectors will require a sand bed and a sand covering for protecting underground conductors, especially in rocky areas and where freezing temperatures are encountered. They may also require a mechanical protection over the conductors. The mechanical protection required is the inspector's prerogative; some may require redwood or treated boards, others may require a plastic strip that has the words **caution** printed along the entire length.

Underground cable run under a building shall be in a raceway that is extended beyond the outside wall of the building.

Before this last paragraph was inserted, UF cable could be buried below a cement floor of a building, and conduit used to sleeve it through the concrete. The latest Code ruling is a very welcome change, as most inspectors never considered it good workmanship to pour a floor over a cable because it was not readily replaceable.

300-8.   Through Studs, Joists and Rafters—

(a) When installing exposed or concealed conductors in insulating tubes, or installing cables in holes bored through studs, joists, or rafters, the holes shall be drilled as near the center of the wood member as possible, but not less than 2 inches from the nearest edge. In drilling, notching, etc., the structure shall not be weakened. It is not within the scope of the Code to cover this fully, but all building codes should be adhered to.

(b) If there is no objection because of weakening the structure, notching for cables of all types is approved by the Code, provided that the notch is covered by a steel plate at least 1/16 inch thick to protect the cable from nails. For the intent of (a) and (b), see Fig. 300-1.

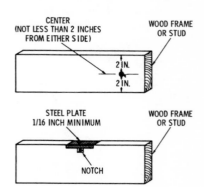

Fig. 300-1. Approved drilling and notching procedure.

300-9.   Grounding Metal Enclosures—*Metal raceways, boxes, cabinets, cable armor and fittings shall be grounded if and as prescribed in* **Article 250.**

It will be recalled that there are many and varied methods of grounding metal enclosures. In ordinary wiring with conduit, armored cable, MI cable, etc., the metal of the raceway is the grounding conductor. On the service entrance and in hazardous locations, hubs or bonding is required. With NM and UF cables, the grounding conductor is to be placed under a screw used only for grounding purposes. They are to be made electrically and mechanically secure, and soldering is not permitted.

300-10. Electrical Continuity of Metal Raceways and Enclosures— *Metal raceways, cable armor, and other metal enclosures for conductors shall be metallically joined together into a continuous electrical conducductor.* Raceways and cable armor shall be securely and effectively connected to boxes, fittings, and cabinets. Locknuts, bushings, and connectors supply this continuity, except where other measures are required to be taken, such as bonding at services, expansion joints, eccentric and concentric knockouts, and in hazardous locations. Where nonmetallic boxes are used, as permitted in **Section 370-7,** they do not have to make a metallic connection with the raceway, but the metallic connection must be carried on by an approved means.

300-11. Secured in Place—All raceways, cable assemblies, boxes, cabinets, fittings, etc., shall be securely fastened in place with approved anchors, except in certain specific instances mentioned elsewhere in the Code. Wooden plugs driven into concrete are not considered acceptable for fastening electrical equipment. Securing of continuous rigid-cable supports will be covered in **Article 318.**

300-12. Mechanical Continuity—Raceways and Cables—*Raceways and cable assemblies shall be continuous from outlet to outlet and from fitting to fitting* as shown in Fig. 300-2.

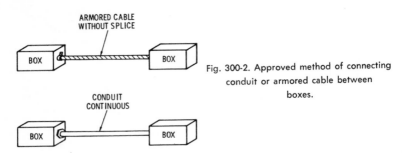

Fig. 300-2. Approved method of connecting conduit or armored cable between boxes.

300-13. Mechanical and Electrical Continuity–Conductors—Conductors shall be continuous between outlets, devices, etc. No splices shall be permitted in raceways, except as permitted for auxillary gutters in **Section 374-8,** for wireways in **Section 362-6,** and **Section 300-15(a).** In other words, conductors in raceways shall be in one piece and without splice except as used above.

A new change has been added in the 1971 NEC to cover continuity of identified grounded conductors in multiwire circuits. Usually the conductor was run to a box and another conductor from that box on to the next box, etc., and the ends were put under separate screws of a receptacle. This will no longer be allowed and the continuity shall not depend upon the device connections, such as lampholders, receptacles, etc. Removal of the device could interupt the continuity and serious results could occur. Now the conductor may be either continuous with loop connections, or approved splices made and a pigtail to the device.

300-14. Free Length of Conductors at Outlets and Switch Points— A minimum of 6 inches of free conductor length shall be left at all outlets and switch points, except if a conductor loops through without connection to any device and is without a splice. This ruling is to provide ample conductor length for making connections to the outlet or switch, and to provide some spare length in the event that a piece should break off in the makeup.

300-15. Boxes and Fittings Where Required—

(a) **Box or Fitting.** *A box or fitting shall be installed at each conductor splice connection point, outlet, switch point, junction point or pull point for connection of conduit, electrical metallic tubing, surface raceways or other raceways.*

Exception No. 1. A box or fitting is not required for a conductor splice connection in surface raceways, wireways, header ducts, multi-outlet assemblies and auxillary gutters having a removeable cover which is accessible after installation.

Exception No. 2. As permitted in **Section 410-26.**

(b) **Box Only.** *A box shall be installed at each conductor splice connection point, outlet, switch point, junction point, or pull point for the connection of metal-clad cable, mineral-insulated metal-sheathed cables, aluminum-sheathed cable, nonmetallic sheathed cable, or other cables and at each outlet and switch point for concealed knob-and-tube wiring.*

Exception No. 1. As permitted by **Section 336-11** *for insulated outlet devices supplied by nonmetallic-sheathed cable.*

Exception No. 2. As permitted by **Section 410-60** *for rosettes.*

Exception No. 3. Where accessible fittings approved for the purpose are used for straight-through splices in mineral insulated metal-sheathed cable.

300-16. Raceway or Cable to Open or Concealed Wiring—

(a) When changing from conduit, EMT, NM cable, MC cable, ALS cable, metal-sheathed cable, or MI cable to open wiring or concealed knob-and-tube wiring, a box or fitting with bushed openings or holes for each conductor may be used. The box or fitting shall contain no splice, nor shall it be used at fixture outlets. See Fig. 300-3.

(b) See NEC.

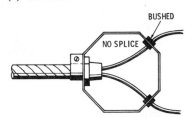

Fig. 300-3. Method of transferring from cable to concealed knob-and-tube wiring.

300-17. Number of Conductors in Raceway—The most commonly used raceways are conduit and EMT. The 1971 NEC has changed the *fill* Tables in Chapter 9.

Table 1 gives us the percent of **Cross Section of Conduit** and tubing for conductors. **Table 2** gives us fill for **Fixture Wires. Table 3A, 3B** and **3C** apply to complete conduit or tubing systems and do not apply to short sections of conduit used for physical protection only. Nipples not exceeding 14 inches may be filled to 60%. Please note that Tables for new and rewire work, no longer exist. Refer to the NEC for Sections of the Code covering specific applications.

300-18. Inserting Conductors in Raceways—

(a) Before conductors are installed in raceways, the raceways shall be installed as a complete system, except those that have removable covers or cappings.

(b) As far as practical, conductors shall not be pulled into the raceways where they might be damaged by weather or mechanical injury during construction.

(c) When pull wires are to be used, they shall not be installed until the raceway system is in place.

(d) Before using any cleaning agents or lubricants to aid in the pulling of conductors, such agents or lubricants should be checked to see that they are approved and have no deteriorating effect on the conductor or the insulation.

300-19. Supporting Conductors in Vertical Raceways—

(a) Due to the weight of the conductors, it is necessary to support them on vertical runs. The Table in this section of the NEC specifies the supports necessary.

(b) The following are approved methods of supporting vertical conductors:

    (1) *By clamping devices constructed of or employing insulating wedges inserted in the ends of the conduits. With cables having varnished cambric or thermoplastic insulation it may also be necessary to clamp the conductor.* The varnished cambric and thermoplastic insulation is inclined to slip on the conductor. Therefore, wedges might not hold this type of conductor and insulation effectively.

    (2) *By inserting boxes at the required intervals in which insulating supports are installed and secured in a satisfactory manner to withstand the weight of the conductors attached thereto, the boxes being provided with covers.* See Fig. 300-4.

    (3) *In junction boxes, by deflecting the cables not less than 90 degrees and carrying them horizontally to a distance not less than twice the diameter of the cable, the cables being carried on two or more insulating supports, and additionally secured thereto by tie wires if desired. When this method is used cables shall be supported at intervals not greater than 20 per cent of those mentioned in the preceding tabulation.* The necessity of supporting at not more than 1/5 of the distances in the Table would seem to make this method the less practical, because additional expenses would be involved.

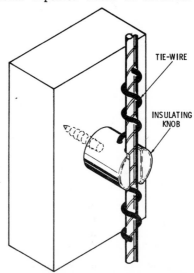

Fig. 300-4. Vertical support of conductors by knobs and tie wires.

157

300-20. Induced Currents in Metal Enclosures—Please note that prior to the 1965 Code, this Section was effective only for circuits carrying 50 amperes or more. The new ruling mentions no minimum value of current.

To accomplish the minimizing of heating effects, the phase conductors, neutral where used, and equipment grounding conductor where used, shall all be in the same enclosure. It is recommended that **Section 300-20** of the NEC be studied for further clarification.

300-21. Prevention of Spread of Fire—Electrical installations shall be planned and installed so as to minimize the spread of fire through:

(1) Fire-stopped partitions.
(2) Hollow spaces.
(3) Fire walls.
(4) Fire partitions.
(5) Vertical shafts.
(6) Ventilating and air-handling ducts.

This safeguarding may be facilitated by sealing openings around boxes and cabinets, keeping drilled holes to a minimum size, keeping notches to a bare minimum, and by the proper routing of raceways. Wall boxes in wallboard, paneling, etc., are to be flush and the space around the box sealed. This will stop possible drafts which cause fires to spread.

300-22. Wiring in Ducts, Plenums and Other Air Handling Spaces— (a) Ducts or Dust, Loose Stock or Vapor Removal.
port:
(1) Loose dust.
(2) Loose stock.
(3) Flammable vapors.
No wiring shall be installed in ducts of duct shafts containing only such ducts that are used for:
(1) Vapor removal for commercial type cooking.
(2) Ventilation of commercial type cooking.
(b) Ducts or Plennums Used for Environmental Air.
(1) MI Cable.
(2) ALS Cable.
(3) E.M.T.
(4) Rigid metal conduit.
(5) Metal-sheathed Cable.
When equipment is permitted in these types of ducts or plenums, flexible metal conduit not to exceed 4 ft. in length may be used to connect physically adjustable equipment and devices. The connectors used with this flexible metal conduit shall effectively close any openings for such connections. *Equipment and devices may only be installed within*

such ducts or plenum chambers if necessary for their direct action upon, or sensing of, the contained air. Where equipment or devices are installed and illumination is necessary to facilitate maintenance and repair, enclosed gasketed type fixtures may be installed.

(c) Hollow Spaces Used as Ducts or Plenums for Environmental Air.

(1) *The wiring materials, including fixtures, are suitable for the expected ambient temperature to which they will be subjected.*

(2) *The wiring system, including fixtures, in no way reduces the fire protective rating of the construction in which they are installed.*

(3) *Flexible metal conduit shall be limited to the connection of devices, equipment, and fixtures in lengths not exceeding six feet. The connectors used with flexible metal conduit shall effectively close any openings in the connection.*

Exception No. 1. The above provisions shall not apply to integral fan systems specifically approved for the purpose.

Exception No. 2. This section does not include habitable rooms or areas of buildings, the prime purpose of which is not air handling.

NFPA Standard for the Installation of Air Conditioning and Ventilating Systems, No. 90A, sets forth requirements of building used for ducts and plenums.

(d) *The wiring systems used for data processing systems and located within air handling areas created by raised floors shall conform to* **Article 645.**

ARTICLE 305—TEMPORARY WIRING

There has been nothing explicit in the NEC covering **Temporary Wiring,** so the 1971 NEC has a new Article covering this subject. This new Articles is well covered and I felt that the Code material, plus any explanations should be included.

305-1. Scope—*The provisions of this Article are applicable to temporary electrical power and lighting methods which may be of a class less than would be required for permanent installations. Except as specifically modified in this Article, all other requirements of this Code for permanent wiring shall apply to temporary wiring installations.*

Temporary wiring has been rather an off breed. This gives the inspection authorities having jurisdiction something to use for decisions.

(a) *Temporary electrical power and lighting installations may be*

159

used during the period of construction, remodeling, or demolition of buildings, structures, equipment, or similar activities.

Each and everyone of us in this field has seen very dangerous practices used in temporary wiring.

(b) *Temporary electrical power and lighting installations may be used for a period not to exceed 90 days for Christmas decorative lighting, carnivals, and similar purposes, and for experimental or development work.*

305-2. General—

(a) Services. *Services shall be installed in conformance to* **Article 230.** *This will be as required for any other service.*

(b) Feeders. *Feeders shall be protected as provided in* **Article 240.** *They shall originate in an approved distribution center. The conductors may be contained within multi-conductor cord or cable assemblies or where not subject to mechanical injury, they may be run as open conductors on insulators not more than 10 feet apart.*

(c) Branch Circuits. *All branch circuits shall originate in an approved distribution cabinet or panelboard. Conductors may be contained within multi-conductor cord or cable assemblies or as open wiring. All conductors shall be protected by overcurrent devices at their rated ampacity. When run as open conductors they shall be fastened at ceiling height every 10 feet. No conductor shall be laid on the floor. Each branch circuit which supplies receptacles or fixed equipment shall contain a separate equipment grounding conductor when run as open wiring.*

The three preceeding parts are a far cry from the temporary wiring so often used on construction sites. If the overcurrent panels, etc., are exposed to the elements, the same types of equipment shall be used as would be used under similar conditions on permanent wiring.

(d) Receptacles. *All receptacles shall be of the grounding-type. Unless installed in a complete metallic raceway all branch circuits shall contain a separate equipment grounding conductor and all receptacles shall be electrically connected to the grounding conductor. See* **Section 210-7** *for receptacles installed on construction sites.*

(e) Earth Returns. *No bare conductors nor earth returns shall be used for the wiring of any temporary circuit.*

(f) Disconnecting Means. *Suitable disconnecting switches or plug connectors shall be installed to permit the disconnection of all ungrounded conductors of each temporary circuit.*

Referring back to **(d)** above, **Section 210-7** states:

All 15- and 20-ampere receptacle outlets on single-phase circuits for construction sites shall have approved ground-fault circuit protection for personnel. This requirement shall become effective on January 1, 1974.

305-3. Grounding—All grounding shall conform with **Article 250.**

ARTICLE 310—CONDUCTORS FOR GENERAL WIRING

310-1. General—

(a) This Article is to assure that conductors for general wiring:

    (1) Have mechanical strength.
    (2) Have adequate current carrying capacity (ampacity).
    (3) Are adequate for the particular usage to which they are to be put (such as wet or dry locations), for the temperature to which they will be subjected, etc.

A large part of this Article is in the form of Tables, which will be explained as they are covered.

(b) *Conductors shall be insulated, except when covered or bare conductors are specifically permitted* elsewhere in the Code.

(c) Conductors that are an integral part of a motor, motor controller, or other equipment, or which are provided for elsewhere in the Code, are not covered by this Article.

310-2. Application and Construction—

(a) Conductor Application. Table 310-2(a) lists the conductor insulation, type letter (Code letter) of the wire, maximum operating temperatures, both in Fahrenheit and Centigrade, for which the wire and insulation is approved, and the general application for which the conductor is intended.

For instance, if the ambient temperature is 140°F, it is known that a higher temperature insulation must be used as there most certainly will be some heat dissipated in the conductor under load unless the conductor is merely a control wire with little or no current flowing through it.

The conductors in **Table 310-2(a)** may be used for wiring methods recognized by this chapter, excepting as provided in the Table or in **Section 310-3,** or as otherwise specified in the Code. They are only suitable for 600 volts or less.

An explanation of the letters in the "Type Letter" column is as follows:

161

F—Fixture Wire	H—Heat Resistant
T—Thermoplastic	A—Asbestos
R—Rubber	W—Water Resistant
V—Varnished Cambric	S—Silicone
L—Lead Covered	N—Nylon Covered

The "Application Provisions" column identifies the use to which the particular type of wire may be put. For example, THWN identifies a moisture- and heat-resistant thermoplastic covered wire which may be used in either dry or wet locations, and has a temperature rating of 75°C or 167°F. The "T" stands for thermoplastic, the "H" for heat-resistant, the "W" for wet locations, and the "N" for Nylon.

(b) Conductor Construction. Conductors insulated for 600 volts or less shall conform to the provisions of **Table 310-2(b).** There are five columns in this Table. Column 1 (Trade Name) identifies the purpose of the conductor; Column 2 (Type Letter) gives the letter identification; Column 3 lists the type of insulation; Column 4 lists the thickness of the insulation for the different sizes of wires; and Column 5 describes the type of covering. The larger the size of the wire, the thicker the insulation—this is to give added protection in the installation.

(c) Identified Conductors. Referring back to **Article 100,** *Identified* means that it is to be recognized as grounded. All insulated conductors, No. 6 or smaller, that are intended to be used as identified conductors of any circuit shall have an outer covering of white or natural gray color. Also, twin or twisted pair conductors, or three-conductor cables, shall have one conductor identified; four-conductor cables shall have one conductor identified in this manner. Refer back to **Section 200-7.** Conductors larger than No. 6 may have the ends identified by white paint (permanent) or by white tape.

Exception No. 1. Multiple-conductor varnished cloth insulated cables.

Exception No. 2. Fixture wires as outlined below.

Exception No. 3. Mineral-insulated metal-sheathed cable. The conductors of MI cable are bare and are to be identified by white sleeving.

Exception No. 4. A conductor identified as required by **Section 210-5.**

For fixture wires the identification shall be as above, or by means of (1) stripes, or (2) by means described in **Sections 400-13 (a), (c), (d)** *and* **(e).** Illustrations of this are shown in Fig. 310-1.

310-3. Insulating Material—

(a) Rubber insulating materials include the following:

    (1) Natural rubber.
    (2) Synthetic rubber.
    (3) Neoprene.
    (4) Other vulcanizable materials.

(b) Thermoplastic insulation may be affected by temperature and may stiffen at temperatures lower than −10°C (14°F). When working with it, care must be taken during installation at these temperatures. Pressure against this type of insulation may also cause deforming—one vulnerable spot is at bushings. **Section 373-6(b)** has taken this into consideration, requiring insulating bushings where No. 4 or larger wire is used. One point comes up quite often—what do you do when a grounding-type bush-ing is required and also an insulating bushing? The answer is a combination insulating and grounding bushing, or fiber inserts made for use with ordinary all-metal bushings.

310-4. Temperature Limitations—Table 310-2(a) gave temperature ratings of various insulations. These were the temperature ratings under load-carrying conditions and were not the ambient temperature. For instance, it is incorrect to use TW wire for wiring boiler controls—a high-temperature wire is required. Also, TW wire is not generally ap-plicable for running to fluorescent lighting fixtures because of the heat of the ballasts.

310-5. Wet Locations—Insulated conductors installed in any of the following locations shall be moisture resistant:

    (1) Underground.
    (2) In concrete slabs or masonry in direct contact with the earth.
    (3) In wet locations.
    (4) Where condensation or accumulation of moisture within the raceway is likely to occur.

The following types of insulation are moisture resistant:

    (1) RHW.
    (2) RUW.
    (3) TW.
    (4) THW.
    (5) THWN.
    (6) XHHW.
    (7) ALS Cable.
    (8) MI Cable.
    (9) Lead-Covered Cable.

These types are not approved for direct burial in the earth unless specifically approved for this purpose.

310-6. Buried Conductors—*Cables of one or more conductors for direct burial in the earth shall be of the type approved for the purpose and use, such as Types USE and UF. Where single conductor cables are installed, all conductors of each service, feeder, sub-feeder or branch circuit, including the neutral conductor, shall be run continuously in the same trench or raceway.*

The authority enforcing the Code may require supplemental mechanical protection, such as a covering board, concrete pad, or raceway. In rocky soil, and more especially where frost is prevalent, the inspection authority will in addition usually require that a bed of fine sand be provided both under and over the conductors and the protection board. Rocks subject to frost heave will cause damage to the insulation.

310-7. Corrosive Conditions—Where conductors are exposed to (1) oils, (2) grease, (3) vapors, (4) gases, (5) fumes, or (6) liquids, or other substances that might cause deterioration of the conductor insulation, a type approved for the condition shall be required. A case in point is a gasoline dispensing island where lead-covered cable or cable with an approved nylon jacket is required. The conductors may be found in the UL listings to be certain whether or not they are approved for the location.

310-8. Minimum Size of Conductors—*Conductors, whether solid or stranded, shall not be smaller than No. 14, except for:*

(1) Printing press control circuits.
(2) Flexible cords, as provided in **Section 400-7.**
(3) Fixture wires, **Section 410-18.**
(4) Fractional horsepower motors, **Section 430-22.**
(5) Cranes and hoists, **Section 610-14.**
(6) Elevator control and signal circuits, **Section 620-12.**
(7) Remote-control, low-energy power, low-voltage power, and signal circuits, **Section 725-13.**

310-9. Stranded Conductors—*Except when used as bus bars or in Type MI Cable, conductors No. 6 and larger, installed in raceways, shall be stranded.* MI cable will come with solid conductors in No. 6 or larger sizes in most cases. Generally, No. 8 or larger conductors will be stranded.

For aerial cable the identification shall be as above, or by means of a ridge so located on the exterior of the cable as to identify it.

Wires having their outer covering finished to show a white or natural gray color but having colored tracer threads in the braid, identifying the source of manufacture, are considered as meeting the provisions of this Section.

(d) Unidentified Conductors. Single conductors and conductors other than the identified conductors of multiconductor cables, shall be colored or have a combination of colors in contrast to white or natural gray. Conductors, larger than No. 6, that are used as unidentified conductors shall have a distinctive marking at their terminals. For indentification requirements for conductors larger than No. 6 see **Section 200-6(b).**

(e) Insulation Thickness–Over 600 Volts. *The thickness of insulation for conductors for use over 600 volts shall conform to* **Tables 310-2(e) (1)** *thru* **(e) (4).**

The requirement that says No. 6 or larger shall be stranded, will be changed to No. 8 or larger, to be effective after January 1, 1973.

310-10. Conductors in Parallel—This Section applies to aluminum or copper conductors connected in parallel so as to in reality form a common conductor and this part is commonly abused. It is recommended that the following conditions for paralleling be followed closely.

When necessary to run equipment grounding conductors with paralleled conductors, these equipment grounding conductors are to be treated the same as the other conductors and sized according to **Table 250-95.**

310-11. Ampacity Reduction Factors—*Where more than three conductors are installed in a raceway or assembled into one or more cables the ampacity of each conductor shall be reduced in accordance with Note 3 to* **Tables 310-12** *through* **310-15.** The Notes to **Tables 310-12** through **310-15** are listed in the NEC and will not be repeated here. However, comments that are considered helpful are given here.

Note 3. Aluminum Conductors. Tables 310-14 and **310-15** cover aluminum conductors. Aluminum has approximately 80% of the conductivity of copper, so a larger size aluminum wire will be required for the same ampacity as copper. For instance, where No. 14 copper is permitted, No. 12 aluminum will have to be used. These Tables should be thoroughly studied. While they may seem dull and uninteresting, there is a great deal of information to be learned from them.

Note 6. Ultimate Insulation Temperature. As will be recalled, the temperature rating of the conductor insulation is not only the ambient temperature, but also includes the temperature rise of the conductor due to current flow. Thus, both the ambient temperature and the conductor rise in temperature shall be used in determining the type of insulation to use. Be sure to follow the correction factors for ambient temperatures listed at the bottom of **Tables 310-12** through **310-15.**

Note 7. Use of Conductors With Higher Operating Temperatures. Where the maximum room temperature is within 10°C of the operating temperature, it is recommended that a higher temperature conductor be used. Conductors approaching the maximum operating temperature of the insulation may be used if the current is reduced in accordance with the Ambient Temperatures. Correction Factors appear as **Note 15.** This **Note 15** is a very important note and applies to the conductors in **Tables 310-12** through **310-15.** The purpose is to avoid the damaging of insulations where ambient temperatures are over 86°F.

Note 8. More Than Three Conductors in a Raceway or Cable. The derating factors given do not apply where wires that carry little current, such as control wires, are installed in the same raceway with three current-carrying conductors. Also, under **Section 210-23(b)** and **220-2,** where percentage factors are to be used, the derating factors there will not apply. Any conductors or cables stacked in continuous rigid cable supports **(Article 318)** will have to be derated in accordance with this Note.

A very controversial item is whether the neutral conductor of a four-wire wye system has a bearing on derating. It is the author's opinion that this question cannot be answered in a broad sense, but would depend upon the types of loads and whether the neutral was carrying any appreciable amount of current or not.

Note 10. Neutral Conductor. This Note also covers what was mentioned in Note 8. In general, the neutral will not be counted as a current-carrying conductor. Refer to **Section 220-4(d-3).**

Note 11. Voltage Drop. Voltage drop is not considered in **Tables 310-12** through **310-15.** It may be found that a certain size conductor is ample for the temperature, but the voltage drop may be out of the limits specified by the Code. Thus, a larger conductor must be used. Carefully study **Tables 310-12** through **310-15** in the NEC. Also note that the conductors are listed according to temperatures, so it may be necessary to refer back to **Table 310-2(a).**

310-12. Marking—

(a) **Required Information.** See NEC.

(b) **Method of Marking.** See NEC.

(c) **Suffixes to Designate Number of Conductors.** See NEC.

310-20. Simplified Wiring Table—*The Simplified Wiring Table,* **Table 310-21** *may be used for the selection of feeder and branch circuit conductor sizes and insulation types only under the conditions stated in this Section. The Simplified Wiring Table shall be used only when a demand factor of 80 per cent or less exists.* See **Tables 310-20(c)** and **310-21.**

166

First determine the load in amperes and whether the load is continuous or noncontinuous. Use **Section 310-20(b)** to arrive at whether the load is continuous or noncontinuous. Decide on whether you will be using aluminum or copper wire. Find the amperes in Column 1 of **Table 310-21,** and then under copper or aluminum, continuous or noncontinuous, find the conductor size.

Determine the ambient temperature under which the conductors will be operating. If it is 30° C or below, **Table 310-20(c)** will not be used. If it is above 30°C, such as in a furnace or boiler room, we find an ambient temperature of 60° C max. In the last column we find that a 90° C insulation will have to be used for the conductors.

This simplified wiring table anticipates the existence of a load factor of less than 100%. Since this anticipation is automatic in the table, it may be used without the consideration of the 80% normally used on conductor loadings. This simplified wiring table is, in essence, taking into consideration load diversities and demands, which are also considered in the NEC.

310-21. Conductor Ampacity—See NEC.

ARTICLE 318—CONTINUOUS RIGID CABLE SUPPORTS

This Article has been completely changed in the 1965 Code, and should therefore be carefully read and the comments noted in order to become familiar with the changes. A considerable portion of the Code will be quoted in order to give a better understanding of the intent.

318-1. Definition—*A continuous rigid cable support is a unit or an assembly of units or sections, and associated fittings, made of metal or other noncombustible materials forming a continuous rigid structure used to support cables. Continuous rigid cable supports include ladders, troughs, channels, and other similar structures.*

It is not the intent of this Article to require that cables be supported by continuous rigid cable supports or to recognize the use of conductors described in **Article 310** *in continuous rigid supports for general wiring.*

It should be noted that this is not the only way that cables may be supported. Regardless of the type, however, they very definitely are to be of noncombustible materials.

When single conductors are subjected to fault currents, they will be repelled from one another. This can cause a problem with supports. Thus, it is easy to see why cables are intended for use in such instances.

318-2. Use—

(a) Continuous rigid cable supports may be used for the following, but the conditions covering the installation of each should be followed as per the Articles referred to:

(1) Mineral-insulated metal-sheathed cable **(Article 330).**

   (2) Aluminum sheathed cable **(Article 331).**

   (3) Metal-clad cable **(Article 334).**

   (4) Non-metallic sheathed cable **(Article 336).**

   (5) Service entrance cable **(Article 338).**

   (6) Underground feeder and branch-circuit cable **(Article 339).**

   (7) Any approved conduit or raceway with its contained conductors.

   (8) Shielded nonmetallic cable.

Please note the absence of reference to individual conductors, such as TW, THW, THWN, etc., as referred to in **Article 310.** Single conductors are not permitted to be used—they shall be multiple-conductor cables.

(b) *Continuous rigid cable supports may be used as the mechanical support for factory-assembled, multiconductor control, signal, and power cables, which are specifically approved for installation in Continuous Rigid Cable Supports, in fire-resistive or noncombustible construction, but shall not be used:*

   (1) In hoistways.

   (2) Where cables supported are subject to severe physical damage.

   (3) In areas having readily combustible contents as determined by the authority enforcing the Code.

Continuous Rigid Cable Supports may be used to support cables in hazardous locations when the cables are specifically approved for such use. (Refer to **Section 501-4, 502-4,** *and* **503-3.**)

It is readily seen from the two Sections above that continuous rigid cable supports have a very definite place but are certainly not intended as a cure-all.

318-3. Construction—See NEC.

318-4. Installation—

(a) *Continuous Rigid Cable Supports shall be installed as a complete support system.* See Fig. 318-1.

(b) *Each run of continuous rigid cable support shall be complete before installation of cables.*

(c) *Continuous rigid cable supports shall be mechanically connected to any enclosure or raceway into which the cables contained in the continuous rigid cable support extend or terminate.* See Fig. 318-2.

(d) *In portions of runs where additional physical protection is required, noncombustible covers or enclosures providing the required protection shall be used.* See Fig. 318-3.

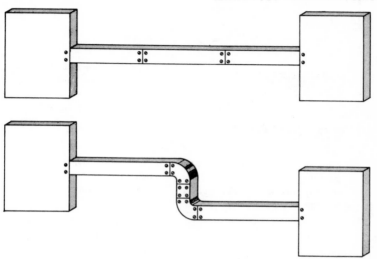

Fig. 318-1. Continuous rigid cable supports shall be continuous as a complete system from the point of origin to the point of termination.

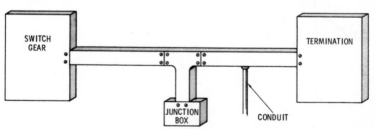

Fig. 318-2. Continuous rigid cable supports shall be mechanically connected to all enclosures or raceways.

(e) *Installations involving different electrical systems shall comply with* **Section 300-3** *and, where separation is required, the separation shall be a solid noncombustible partition or compartment. Where cables, as permitted by* **Section 318-2(b),** *are installed in the same continuous rigid cable support as the cables permitted by* **Section 318-2(a),** *the requirements of this section shall apply.*

Section 300-3 fundamentally requires insulation for the highest voltage. See Fig. 318-4.

(f) *When continuous rigid cable supports are installed in tiers, the minimum vertical clearance between tiers shall be 12 inches.* See Fig. 318-5.

169

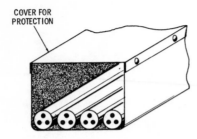

Fig. 318-3. Covers shall be used where necessary for protection.

(g) *Continuous rigid cable supports may extend transversely through partitions or walls, other than firewalls, provided the section of the support within the wall is continuous and unventilated. See* **Section 300-21.**

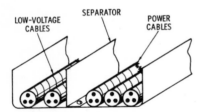

Fig. 318-4. Separators shall be used where required.

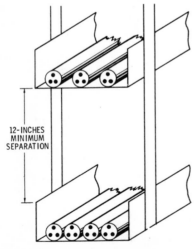

Fig. 318-5. A 12-inch minimum separation shall be maintained between continuous rigid cable supports in tiers.

The purpose of this part is to assure that there will be no path for fire between the various parts of the building. Note that they are prohibited through fire walls. See Fig. 318-6.

Exception: Where an opening in a partition or wall provides two inches minimum clearance above and on both sides, the continuous rigid cable support may be of the ventilated type.

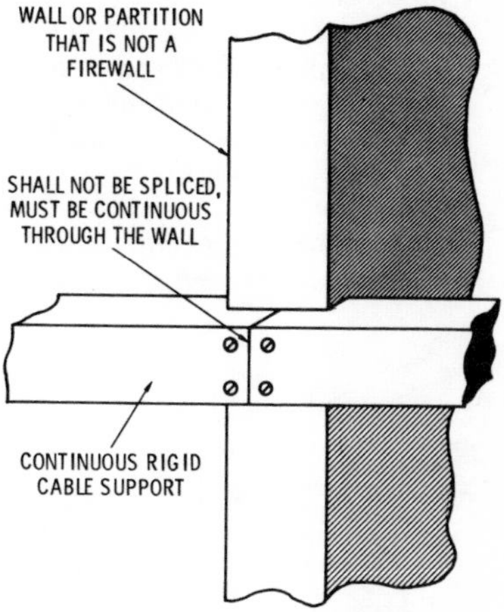

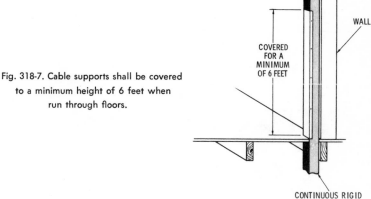

Fig. 318-6. Cable supports shall be continuous through walls or partitions.

WALL OR PARTITION THAT IS NOT A FIREWALL

SHALL NOT BE SPLICED, MUST BE CONTINUOUS THROUGH THE WALL

CONTINUOUS RIGID CABLE SUPPORT

Fig. 318-7. Cable supports shall be covered to a minimum height of 6 feet when run through floors.

WALL

COVERED FOR A MINIMUM OF 6 FEET

CONTINUOUS RIGID CABLE SUPPORT

(h) *Continuous rigid cable supports may extend vertically through dry floors and platforms provided the continuous rigid cable support is totally enclosed where it passes through the floor or* platform opening and for a distance of six feet above the floor or platform to provide protection from physical injury. See **Section 300-21.** The purpose of this ruling is also to stop fire from spreading. See Fig. 318-7.

(i) *Continuous rigid cable supports may extend vertically through floors and platforms in wet locations where (1) there are curbs or other suitable means to prevent water flow through the floor or platform opening and (2) the continuous rigid cable support is totally enclosed where it passes through the floor or platform opening and for a distance of six feet above the floor or platform to provide protection from physical injury. See* **Section 300-21.** Also see Fig. 318-8.

(j) *Cable splices and cable taps shall be made only in junction boxes or fittings approved for the purpose.* See Fig. 318-9.

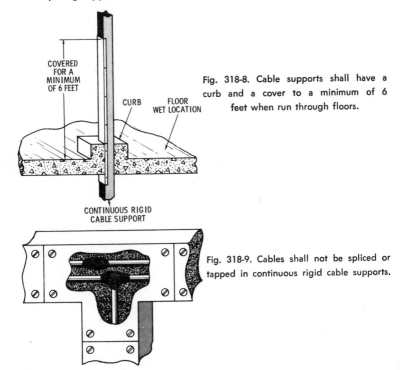

Fig. 318-8. Cable supports shall have a curb and a cover to a minimum of 6 feet when run through floors.

COVERED FOR A MINIMUM OF 6 FEET

CURB

FLOOR WET LOCATION

CONTINUOUS RIGID CABLE SUPPORT

Fig. 318-9. Cables shall not be spliced or tapped in continuous rigid cable supports.

(k) *In other than horizontal runs, and where side rails do not provide adequate containment of the cables, they shall be fastened secure-*

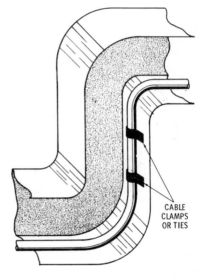

Fig. 318-10. Cables shall be securely fastened by a suitable means when required.

CABLE
CLAMPS
OR TIES

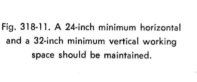

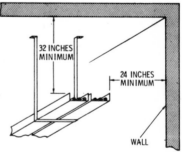

Fig. 318-11. A 24-inch minimum horizontal and a 32-inch minimum vertical working space should be maintained.

32 INCHES MINIMUM

24 INCHES MINIMUM

WALL

ly to transverse members of the continuous rigid cable support. See Fig. 318-10.

(l) *Where continuous rigid cable supports are located adjacent to one another an adequate working space of 24 inches minimum should be maintained on one side of each continuous rigid cable support or where grouped in rows adjacent to each other a minimum working space of 32 inches should be maintained over each continuous rigid cable support.* See Fig. 318-11.

(m) *Except as provided in* **Section 318-4(g),** *a minimum vertical clearance of 6 inches should be maintained from the top of the continuous rigid cable support to all ceilings, beams, and other obstructions.* See Fig. 318-12.

173

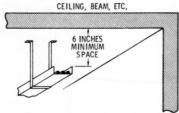

CEILING, BEAM, ETC.

6 INCHES MINIMUM SPACE

Fig. 318-12. A minimum 6-inch clearance should be provided from the top of the cable support to the ceiling, beams, etc.

318-5. Grounding—All metal sections of continuous rigid cable supports and fittings shall be effectively grounded and bonded as required, but the metal continuous rigid cable supports shall in no case be used as a grounded circuit conductor (neutral) or as an equipment grounding conductor as would be the case with metal raceways. Where completely isolated, 25 feet or less in length, not in contact with other metals, and out of reach of nonqualified persons, grounding is not required as in **Section 250-33.**

318-6. Ampacity—*The ampacities of cables installed in continuous rigid cable supports shall be as follows:*

(a) *Where cables containing not more than three current-carrying conductors are installed in ventilated continuous rigid cable supports and spacing is maintained at from one-quarter to one cable diameter, the factors of* **Table 318-6(a)** *shall be applied to the ampacities of the cables used.*

Please note that the cables shall not have more than three current-carrying conductors; the continuous rigid cable supports shall be ventilated; and the spacing between cables shall be not less than one-quarter of the cable diameter up to one times the cable diameter, in order to use **Table 318-6(a).** Also note that the percentage varies as to whether the cables are vertical or horizontal.

(b) The percentage of ampacity as required in Note 8 that accompanies **Tables 310-12** through **310-15** are to be used under the following conditions:

(1) Cables are not spaced, but are located adjacent or less than the required spacing in **(a)** of this Section.

(2) Where the spacing is maintained but the cables have more than three current-carrying conductors.

(3) Where unventilated continuous rigid cable supports are used.

ARTICLE 320—OPEN WIRING ON INSULATORS

320-1. Definition—*Open wiring is a wiring method using cleats, knobs, tubes and flexible tubing for protection and support of insulated*

174

conductors run in or on buildings, and not concealed by the building structure.

This type of wiring should not be confused with that covered in **Article 324** which deals with concealed knob-and-tube work. The fact remains that open wiring is seldom used but is still part of the Code.

320-2. Use—

(a) Open wiring on insulators may be used for:

(1) Exposed work, either inside or outside of the building.
(2) In wet or dry locations.
(3) Where subject to corrosive vapors, as in **Article 480** covering storage batteries, providing that the conditions of **Article 480** are complied with.
(4) For services as covered in **Article 230,** provided that all conditions applying to **Article 230** are met.

(b) Open wiring on insulators shall not be used:

(1) In commercial garages. (See definition of commercial garages.)
(2) In theaters.
(3) In motion-picture studios.
(4) In hazardous locations, except in storage compartments of Class III locations as provided in **Section 503-3(b).** This paragraph refers back to **Article 320,** where protection is required as provided in **Section 320-12.**

320-3. Other Articles—Not only does the wiring methods of this Article prevail, but also the provisions of **Article 300** which covers General Wiring-Methods, and **Article 730** which covers Outside Branch Circuits and Feeders.

320-4. Conductors—Any conductors used shall be insulated and must conform to **Article 310.** Only single conductors may be used. Thus, conductors such as TW, THW, RH, RHW, THWN, etc., are permitted, but conductors with an F prefix are not permitted as these are for fixture wiring.

(a) In figuring the ampacities allowed, **Table 310-13** for copper and **Table 310-15** for aluminum conductors are to be used.

320-5. Supports—

(a) Conductors must be separated from making contact with any object other than its insulating supports. The supports shall be noncombustible and nonabsorptive. The requirements for the supports shall be as follows:

ARTICLE 320—OPEN WIRING

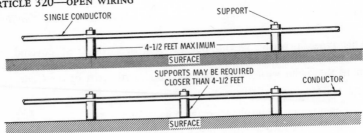

Fig. 320-1. Spacing of supporting knobs.

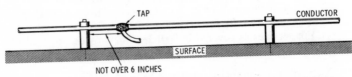

Fig. 320-2. Distance between a support and a tap should never exceed 6 inches.

(1) Under ordinary conditions the conductor supports shall not be more than 4-1/2 feet apart, but it may be required that they be placed closer together if conditions warrant. Where the conductors are subject to disturbance, the inspection authority may require the supports to be spaced closer than 4-1/2 feet if it is deemed necessary. See Fig. 320-1.

(2) Where taps are to be made from the conductors, the taps shall be within 6 inches of a support. See Fig. 320-2.

(3) Where conductors are to be dead ended at a lampholder, rosette, or receptacle, the last support shall be within 12 inches of the device. Switches are not mentioned, but they are a device and the same support conditions are required. See Fig. 320-3.

(b) Exceptions are permitted for **Section 320-5(a),** as follows:

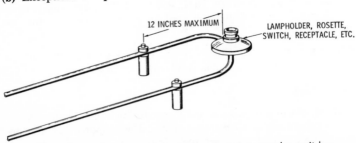

Fig. 320-3. Distance of supports when connecting receptacles, switches, rosettes, and other devices.

176

Exception No. 1. *For the use of flexible nonmetallic tubing, see* **Section 320-7.**

Exception No. 2. Conductors of No. 8 or larger that are installed across open spaces where they are not liable to be disturbed may have the supports spaced a maximum of 15 feet apart. However, noncombustible, nonabsorptive supports shall be spaced at intervals not to exceed 4-1/2 feet apart, and with a minimum spacing of 2-1/2 inches between the conductors. See Fig. 320-4.

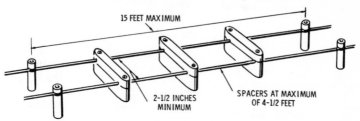

Fig. 320-4. A 15-foot span requires spacers.

Exception No. 3. In buildings of mill construction where feeders of No. 8 or larger are used, and a minimum spacing of 6 inches between conductors is maintained, the conductors may be supported at the timbers only. See Fig. 320-5.

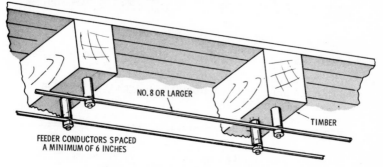

Fig. 320-5. Mill construction installation.

(c) If nails are used in the mounting of knobs for conductor support, they shall be no smaller than 10-penny nails. Where screws are used for mounting the knobs, they shall be of sufficient length to penetrate the wood no less than 1/2 the height of the knob or no less than the thickness of the cleat when cleats are used. Where nails are used, there shall be a cushion under the nail head to prevent damage to the knob or cleat. See Fig. 320-6.

177

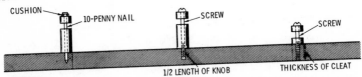

Fig. 320-6. Length of nails and screws for knobs and cleats.

320-6. Conductor Separation—*Open conductors shall be separated as follows:*

(a) *For voltages not exceeding 300 volts between conductors:*

(1) A minimum of 2-1/2 inches separation between conductors.
(2) A minimum of 1/2 inch from the surface over which they are run, provided they are in dry locations. See Fig. 320-7.

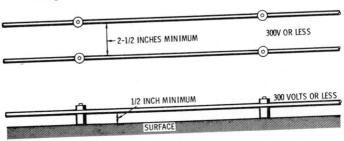

Fig. 320-7. Minimum spacings for 300 volts or less.

(b) For voltages between 301 and 600 volts between conductors:

(1) A minimum of 4 inches between conductors.
(2) A minimum of 1 inch from the surface over which they are run. See Fig. 320-8.

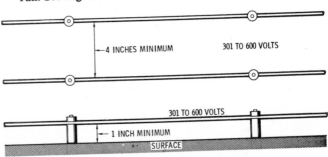

Fig. 320-8. Minimum spacings for 301 to 600 volts.

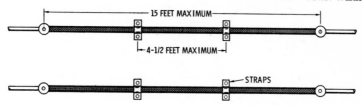

Fig. 320-9. Use of approved nonmetallic tubing.

(c) *In damp or wet locations, a separation of at least 1 inch from the surface wired over shall be maintained for all voltages.* The term "all voltages" means up to 600 volts between conductors.

320-7. Flexible Nonmetallic Tubing—Approved flexible nonmetallic tubing may be used over the conductors in a continuous length not to exceed 15 feet when not exposed to physical damage and in a dry location. In addition the nonmetallic tubing shall be secured by means of straps that are not more than 4-1/2 feet apart. See Fig. 320-9.

320-8. Tie Wires—Tie wires may be used to fasten No. 8 or larger conductors to knobs, but they shall be tied securely and shall have insulation equivalent to the conductor which they are securing to the knobs.

320-9. Passing Through Walls and Floors—Open conductors that pass through floors, walls, timbers, etc., shall pass through tubes or bushings that are made of noncombustible, nonabsorptive material. Where the bushings or tubes are shorter than the hole, a sleeve of noninductive material may be slipped over the conductor and bushings inserted into the sleeve. The sleeve material must be waterproof and the conductor must not touch the sleeve at any point.

320-10. Separation from Metal Work—All open conductors shall be separated from conduit, pipes, or any other conductive material, by at least 2 inches. The same separation must be maintained from any exposed lighting, power, or signal circuits. Where this distance cannot be maintained, insulating tubes may be used for additional insulation, providing these tubes are secured at both ends to keep them from moving out of place. Any deviation from this requirement must be approved by the Code enforcing authority.

320-11. Separation from Piping in Damp Locations—Open conductors that must be located close to piping or tanks shall be so placed that there is a permanent air space between them and the piping. If there is a chance that condensate or water might drip on the conductors, they shall be run above the pipes or tanks, if at all possible. The minimum 2-inch clearance mentioned in Section 320-10 shall also be maintained.

179

320-12. Protection from Physical Damage—*Where open conductors cross ceiling joists and wall studs, and are exposed to physical damage, they shall be protected by one of the following methods. Conductors within 7 feet from the floor shall be considered exposed to physical damage.*

(a) *By guard strips not less than 7/8 inch in thickness and at least as high as the insulating supports, placed on each side of and close to the wiring.* See Fig. 320-10.

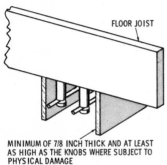

MINIMUM OF 7/8 INCH THICK AND AT LEAST AS HIGH AS THE KNOBS WHERE SUBJECT TO PHYSICAL DAMAGE

Fig. 320-10. Protecting conductors from physical damage.

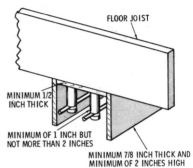

MINIMUM 1/2 INCH THICK

MINIMUM OF 1 INCH BUT NOT MORE THAN 2 INCHES

MINIMUM 7/8 INCH THICK AND MINIMUM OF 2 INCHES HIGH

Fig. 320-11. Use of running board and sides for protection.

(b) *By a substantial running board at least 1/2 inch thick back of the conductors with side protections. Running boards shall extend at least 1 inch outside the conductors, but not more than 2 inches and the protecting sides shall be at least 2 inches high and at least 7/8 inch thick.* See Fig. 320-11.

(c) *By boxing made as above and furnished with cover kept at least 1 inch away from the conductors within.* See Fig. 320-12. *Where protecting vertical conductors on side walls the boxing shall be closed at the top and the holes through which the conductors pass shall be bushed.* See Fig. 320-13.

(d) Conduit or electrical metallic tubing may be used for protection of open conductors. The installation of the conduit shall comply with **Article 346** and of electrical metallic tubing with **Article 348.** Metal piping may also be used, but the conductors shall be encased in a continuous length of approved flexible tubing. Where conductors are encased in conduit, piping, etc., they shall be so installed that the current passing in both directions is approximately equal so as to counteract induction and resultant heating. Where entering the conduit proper, approved insulated fittings or the equivalent shall be used.

320-13. In Accessible Attics—See NEC.

180

320-14.   Entering Spaces Subject to Dampness, Wetness or Corrosive Vapors—All conductors of open wiring that enter or leave a damp, wet, or corrosive space, shall have drip loops as provided for in **Section 230-49,** and the tubes entering the walls shall be noncombustible and nonabsorptive and mounted on a slope so that the moisture will not enter the other parts of the building.

320-15.   Switches—Surface-type snap switches are not required to be mounted in metal boxes (see **Section 380-3).** Where surface-mounted snap switches are used, they are required to be mounted on insulated material

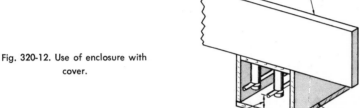

Fig. 320-12. Use of enclosure with cover.

FLOOR JOIST

1 INCH MINIMUM

BOXED IN WITH COVER

SEE FIG. 320-11 FOR OTHER DIMENSIONS

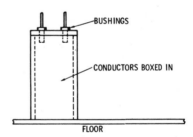

Fig. 320-13. Vertical enclosure for conductors.

BUSHINGS

CONDUCTORS BOXED IN

FLOOR

that is at least 1/2 inch thick in order to keep the conductors away from the surface over which they pass. This is covered in **Section 380-10.**

NOTE: A lot of similarity exists between this Article **(320)** and the next Article **(324)** which covers concealed Knob-and-Tube Work. It is very seldom that it will be required to use either Article, but there are installations existing that may have to be modified or added to. Therefore, it is well to have an understanding of how to do the installation.

ARTICLE 324—CONCEALED KNOB-AND-TUBE WORK

A great deal of similarity exists between this Article and preceding **Article 320.**

ARTICLE 324—KNOB-AND-TUBE WIRING

324-1. Definition—*Concealed knob-and-tube wiring is a wiring method using knobs, tubes and flexible nonmetallic tubing for the protection and support of insulated conductors concealed in the hollow spaces of walls and ceilings of buildings.*

324-2. Use—*Concealed knob-and-tube work may be used in the hollow spaces of walls and ceilings. It shall not be used:*

(1) In commercial garages.
(2) In theaters, except under some conditions in assembly halls (refer to **Section 520-4**).
(3) In motion-picture studios.
(4) In hazardous locations.

324-3. Other Articles—As with open wiring in preceding **Article 320,** other parts of the Code are applicable, especially **Article 300** on Wiring Methods—General.

324-4. Conductors—Only single conductors are permitted (as in **Article 320**) and the insulation shall be that which is approved for general wiring, not the type used for special cases (such as AF). The ampacity is determined by the table in **Article 310.**

324-5. Supports—The same spacing governs as in **Section 320-5(a).** Tie wires may be used on No. 8 or larger conductors (See **Section 320-8**). Where supporting is impractical, conductors that are encased in nonmetallic tubing may be fished in dry locations, provided the tubing is continuous from one support to the next or from one box to the next.

324-6 Conductor Separation—

(a) *Conductors shall be separated at least 3 inches and maintained at least 1 inch from the surface wired over.* Notice that this is different from **Article 320.**
(b) *At distributing centers, meters, outlets, switches or other places where space is limited and the 3-inch separation cannot be maintained, each conductor shall be encased in a continuous length of flexible tubing.*
(c) *Where practicable, conductors shall run singly on separate timbers or studding.*

324-7. Separation from Other Objects and Protection—*Conductors shall be separated from other conductors and objects as follows:*

(a) This part is the same as **Section 320-9, 320-10, 320-11,** and **320-15** of the preceding Article, so will not be repeated here.

(b) *Conductors passing through cross timbers in plastered partitions*

182

shall be protected by an additional noncombustible, nonabsorptive insulating tube extending at least 3 inches above the timber.

324-8. In Unfinished Attics and Roof Spaces—*Conditions in unfinished attics or roof spaces shall comply with the following:*

(a) *Conductors in unfinished attics and roof spaces shall be run through or on the sides of joists, studs and rafters, except in attics*

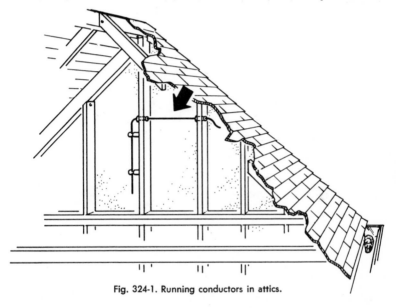

Fig. 324-1. Running conductors in attics.

and roof spaces having head room at all points of less than 3 feet in buildings completed before the wiring was installed. See Fig. 324-1.

(b) *Where conductors in accessible unfinished attics or roof spaces reached by stairway or permanent ladder are run through bored holes in floor joists or through bored holes in studs or rafters within 7 feet of the floor or floor joists, such conductors shall be protected by substantial running boards extending 1 inch on each side of the conductors and securely fastened in place. See Fig. 324-2.*

(c) *Where carried along the sides of rafters, studs or floor joists, neither running boards or guard strips will be required.*

324-9. Boxes of Insulating Material—In **Sections 370-3** and **370-7,** the use of nonmetallic boxes is permitted, provided that the conductors are supported within 8 inches of the boxes. These nonmetallic boxes are also permitted on concealed knob-and-tube work.

324-10. Switches—Surface-type snap switches are not required to be mounted on metal boxes (see **Section 380-3**). Where surface-mounted snap switches are used, they are required to be mounted on insulating material at least 1/2 inch thick so as to keep the conductors away from the surface over which they pass. This is covered in **Section 380-10.**

RUNNING BOARD
ONE INCH OVER
EACH SIDE

Fig. 324-2. Protection by running boards in attics accessible by stairs or permanent ladder.

324-11. Splices—*Splices shall be made only where close to knobs or tubes using solder or specially approved splicing devices. In line or strain splices shall not be used.*

ARTICLE 330—MINERAL INSULATED-METAL SHEATHED CABLE
Type MI

MI cable is a wiring method which seems to cause confusion in the trade. There is no reason why it should, except that it is not the most widely used method of wiring, but it probably has more applications to which it lends itself than any other wiring method.

A. General

330-1. Definition and Construction — Mineral-insulated, metal-sheathed Type MI cable is composed of one or more conductors insulated by a highly compressed refractory mineral insulation and enclosed in a gastight metal tube sheath. The highly compressed refractory mineral insulation is magnesium oxide powder. The conductors are normally copper. MI cable is also made up into a heating cable in which the outside or sheath is a seamless phosphorized copper tubing. As a word of explanation, magnesium oxide is the material which is used in many range burners as the insulation in the tube elements to enclose and insulate the nichrome elements from the outer sheath of the units. See Fig. 330-1.

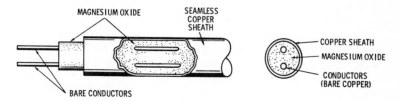

Fig. 330-1. Construction of MI Cable.

It is required that MI cable be used only with approved fittings for terminating and connecting boxes, outlets, etc. See Fig. 330-2.

330-2. Use—Mineral-insulated metal-sheathed cable MI may be used for:

(1) Services.
(2) Feeders.
(3) Branch circuits.
(4) Open wiring (exposed).
(5) Concealed wiring.
(6) Wet locations.

MI cable may be used in practically all locations except that, if used in a highly corrosive location (such as cinder fill), it shall be protected. It may be used for all of the following:

(1) All hazardous areas: Class I, Class II, and Class III locations.
(2) Under plaster extensions.
(3) Embedded in plaster finish.
(4) On brick or masonry.
(5) Exposed to weather or continuous moisture.
(6) Embedded in concrete or fill.
(8) Buildings under construction.
(9) Exposed to oils and gasoline.
(10) Any other location that will not have a deteriorating effect on the copper sheath.

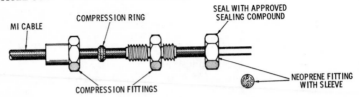

Fig. 330-2. Fittings for MI cable.

The following is not a part of the Code, but it is felt that it should be mentioned here as a precaution in the installation of MI Cable.

Magnesium oxide will draw some moisture when exposed to the air. Therefore, when the cable is cut, the end should be taped. When using a piece of MI cable, about 6 inches should be cut off from the end, or start back from the cut end a couple of feet and heat it with a torch, working toward the cut end, thus driving any moisture out of the cable.

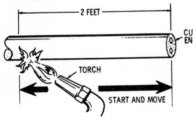

Fig. 330-3. One method of driving out moisture.

See Fig. 330-3. The temperature to which the cable may be heated is limited only by the melting point of the sheath. In **Article 310** it is mentioned that MI cable is an 85°C cable. This will not prevent the use of a torch in driving out the moisture, however.

330-3.   Other Articles—See NEC.

B. Installation

330-4.   Supports—*Mineral insulated-metal sheathed cable shall be securely supported by approved staples, straps, hangers or similar fittings, so designed and installed as not to injure the cable. Cable shall be secured at intervals not exceeding 6 feet except where cable is fished.* Please note the term "approved." Consideration must always be given to electrolysis which is ever present between dissimilar metals.

330-5.   Through Studs, Joists and Rafters—Reference is made to **Section 300-8.** Part **(b)** permits notching, provided a steel plate of not less than 1/16 inch is provided so as to give protection from nails.

330-6.   Wet Locations—Reference is made to **Section 300-5** which gives the precautions that must be taken on corrosive locations.

330-7. Bends—All bends shall be so made that the cable will not be damaged and the radius of the curve of the inner edge of any bend shall be not less than 5 times the diameter of the cable. See Fig. 330-4.

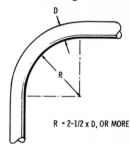

Fig. 330-4. Radius of bends.

R = 2-1/2 x D, OR MORE

330-8. Terminating Seal—Where MI cable is terminated, approved seals shall be used. Refer to Fig. 330-2. These seals have a compression ring and fittings similar to those used on copper tubing. In addition, there is a neoprene bushing which slips into these fittings and is sealed with an epoxy resin, after which a neoprene bushing with holes for the conductors and the sleeves is inserted. This sealing should be done immediately after stripping or heating so as to prevent the entrance of any moisture. The bare conductors are of course insulated with sleeving, the color of which must be correct for the particular use of the conductor.

330-9. Fittings—Approved fitting shall be used with MI cable for the conditions of service. Type MI cable of single conductor must be used when entering metal boxes, as outlined in **Section 300-20**, to prevent induced currents from causing heating.

330-10. Insulation Resistance—Section 110-20 covering insulation resistance of a completed wiring system applies to MI cable as well as to other methods of wiring. Refer to **Section 110-20.**

C. Construction Specifications

NOTE: The Code does not specify the sizes that are available in MI Cable, so the following information is included for the reader's convenience:

Single-conductor cable is available from No. 16 through 4/0.
Two-conductor cable is available from No. 16 through No. 4.
Three-conductor cable is available from No. 16 through No. 4.
Four-conductor cable is available from No. 16 through No. 6.
Seven-conductor cable is available from No. 16 through No. 10.

Remember that No. 14 wire is the smallest allowable under the Code for general wiring—smaller sizes may be used for low-voltage thermostat wiring, as permitted. There is also MI low-energy cable rated at 300 volts available in two- three-, four-, and seven-conductor cable, but a check should be made to be certain that this low-energy cable is approved by UL.

Mention was also made of heating cable. This is not considered a wiring cable, so it would have to be approved by UL for the purpose to which it is to be used.

330-11. General—See NEC.

ARTICLE 331—ALUMINUM SHEATHED CABLE
Type ALS

This type of cable is not exactly new as it has been used with success in Canada and Great Britain. However, it was approved and appeared for the first time in the 1962 National Electrical Code.

A. General

331-1. Definitions and Construction—See NEC.

331-2. Use—Aluminum sheathed type ALS cable is approved for:

(1) Exposed work.
(2) Concealed work.
(3) Dry locations.
(4) Wet locations.

ALS cable shall be protected:

(1) When exposed to destructive corrosive conditions such as strong chlorides or caustic alkalies.
(2) Where exposed to vapors of chlorine or hydrochloric acid.
(3) Where installed underground by materials suitable for the conditions to which it is exposed. Also supplementary protection may be required by the inspection authority. See **Sections 300-5** and **310-6.**

There is a new addition to this section in the 1965 Code: *Aluminum sheathed cable and fittings shall not be embedded or buried directly in concrete or used in areas subject to severe corrosive influences unless suitable supplemental corrosion protection is provided.*

331-3. Other Articles—As with all other wiring methods, ALS is subject to other applicable provisions of the Code and particularly **Article 300.**

B. Installation

331-4. Supports—ALS cable shall be supported at intervals not exceeding 6 feet by approved staples, straps, or hangers, so that the cable will not be injured. The staples, etc., should be of such a material that electrolysis to the cable sheath will not be caused. These fastening requirements are not necessary where the cable is fished.

331-5. Through Studs, Joists and Rafters—The same provisions as required by **Section 300-8** apply to ALS cable in running through or notching studs, joists, or rafters.

331-6. Wet Locations—The same provisions apply to ALS cable in wet locations as with other wiring methods, as explanied in **Section 300-5,** namely that the 1/4-inch spacing applies.

331-7. Bends—Bends shall be made in such a manner as to protect the ALS cable from damage, but the radius of the bend on the inner edge shall not be less than:

(a) Ten times the external diameter of the cable, if 3/4 inch or less.

(b) Twelve times the external diameter of the cable sheath that is more than 3/4 inch but not more than 1-1/2 inch in diameter.

(c) Fifteen times the external diameter of the cable sheath for ALS cable more than 1-1/2 inches in diameter.

331-8. Fittings—*When aluminum sheathed cable is connected to boxes or equipment, the fittings shall be approved for the conditions of service. When single conductor aluminum sheathed cables enter metal boxes through separate openings refer to* **Section 300-20. Section 300-20** provides for heating from induction.

C. Construction

331-9. General—See NEC.

ARTICLE 334—METAL-CLAD CABLE
Type MC and AC Series

Prior to the 1962 edition of the National Electrical Code, this Article was termed ARMORED-CABLE. In the 1962 edition, it was changed to include both MC and AC Types of cables. The first five Sections are combined here as they tie together so closely.

334-1. Definition—

334-2. Voltage—

334-3. Marking—

334-4. Construction—

334-5. Conductors—

By definition, a metal-clad cable is a fabricated assembly of insulated conductors in a flexible metallic enclosure. There are two types—the MC series and the AC series. The MC Series are power cables for 600 volts or less. Chapter 3 covered 600 volts or less, with higher voltages covered in **Article 710.** Copper conductors have a minimum size of No. 4 and aluminum conductors a minimum size of No. 2. The metal enclosure may be either of an interlocking metal type or an impervious close-fitting corrugated tube. A supplemental outer covering, such as neoprene or other corrosion-resistant material, is required in locations that require corrosion protection. The outer metallic covering shall provide an adequate path for grounding purposes. This is for equipment grounding—not for a neutral.

The insulated conductors in MC cable shall be of the types listed in **Table 310-2(b)** for:

(1) Rubber.
(2) Thermoplastic.
(3) Varnished cloth.
(4) Asbestos-varnished cloth.
(5) Special types approved for the purpose.

MC Cables shall have the conductors marked as specified in the provisions of **Section 310-2.**

There are a number of types of AC cable, such as AC, ACL, ACT, etc. The voltages and definition are the same as for MC cable. Type AC cables are for branch circuits and feeder circuits. These cables are made up of flexible metal tape, but an internal strip of bonding composed of copper or alumnium shall be continuous throughout the length and in intimate contact with the outer covering. This is for additional protection when serving as an equipment ground. The old BX, when subjected to a grounded condition, very often got hot and fires have been known to start from this cause. The bonding strip lowers the impedance and reduces the heating.

The insulated conductors shall be of the same type as for type MC cable, but, in addition, an overall moisture-resistant and fire-retardant fiberous covering is to be added. On Type ACT, a moisture-resistant fiberous covering is required only on the individual conductors.

334-6. Use—Metal-clad cable may be used for exposed or concealed work, except where otherwise specified.

(a) **Type MC.** This power type of cable may be used in partially protected places, on continuous rigid cable supports, and in dry locations. It may also be used in wet locations when the following conditions are met:

(1) *The metallic covering is impervious to moisture.*

(2) *A lead sheath or moisture impervious jacket is provided under the metal covering.*

(3) *The insulated conductors under the metallic covering are approved for use in wet locations.*

(b) Type AC. Type AC metal-clad cable may be used:

(1) For dry locations.

(2) Under plastic extensions.

(3) Embedded in plaster finish.

(4) Embedded in brick or other masonry, except in wet or damp locations.

(5) May be run or fished in air voids of masonry, block or tile walls that are not exposed to moisture or dampness or are below grade line.

(6) As in (5), but in damp places, and where exposed to oil or other conditions that might deteriorate the insulation, if of the ACL (lead-covered) type.

(7) Far underground runs in duct or raceway.

Type AC metal-clad cable may not be used in the following locations:

(1) In theaters, except as provided in **Section 520-4.**

(2) In motion-picture studios.

(3) In any hazardous location.

(4) Where exposed to corrosive fumes or vapors.

(5) On cranes or hoists, except as provided for in **Section 610-11** (Exception 3).

(6) In storage-battery rooms.

(7) In hoistways or an elevators, except as provided in **Section 620-21.**

(8) Commercial garages where prohibited in **Article 511.**

(9) Type ACL cable shall not be used for direct burial in earth.

334-7. Other Articles—Metal-clad cable, of course, is subject to any other applicable provisions in the Code, but more especially to **Article 300.**

334-8. Supports—All supports for both MC and AC cables must be of the approved type and must be installed so as not to damage the cable.

(a) Except where fished, MC cable must be secured within 2 feet of every box or fitting and at intervals not to exceed 6 feet. It may be installed on metal racks, trays, troughs, or continuous rigid cable supports, but all of these must be grounded as required by **Article 250.** MC cables must be separated by a distance of not

191

less than one-quarter the diameter of the cable. There shall not be more than one layer of cable and each cable shall be attached to the support, such as continuous rigid cable supports at intervals not to exceed 10 feet horizontally or 2 feet vertically

(b) AC type cable shall be secured at intervals not to exceed 4-1/2 feet and within 12 inches of a box or fitting, except where fished, and except that the 12 inches may be extended to not over 24 inches at terminals where there is a necessity for flexibility.

334-9. Bends—All bends are to be made so as not to damage the cable. For MC type cable, the radius of the inner edge of the curve shall not be less than seven times the diameter of the cable. For AC type cable, the bend radius shall not be less than five times the diameter of the cable.

334-10. Boxes and Fittings—

(a) Approved fittings suitable for the particlular wiring cable shall be used at all terminals where type MC cable is used.

(b) For Type AC cable, approved fittings to prevent abrasion of the conductors and their insulation shall be used. In addition to this, an approved insulating bushing is required to be inserted at the end between the conductors and the outer metallic covering. The connection to the fitting or box must be so designed that the insulated bushing will be visible for inspection without removing the fitting. This is an excellent requirement, because it seems that in the haste of installation, this bushing is so often overlooked, and it is a vital spot for a breakdown in the insulation. The insulated bushing is not required where a lead covering is used on the conductors, such as ACL type. Any splices or connections to other raceways must be in approved junction boxes.

334-11. Through Studs, Joists and Rafters—The same precautions must be taken as outlined in **Section 300-8** to protect the cable from being punctured by nails, etc.

334-12. Exposed Work—The cable runs on exposed work shall follow the surface of the building finish or of running boards. Please remember the limitations on bends and do not try to form the cable to a right angle as this would damage the cable. The provisions of **Section 334-8(a)** also apply.

334-13. In Accessible Attics—Where run across the top of floor joists, or within 7 feet of the floor, or floor joists across the face of rafters or studding in attics and roof spaces that are accessible, the cables are to be protected by substantial guard strips that are as high as the thickness of the cable. Where such spaces are only accessible by scuttle holes, or the equivalent, protection will be required for any cable within 6 feet of the scuttle hole. Where the cable is run along the sides of rafters, studs, or floor joists, the guard strips or running boards will not be required.

This may sound like a lot of extra work for space that will probably not be used. Remember, however, that plans change. The attic may become a storage space or room, in which case damage to the cable may result and the work will have to be redone.

ARTICLE 336—NONMETALLIC-SHEATHED CABLE
Types NM and NMC

By definition, a nonmetallic sheathed cable is an assembly of two or more conductors having an outer sheath of moisture-resistant, flame-resistant, nonmetallic material. This is commonly known as loom wire, Romex, or other common trade names.

Nonmetallic sheathed cable shall be of an approved type. From time to time, some appear on the market that do not meet the UL listing. This kind should not be used.

This type of cable is available in sizes from No. 14 to and including No. 2. The No. 2 was an addition in the 1962 Code. This cable may have an uninsulated conductor or a green insulated conductor for equipment grounding purposes in addition to the current-carrying conductors. **Table 250-95** lists the size of this grounding conductor in reference to the current-carrying conductors. In the event that the cable is not equipped with the grounding conductor, a green No. 14 or larger conductor may be run with it to serve as the equipment ground.

Type NM cable is the type most commonly used, especially in residential occupancies, but there is an NMC type that not only has an overall covering that is flame-retardant and moisture-resistant, but also is fungus-retardant and corrosion-resistant.

There must be a distinctive marking on the exterior of the cable for its entire length that specifies cable type and the name of the manufacturing company. The box in which the cable is packaged will have the UL listing, if any, on it. NM cable is also made in No. 12 through No. 2 sizes for aluminum conductor.

336-3. **Use**—Nonmetallic cable may be used for both the exposed and concealed installations.

(a) Type NM Cable may be used for the following:

    (1) Concealed or exposed installation.
    (2) Installed or fished in the hollow voids of masonry or tile walls that are not exposed to excessive moisture or dampness.

Type NM Cable may not be used where:

(1) Exposed to corrosive vapors or fumes.
(2) Embedded in masonry concrete, fill, or plaster.
(3) Run in shallow chase in masonry or concrete and covered with plaster or similar finish.
(4) For direct burial.

(b) Moisture- and corrosion-resistant Type NMC cable may be used for the following:

(1) Concealed or exposed work in dry, moist, damp, or corrosive locations.
(2) Outside and inside walls of masonry block or tile. Where embedded in plaster or run in a shallow chase in masonry walls and covered with plaster within 2 inches of the finished surface, it must be protected against damage by nails by a corrosive-resistant steel plate of not less than 1/16 inch in thickness and 3/4 inch in width which shall be placed in the chase and under the final finish coat.

(c) Type NM or NMC cannot be used for:

(1) Service-entrance cable.
(2) In commercial garages.
(3) In theaters and assembly halls, except as provided in **Section 520-4.**
(4) In motion-picture studios.
(5) In storage-battery rooms.
(6) In hoistways.
(7) In hazardous locations.
(8) Embedded in poured cement, concrete, or aggregate.

In the next Article, it will be seen that service-entrance cable cannot be used for feeders under certain conditions. However, NM and NMC cable may be used for this purpose, and this was apparently the intent of increasing the size of conductors to No. 2. This cable, of course, may be purchased with or without a grounding conductor.

It might be stated here that, too often, changes that are made in the NEC are not noticed by the wiremen and engineers. The NEC always notes the changes that have been made over the previous edition. It takes only a little time to thumb through the Code and observe these changes.

336-4. Other Articles—As with all other wiring methods, any other applicable article applies to the installation of nonmetallic sheathed cable, especially **Article 300.**

336-5. Supports—Approved staples, straps, or other fittings shall be used to support nonmetallic sheathed cable, and shall be so designed and installed so as to not cause damage to the cable. Too often it is the last blow of the hammer that should never be given. Inspectors find much insulation damaged in this fashion. It is also easy to use a nail bent over to secure a cable. This should never be tolerated.

Cables shall be secured at intervals not exceeding 4-1/2 feet and within 12 inches of the box or fitting, except that in concealed work in finished buildings or finished panels of prefabricated buildings, it may be fished into the walls.

336-6. Exposed Work—General—In exposed work, except as provided in **Sections 336-8** and **336-9**, the cable is to be installed as follows:

It shall follow the surface of the building finish or of running boards. It shall be protected from physical damage where necessary by conduit, pipe, guard strips, or other satisfactory means, and when passing through a floor, it shall be protected by conduit or pipe to a minimum height of 6 inches above the floor.

336-7. Through Studs, Joists and Rafters—See **Section 300-8**.

336-8. In Unfinished Basements—If the cable is run at an angle with joists in unfinished basements, assemblies not smaller than two No. 6 or three No. 8 conductors may be fastened directly to the lower edges of the joists. Small assemblies shall be either run through bored holes or on running boards. Cables of any size that are run parallel to the joists may be attached to the sides of the joists or to the face.

336-9. In Accessible Attics—See **Sections 110-12** and **334-13**.

336-10. Bends—All bends are to be made so as not to damage the cable or its protective covering, but no bend shall have a radius of less than five times the diameter of the cable.

336-11. Devices of Insulating Materials—For exposed work, concealed work for rewiring existing buildings where the cable is concealed or fished, switch, outlet, and tap devices made of insulating materials may be used without the use of boxes if approved types make a close fit around the outer covering of the cable and fully covers the part from which the outer covering has been removed. Also, there shall be one terminal screw for each conductor, or a type of connector that is approved for multiple conductor connections.

336-12. Boxes of Insulating Materials—Nonmetallic outlet boxes are approved for nonmetallic cable and provision for their use is made in **Section 370-3**.

ARTICLE 337—SHIELDED NONMETALLIC-SHEATHED CABLE

ARTICLE 337—SHIELDED NONMETALLIC-SHEATHED CABLE

337-1. Scope—*This Article covers a wiring method of shielded nonmetallic-sheathed cable and fittings and defines installation and construction specifications.*

337-2. Definitions—Type SNM Cables:

(1) A factory assembly of two or more insulated conductors in an extruded core of:

  (a) Moisture-resistive material.
  (b) Flame-retardant nonmetallic material.
  (c) Covered with an overlapping spiral metal tape and wire shield.

  (d) Covered with an extruded covering which is:

    (1) Moisture resistant.
    (2) Flame retardant.
    (3) Oil resistant.
    (4) Corrosion resistant.
    (5) Fungus resistant.
    (6) Sunlight-resistant.

337-3. Other Articles—*In addition to the provisions of this Article, installations of Type SNM cable shall conform to other applicable provisions, such as* **Articles 300** *and* **318** *of the Code.*

337-4. Uses Permitted—*Type SNM cable may be used only as follows:*

(1) Where operating temperatures do not exceed the rating marked on the cable.
(2) In continuous rigid cable supports or in raceways.
(3) In hazardous locations where permitted in **Articles 500** *through* **516.**

337-5. Bends—*Bends in Type SNM cable shall be so made as not to damage the cable or its covering. The radius of the inner edge shall not be less than 5 times the cable diameter.*

337-6. Handling—*Type SNM cable shall be handled in such a manner as not to damage the cable or its covering.*

337-7. Fittings—*Fittings for connecting SNM cable to enclosures or equipment shall be approved for the purpose and for the conditions of use.*

The most practical way that I know of to determine whether fittings are approved or not is to look for listing in the UL books.

337-8. Construction—See NEC. The shield is used as the equipment grounding conductor.

337-9. Marking—See the NEC.

ARTICLE 338—SERVICE-ENTRANCE CABLE
Types SE and USE

Type ASE cable was eliminated in the 1965 Code. After considerable checking, the Code Making Panel found that this cable was not being made, so it no longer need appear in the Code.

There has been considerable misuse of service-entrance cables. It will be attempted here to bring out some of these abuses so that one may secure a better understanding of the uses for which service-entrance cable is intended.

338-1. Definition—*Service-entrance cable is a conductor assembly provided with a suitable over-all covering, primarily used for services and of the following types. When consisting of two or more conductors, one may be without individual insulation.*

Please take note of the *conductor assembly provided with a suitable over-all covering,* and *primarily used for services.*

(a) *Type SE, having a flame-retardant, moisture-resistant covering, but not required to have inherent protection against mechanical abuse.*

This may be one of two types—one with a bare neutral conductor and the other with all conductors insulated and with or without a grounding conductor for the purpose of grounding equipment. This is mentioned because it is very important as one will see in the following information.

Type SE cable has no inherent mechanical protection against abuse. Therefore, it may be necessary to provide mechanical protection should the Code enforcing authority require it.

(b) *Type USE, recognized for underground use, having a moisture-resistant covering, but not required to have a flame-retardant covering or inherent protection against mechanical abuse. Single conductor cables having rubber insulation specifically approved for the purpose do not require an outer covering.*

It is intended that USE cable be a conductor assembly provided with a suitable over-all covering. This brings up the point of single conductors that might be marked RHW-USE. Most certainly if the Code enforcing authority approves these conductors for direct burial, they would demand that they be buried side by side and possibly require other provisions in the installation of same, such as mechanical protection. If the conductors are marked USE they are approved for direct burial.

338-2. Use as Service-Entrance Conductors—As was stated, this is their primary use and their installation comes under **Article 230.** They may be used for other purposes, as explained following this. SE cable is not a cure-all, but does have a definite use. See **Section 230-70(b)** and check with the inspector for length of runs permitted. Also see **Section 230-44**.

338-3. Use as Branch Circuit or Feeders—Service-entrance cables may be used for branch circuits and for feeders, with the provisions that are noted here.

(a) *Service-entrance cables may be used in interior wiring systems where all of the circuit conductors of the cable are of rubber-covered or thermoplastic type.* This means that service-entrance cables may be used for branch circuits and feeders provided that all current-carrying conductors are insulated, with the exceptions covered in **(b).** In practically all cases where they are used for this purpose, there must also be a grounding conductor, either bare or covered with green insulation, to be used as an equipment ground. USE cable may also be used in the place of UF cable, as covered in **Article 339,** but this is not often required as UF cable comes in sizes from No. 14 to No. 4/0. Fig. 338-1 illustrates SE cable with a bare neutral, Fig. 338-2 illustrates SE cable with all current-carrying conductors insulated, and Fig. 338-3 illustrates SE cable with all current-carrying conductors insulated and with an equipment ground, either bare or green colored.

(b) *Service-entrance cables without individual insulation on the grounded conductor shall not be used as a branch circuit or as a feeder within a building, except a cable which has a final non-metallic outer covering and when supplied by alternating current at not exceeding 150 volts to ground, may be used: (1) As a branch circuit to supply only a range, wall-mounted oven, counter-mounted cooking unit, or clothes dryer, or (2) as a feeder to supply only other buildings on the same premise. It shall not be used as a feeder terminating within the same building in which it originates.*

OUTER COVER   SEAL TAPE   INSULATED CONDUCTORS

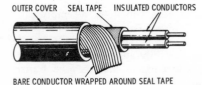

Fig. 338-1. SE cable with bare neutral.

BARE CONDUCTOR WRAPPED AROUND SEAL TAPE

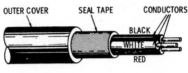

Fig. 338-2. SE cable with all insulated conductors.

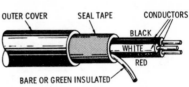

Fig. 338-3. SE cable with insulated conductors and equipment grounding conductor.

An interpretation of this is that service-entrance cable used for branch circuits and feeders shall have all current-carrying conductors insulated, except as noted in (1) and (2). Fig. 338-4 illustrates (1) and Fig. 338-5 illustrates (2). All other branch circuits and feeders using SE cable shall have all current-carrying conductors insulated.

SE cable with a bare current-carrying conductor may be used for branch circuits or feeders if the insulated current-carrying conductors are used for this purpose and the bare conductor used as an equipment ground. An example of this would be a 240-volt single-phase supply to a motor, with the insulated conductors carrying the current and the bare conductor used as an equipment ground. See Fig. 338-6.

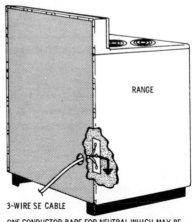

Fig. 338-4. SE cable for ranges and dryers.

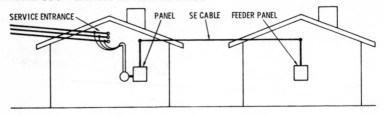

Fig. 338-5. SE cable for feeder or branch circuit to other buildings on the same premises.

X-CEL **SE** 2-6 + 1-8

Fig. 338-6. Marking of SE cable.

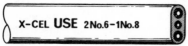

X-CEL **USE** 2No.6 - 1No.8

You are referred to **Section 250-60** which prohibits the use of SE cable with a bare neutral as branch circuit conductors to ranges and dryers if they originate from other than service equipment panels.

(c) *Service-entrance cable used to supply appliances shall not be subject to conductor temperatures in excess of the temperature specified for the type of insulation involved.* See **Table 310-2(a).**

The connecting point on an appliance such as a range or dryer should not be subject to the heat of the appliance. When installing SE cable, be sure that the inspector can see the insulation temperature rating marked on the cable.

338-4. Installation Methods—As with other wiring methods, the installation of this type of cable must not only conform to provisions of this Article, but also to any applicable provisions of **Article 300.** Unarmored cable shall be installed in the same manner as the nonmetallic sheathed cable requirement in **Article 336.** Also, if run through or notched into studs, joists, or rafters, protection shall be given from nails, etc., as per **Section 300-8.**

338-5. Marking—Marking of cables and of conductors was covered in **Section 310-12.** This marking will include manufacturer's name, type of cable, size of conductors in the cable, and an indication if the cable contains a derated neutral. See **Fig. 338-6.** If the neutral conductor is smaller than the ungrounded conductor, the cable shall be so marked.

ARTICLE 339—UNDERGROUND FEEDER AND BRANCH CIRCUIT CABLE
Type UF

339-1. Description and Marking—This is a cable that is used for underground branch circuits and feeders. It is not to be confused with USE which is a direct burial cable for services. UF is not to be used for services. Approved UF cable comes in conductor sizes from No. 14 to 4/0 AWG inclusive. The conductors within the outer sheath may be TW, RHW, etc., as approved for this purpose. Over the conductors and their insulation is placed an outer covering which shall be flame-retardant, moisture-resistant, fungus-resistant, and corrosive-resistant—this outer covering shall be approved for direct burial in the earth. UF cable may also carry a bare or insulated conductor to be used for a grounding conductor, provided that it is the proper size.

In addition to the provisions of the insulation, as provided for in **Section 310-2**, the outer covering shall have distinctive markings along its entire length showing the size of conductors, number of conductors, whether with ground or not, and have the UF marking.

339-2. Other Articles—The provisions of this Article not only apply to the use and installation of UF cable, but the provisions covering general wiring methods in **Article 300** also apply as well as the uses of the insulation as outlined in **Section 310-2(b).**

339-3. Uses—

(a) UF cable may be used as a direct burial cable for branch circuits and feeders, if installed properly and the conductor sizes are protected by proper overcurrent devices and if all other conditions as outlined are met. It will be well to refer back to **Section 300-7** which states: *Underground cable run under a building shall be in a raceway that is extended beyond the outside wall of the building.*

(b) UF single-conductor cables may be installed for feeders, subfeeders, and branch circuits, including the neutral. However, they shall be run together in the same trench or raceway. In mentioning the neutral, be assured that in no case will a bare neutral be permitted in direct burial. Also, in running these circuits, in

practically every case an equipment ground will have to be used, and one must remember that bare equipment grounding conductors are not permitted for direct burial.

(c) The Code stipulates a minimum of 18-inch burial unless the conductors or cable are protected by a covering board, concrete

ARTICLE 342—NONMETALLIC EXTENSIONS

pad, raceway, etc. It will also be found that many Code enforcing authorities will require, in addition to the 18-inch burial (and especially in rocky ground), the protection of a sand bed and covering for the cable. This is easy to understand, for in frost areas, rocks may damage the insulation of the cable. The enforcing authority has the right to require this, as all work shall be done in a proper and workmanlike manner. *This depth may be reduced to 12 inches provided supplemental protective covering such as a 2 inch concrete pad, metal raceway, pipe or other suitable protection is used.*

(d) The use of UF cable for interior wiring is not prohibited provided that it meets the requirements of the Code. If used as nonmetallic sheathed cable, **Article 336** will apply. It is very common practice to use UF cable in concrete-block walls (especially basement walls) instead of NMC cable, as it will stand any dampness that is present. When used for interior wiring, UF cable shall consist of multiple conductors, unless it is to be used for nonheating leads of heat cable as allowed in **Section 424-43.**

(e) UF cable shall not be used:

(1) As service-entrance cables.
(2) In commercial garages.
(3) In theaters, except those having a capacity of less than 200 persons. In many places this type of cable is outlawed in any public building.
(4) In motion-picture studios.
(5) In storage-battery rooms.
(6) In hoistways.
(7) In hazardous locations.
(8) Embedded in poured concrete or aggregate, with possible exceptions in **Article 422.**
(9) It shall not be exposed to sunlight, unless the particular cable is specifically approved for same, because ultraviolet light has a deteriorating effect on most UF cable.

339-4. Overcurrent Protection—UF cable must have proper overcurrent protection as provided in **Section 240-5.**

339-5. Rated Ampacity—UF cable ampacity is rated according to **Tables 310-12** and **310-14.** The derating notes accompanying these tables shall be used as with any other current-carrying conductor.

ARTICLE 342—NONMETALLIC EXTENSIONS

342-1. Description—*Nonmetallic extensions are an assembly of two* *insulated conductors within a nonmetallic jacket or an extruded thermoplastic covering. The classification includes both surface extensions, intended for mounting directly on the surface of walls or ceilings, and aerial cable, containing a supporting messenger cable as an integral part of the cable assembly.*

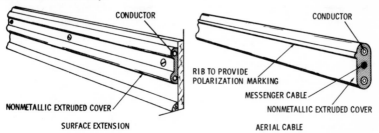

Fig. 342-1. Cross-sectional view of nonmetallic surface extension cable and nonmetallic aerial cable.

This is a wiring method that is intended for specific purposes, mainly that of extensions either on the surface or in the form of an aerial cable assembly. Reference to Fig. 342-1 will give an idea of its construction and will facilitate its application. This illustration shows a cross-section and how it is mounted on the surface.

342-2. Other Article—Not only do the provisions of this Article apply to nonmetallic extensions, but as with other wiring methods, any other applicable provisions of the Code will also apply.

342-3. Use Permitted—The use of nonmetallic extensions are permitted where the following conditions are met:

(a) These extensions are only permitted from existing 15- or 20-ampere branch circuits that meet all of the requirements in **Article 210.**

(b) The extension is never to be run concealed and must always be used in dry locations.

(c) Nonmetallic surface extensions are to be used only in residential and office buildings. They are not intended for use in industrial and commercial occupancies.

(d) Aerial cable is to be used for industrial purposes where flexibility is required for connecting equipment. It is not intended for use in offices and residences.

Fig. 342-2 illustrates the use of nonmetallic surface extensions. Fig. 342-3 illustrated the use of aerial nonmetallic cable with fluorescent lighting.

203

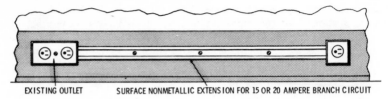

EXISTING OUTLET   SURFACE NONMETALLIC EXTENSION FOR 15 OR 20 AMPERE BRANCH CIRCUIT

Fig. 342-2. Purpose of nonmetallic surface extensions.

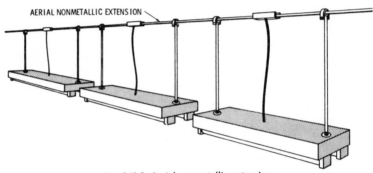

AERIAL NONMETALLIC EXTENSION

Fig. 342-3. Aerial nonmetallic extension.

342-4. Use Prohibited—*Nonmetallic extensions shall not be installed:*

(a) This method of wiring is not intended to be used as aerial cable to take the place of other approved methods as provided by the Code.

(b) They are never to be used in unfinished basements, attics, or roof spaces, but are intended for use only in finished places and must be exposed.

(c) The maximum voltage shall not exceed 150 volts between conductors for nonmetallic surface extensions and shall not exceed 300 volts between conductors for aerial cables.

(d) They shall not be used where subject to corrosive vapors.

(e) They are to be installed only within the room in which they originate and are not to be run through walls, floors, or partitions.

342-5. Splices and Taps—*Extensions shall consist of a continuous unbroken length of the assembly, without splices, and without exposed conductors between fittings. Taps may be made where approved fittings completely covering the tap connections are used. Aerial cable and its tap connectors shall be provided with an approved means for polarization. Receptacle type tap connectors shall be of the locking type.* Refer to Fig.

342-1 which shows a rib on the aerial cable for polarization. Taps other than by means of devices approved for this purpose are prohibited.

342-6. Fittings—The fittings and devices used with this method of wiring are to be approved for the purpose and each run shall be terminated so that the end of the assembly is covered and no bare conductors exposed.

342-7. Installation—*Nonmetallic extensions shall be installed in conformity with the following requirements:*

(a) Nonmetallic Surface Extensions.

(1) *One or more extensions may be run in any direction from an existing output, but not on the floor or within 2 inches from the floor.* See Fig. 342-4.

(2) *Nonmetallic surface extensions shall be secured in place by approved means at intervals not exceeding 8 inches, except that where connection to the supplying outlet is made by means of an attachment plug the first fastening may be placed 12 inches or less from the plug. There shall be at least one fastening between each two adjacent outlets supplied. An extension shall be attached only to woodwork or plaster finish, and shall not be in contact with any metal work or other conductive material except with metal plates on receptacles.* See Fig. 342-5.

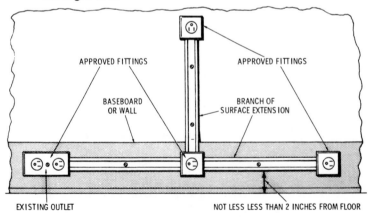

Fig. 342-4. Branches of nonmetallic surface extensions and clearance.

(3) *A bend which reduces the normal spacing between the conductors shall be covered with a cap to protect the assembly from physical damage.* See Fig. 342-6.

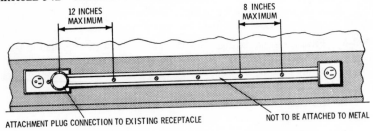

Fig. 342-5. Supporting distances for nonmetallic surface extensions.

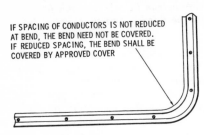

IF SPACING OF CONDUCTORS IS NOT REDUCED AT BEND, THE BEND NEED NOT BE COVERED. IF REDUCED SPACING, THE BEND SHALL BE COVERED BY APPROVED COVER

Fig. 342-6. Bends in nonmetallic surface extensions.

(b) Aerial Cable.

(1) Aerial cable shall be supported by the messenger cable in the assembly, and not by the conductors or insulation. The messenger cable is to be fastened securely at both ends by means of approved cable clamps and turnbuckles for taking up any sag in the assembly. If the span is over 20 feet, the assembly shall be supported by approved hangers at intervals not to exceed 20 feet. The cable shall be so suspended as to eliminate excessive sag and shall clear any metal by a minimum of 2 inches. The assembly is not to contact any metal and the messenger cable is to take the strain of supporting the assembly with added supports as required.

(2) Aerial cable shall have a minimum height of 10 feet above areas of pedestrian traffic only and a minimum height of 14 feet above vehicular traffic. See Fig. 342-7.

(3) Cable assemblies that are over workbenches, but not over vehicular or pedestrian traffic areas, may have a minimum height of 8 feet. See Fig. 342-8.

(4) *Aerial cable may serve to support lighting fixtures when the total load on the supporting messenger cable does not exceed that for which the assembly is intended.* The supporting capabilities of the assembly may be found by contacting the manufacturer for specifications.

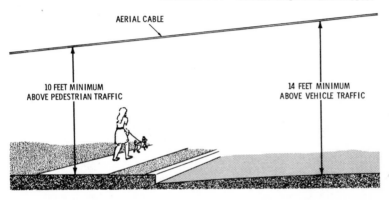

Fig. 342-7. Clearances above floors for aerial nonmetallic surface extensions.

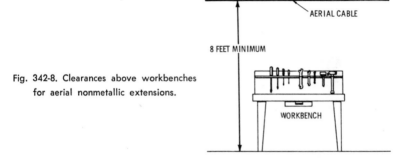

Fig. 342-8. Clearances above workbenches for aerial nonmetallic extensions.

(5) If the supporting messenger cable meets the requirement of **Article 250** for grounding conductors for grounding of equipment, it may be used for this purpose if all provisions covering same in **Article 250** are met, but under no condition is it to be used as a grounded or hot conductor of a branch circuit.

ARTICLE 344—UNDERPLASTER EXTENSIONS

344-1. Use—It is sometimes necessary to make an extension to an existing receptacle (or similar device) or other branch circuits. This Article covers these extensions. They are to be installed only in fire-resistive buildings, such as brick, concrete block, and masonry. It is not necessary to cover extensions in frame buildings as they are covered under other Articles of the Code.

344-2. Materials—Underplaster extensions shall be run in:

(1) Rigid conduit.
(2) Flexible conduit.
(3) Type AC metal-clad cable.
(4) Electrical metallic tubing.
(5) Type MI cable.
(6) Metal raceways approved for this purpose.

Standard sizes of the above shall be used, except for a single conductor where only conduit or tubing having not less than 5/16-inch inside diameter, MI single-conductor cable, or single conductor Type AC cable, may be used.

344-3. Box and Fittings—The same provisions that apply to boxes and fittings in **Article 370** apply to underplaster extensions.

344-4. Installation—Underplaster extensions are to be laid on the face of masonry or other subsurface material and buried in the plaster finish. The provisions of other Articles in the Code which cover the specific material or wiring method to be used will apply in the installation of underplaster extensions.

344-5. Extension to Another Floor—See NEC.

ARTICLE 346—RIGID METAL CONDUIT

A note precedes this Article—*Where conduit is threaded in the field, it is assumed that a standard conduit cutting die providing 3/4 inch taper per foot will be employed.* It must be kept in mind that conduit couplings are different from water-pipe couplings—conduit couplings have no taper in the threads inside the coupling, whereas pipe couplings do have.

346-1. Use—Rigid conduit is the old standby in wiring methods. It may be used in all atmospheric conditions and occupancies, but there are some provisions that cover its use. Ferrous conduit and fittings that have enamel protection from corrosion can only be used indoors and even then shall not be subject to severe corrosive influences. Where practical, ferrous conduit shall be used with ferrous fittings, and nonferrous conduit shall be used with fittings of similar material. This is to avoid galvanic action between the dissimilar metals.

The following leaves considerable to the judgement of the inspection authority: *Unless made of a material judged suitable for the condition, or unless corrosion protection approved for the condition is provided, ferrous or nonferrous metallic conduit, elbows, couplings, and fittings shall not be installed in concrete or in direct contact with the earth, or in areas subject to severe corrosive influences.* This places considerable responsibility upon the inspector to use discretionary powers in its enforcement. It is recommended that, if in doubt, the inspection authority be contacted for a decision before installation.

Section 300-5 is referred to, which states: *Where protected from corrosion solely by enamel, they* (conduit, fittings, etc.) *shall not be used out of doors or in wet locations as described in* (c) which lists a number of locations which would be judged corrosive or damp.

346-2. Other Articles—See NEC.

A. Installation

346-3. Cinder Fill—Cinder fill causes considerable corrosion. Therefore, unless conduit is of a corrosion-resistant material which will withstand this corrosive condition, it shall not be buried under or in cinder fill unless protected by a noncinder concrete covering of a minimum of 2 inches thickness, or unless it is buried a minimum of 18 inches below the fill. See Figs. 346-1 and 2.

346-4. Wet Locations—All supports, bolts, straps, screws, etc., shall *be of corrosion-resistant materials or protected against corrosion by approved corrosion-resistant materials.* Referral is made to **Section 300-5,** which requires a 1/4-inch air space between the wiring system, including boxes and fittings in damp or wet locations.

Also note that the above requires that screws and bolts used in the installation shall be corrosion-resistant or plated by corrosion-resistant ma-

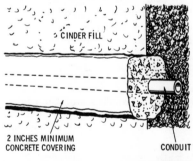

Fig. 346-1. Concrete covering for conduit under cinder fill.

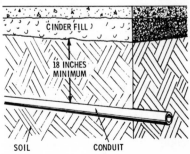

Fig. 346-2. No concrete required if buried a minimum of 18 inches below cinder fill.

terial. This prohibits the use of common steel nails, screws, and bolts in these locations. Galvanized 1/4-inch spacers may be purchased for the purpose of giving the 1/4-inch air space required—common steel washers are not permitted as they are not coated with corrosion-resistant material.

346-5. Minimum Size—For practical purposes, 1/2-inch trade size rigid conduit is the smallest allowable. However, for underplaster extensions, conduit with a minimum inside diameter of 5/16 inch is permitted in some cases, and 3/8 inch conduit is permitted in some cases listed in **Section 430-145(b).**

346-6. Number of Conductors in Conduit—*The number of conductors permitted in a single conduit shall be in accordance with the percentage fill specified in* **Table 1,** *Chapter 9.*

The 1971 NEC has changed. We formerly had New York Fill and Rewire Fill. **Table 1** of Chapter 9, now covers both **Tables 2, 3A, 3B** and **3C,** and are worked out so that one may easily find the number of conductors allowed for fill without calculating same.

346-7. Reaming—*All cut ends of conduit shall be reamed to remove rough edges.* This is to prevent abrasion to the conductor insulation.

346-8. Bushings—Bushings are required on conduits wherever they enter boxes or fittings to protect the wire from abrasion, unless the design of the box or fitting is such that it provides an equivalent protection. **Section 373-6 (b)** requires insulated bushings where No. 4 or larger conductors are used. This may be an insulated bushing, a fiber insert for a metal bushing (provided that it is an approved insert), or it may be a grounding-type bushing which is a combination of metal and insulation, where grounding bushings are required, or the approved fiber insert may be used with a grounding type of bushing.

346-9. Couplings and Connectors—

(a) *Threadless couplings and connectors used with conduit shall be made tight. Where buried in masonry or concrete, they shall be of the concrete-type, or where installed in wet locations, shall be of the raintight type.*

(b) *Running threads shall not be used on conduit for connection and couplings.* There is no taper to running threads—all of the thread is the same size throughout its length, tending to make a loose fit. In addition, there is no corrosion-resistant covering on the threaded portion.

346-10. Bends—How Made—Conduit may be bent, but it shall be done in such a way so as not to damage the conduit nor reduce its internal diameter. Conduit is often kinked while being bent. Installation of kinked conduit is not permitted, as the internal diameter will be reduced, making the pulling of conductors increasingly difficult and making damage to the insulation more probable. Torches have been used to heat conduit to facilitate the bending, but this will damage the galvanizing or other protective coating and is not permitted.

Table 346-10 lists the minimum radius of the inside bend allowed for various sizes of conduit. Factory ells will have a shorter radius than those listed, but this is permissible as they are approved items.

There is an exception on bends, which we have not had before. This is the permitting of bends of less radius than permitted by **Table 336-10,** provided that a one-shot bender is used and that it is the type approved for this purpose. Also **Table 346-10(b)** has been added to cover these bends.

346-11. Bends—Number in One Run—There is a limit of four 90° bends, or the equivalent of 360°, between outlet and outlet, between fitting and fitting, or between outlet and fitting. This is to control the number of bends so that pulling of conductors is not made too difficult. See Fig. 346-3.

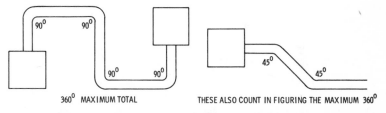

360° MAXIMUM TOTAL   THESE ALSO COUNT IN FIGURING THE MAXIMUM 360°

Fig. 346-3. A maximum of 360° allowed between outlets and/or fittings.

346-12.   Supports—This Section is a new addition to the 1965 Code. *Rigid metal conduit shall be installed as a complete system as provided in* **Article 300** *and shall be securely fastened in place. Conduit shall be firmly fastened within 3 feet of each outlet box, junction box, cabinet, or fitting. Conduit shall be supported at least every ten feet except that straight runs of rigid conduit made up with approved threaded couplings may be secured in accordance with* **Table 346-12,** *provided such fastening prevents transmission of stresses to terminus when conduit is deflected between supports.*

346-13.   Boxes and Fittings—See **Article 370.**

B. Construction Specifications

346-14.   General—The requirements of this Section are very plain— *Rigid metal conduit shall conform to the following:*

(a) *Rigid conduit as shipped shall be in standard lengths of 10 feet* *including coupling, one coupling to be furnished with each length. Each length shall be reamed and threaded on each end. For specific applications or uses, lengths shorter or longer than 10 feet, with or without couplings, may be shipped.* The latter part of the above is quite a change. This is the first time that shorter or longer lengths than 10 feet have been permitted. Note especially the part that states: *For specific applications or uses.*

(b) *Steel conduit shall have an interior coating of a character and appearance so as to readily distinguish it from ordinary pipe commonly used for other than electrical purposes.* Greater care must be exercised in applying the interior coating on conduit in order that no abrasion to the insulation will result.

(c) *Nonferrous conduit of corrosion-resistant material shall have suitable markings.*

(d) *Each length shall be clearly and durably identified in every 10 feet with the manufacturer's name or trademark and type of material.* This is highly important so that it will be easy to identify what type of rigid conduit is being used.

ARTICLE 347—RIGID NONMETALLIC CONDUIT

The use of rigid nonmetallic conduit is a rather new wiring method that has rapidly gained favor. It first became a part of the NEC in the 1962 Edition, with a number of changes made in the 1965 Edition. With its popularity and the general usage to which it is being put, great care should be taken to become familiar with this product.

347-1. Description—*The provisions of this Article shall apply to a type of conduit and fittings of suitable nonmetallic material which is resistant to moisture and chemical atmospheres. For use above ground, it shall also be flame retardant, resistant to impact and crushing, shall resist distortion due to heat under conditions likely to be encountered in service and shall be resistant to low temperature and sunlight effects. For use underground, the material shall be acceptably resistant to moisture and corrosive agents and shall be of sufficient strength to withstand abuse, such as by impact and crushing, in handling and during installation. Where intended for direct burial, without encasement in concrete, the material shall also be capable of withstanding continued loading which is likely to be encountered after installation.*

Materials which have been recognized as having suitable physical characteristics when properly formed and treated include fiber, asbestos cement, soapstone, rigid polyvinyl chloride and high density polyethylene for underground use and rigid polyvinyl chloride for use above ground.

The difference here between the 1962 and the 1965 Code is the recognition of high density polyethylene for underground use.

If in doubt about the application of rigid nonmetallic conduit, it is well to check the UL listings for the application for which the particular type intended to be used is applicable.

347-2. Use Permitted—The intent of this Article regarding rigid non-metallic conduit is that it shall be used for voltages of 600 volts or less, unless otherwise stated, and it is not to be used where prohibited in **Section 347-3** of this Article.

(a) *Direct earth burial not less than 18 inches below the surface. If less than 18 inches it shall be encased in not less than 2 inches of concrete.*

(b) *In walls, floor and ceilings.*

(c) It may be used where subject to severe corrosive influences, such as locations listed in **Section 300-5** which include the following: *Meat packing plants, tanneries, hide cellars, casing rooms, glue houses, fertilizer rooms, salt storage, some chemical works, metal refineries, pulp mills, sugar mills, round houses, some stables and similar locations are judged to be occupancies where severe corrosive conditions are likely to be present.* A check should be made to ascertain that the conduit material is specifically approved for the corrosive influence to which it is to be subjected.

(d) *Cinder fill.* The 24-inch burial mentioned in (b) above will apply here.

(e) *Wet Locations. In portions of dairies, laundries, canneries or other wet locations and in locations where walls are frequently washed, the entire conduit system including boxes and fittings used therewith shall be so installed and equipped as to prevent water from entering the conduit. All supports, bolts, straps, screws, etc., shall be of corrosion-resistant materials.*

(f) In dry and damp locations not prohibited by Section 347-3.

347-3. Use Prohibited—*Rigid nonmetallic conduit shall not be used:*

(a) *In hazardous locations except as covered in* **Section 514-8.** **Article 514** covers Gasoline Dispensing and Service Stations. In **Section 514-8,** rigid metal conduit or, where buried not less than 2 feet in the earth, nonmetallic rigid conduit may be installed. When nonmetallic rigid conduit is installed, there shall be a grounding conductor installed, conforming in size to **Table 250-95,** for the purpose of grounding the metallic noncurrent carrying parts of any equipment. The use of rigid nonmetallic conduit in this type of location will not change the use of seal-offs, as covered elsewhere in **Article 514.** Also see **Section 515-5.**

(b) *For the support of fixtures and other equipment.*

(c) *Where subject to physical damage unless approved for the purpose.*

(d) *Where subect to ambient temperatures exceeding those for which the conduit had been approved.*

(e) *For conductors whose insulation temperature limitations would exceed those for which the conduit had been approved.*

(f) *For potentials exceeding 600 volts unless encased in not less than 2 inches of concrete.*

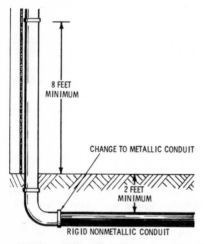

Fig. 347-1. Running nonmetallic conduit above ground.

347-4. **Other Articles**—As with all wiring methods, **Article 300** covering General Wiring Methods is always referred to. Where **Article 250** requires an equipment grounding conductor, one shall be installed.

A. Installations

347-5. **Trimming**—*All cut ends shall be trimmed inside and outside to remove rough edges.* This is for the same reason that rigid metal conduit has to be reamed, namely to prevent damage to the conductor insulation.

347-6. **Joints**—In the makeup of rigid nonmetallic conduit, various methods are used, depending upon the material. The instructions for the particular conduit shall be followed in making up lengths and between conduit and couplings, fittings, and boxes. Some conduit is threaded, while other types use a solvent or similar substance to be applied to the joints and fittings before putting them together.

347-8. Supports—Rigid nonmetallic conduit shall be supported within 4 feet of each box, cabinet, or other conduit termination, and elsewhere according to **Table 347-8.**

347-9. Expansion Joints—Where expansion and contraction due to temperature differences might be encountered, approved rigid nonmetallic conduit expansion joints shall be used. Practically all substances expand and contract with temperature changes, which will put undue strain on the conduit. Expansion joints absorb this expansion and contraction, thus avoiding damage to the conduit and fittings.

347-10. Minimum Size—One-half inch electrical trade size is the smallest permissible size of rigid nonmetallic conduit that can be used.

347-11. Number of Conductors—The fill for both new work and rewire are governed by the same rules as are applicable to rigid metal conduit. This will not be repeated here, but refer back to **Section 346-6** of this book.

347-12. Bushings—This ruling is practically the same as for rigid metallic conduit, except that it says bushing or adapter. As with metal conduit (**Section 373-6(b)**) an insulated bushing is required where No. 4 or larger conductors are used.

347-13. Bends, How Made—See NEC.

347-14. Bends, Number in One Run—See NEC.

347-15. Boxes and Fittings—See **Article 370.**

B. Construction Specifications

347-16. General—See NEC.

ARTICLE 348—ELECTRICAL METALLIC TUBING

Electrical metallic tubing is commonly known as EMT, thin wall conduit, or merely thin wall.

348-1. Use—EMT may be used for:

(1) Exposed work.
(2) Concealed work.
(3) Installation in cinder concrete or cinder fill if protected by a layer of at least 2 inches of noncinder concrete or buried at least 18 inches below the fill. The burial of EMT may be prohibited by the inspection authority under certain conditions.
(4) Installation in damp or wet locations, providing that all condi-

tions (such as water-tight connectors, 1/4-inch spacing, etc.) as specified in **Section 300-5** are met.

The use of EMT is prohibited as follows:

(1) Where it is protected solely by enamel.

(2) Where subject to severe physical damage during or after installation.

(3) In cinder concrete or cinder fill unless protected as per (3) above.

A new paragraph has been added to the 1965 Code—*Unless made of a material judged suitable for the condition, or unless corrosion protection approved for the condition is provided, ferrous or nonferrous electrical metallic tubing, elbows, couplings and fittings shall not be installed in concrete or in direct contact with the earth, or in areas subject to severe corrosive influences.* This ruling also appeared in **Section 346-1**, and has been added because that, even in concrete, conditions have caused corrosion which has cracked the concrete or collapsed the EMT. Therefore, it is up to the inspection authority to decide if its use is prohibited or not. A check with the authority should always be made before making direct burial in concrete or earth.

348-2. Other Articles—The installation of EMT, as with other wiring methods, shall be governed by **Article 300** as well as by this Article.

A. Installation

348-4. Wet Locations—See NEC.

348-5. Minimum and Maximum Sizes—One-half inch electrical trade size is the minimum EMT size allowed, except for underplaster extensions (**Article 344**), where 5/16-inch inside diameter tubing is permitted, and for some cases of motor-lead installation (**Section 430-145(b)**), where 3/8-inch trade size tubing is allowed. The maximum size of EMT permissible has been increased to 4-inch electrical trade size.

348-6. Number of Conductors in Tubing—The requirements for conductors in EMT are exactly the same as for rigid metal conduit as provided in **Section 346-6.**

348-7. Threads—Basically, EMT is not meant to be connected to boxes or fittings or coupled together by means of threads in the wall of the tubing. There is an exception for fittings approved for this purpose, but the threads of these devices are not standard pipe threads.

348-8. Couplings and Connectors—*Threadless couplings and connectors used with tubing shall be made up tight. Where buried in masonry or concrete, they shall be concrete-tight, or where installed in wet locations, shall be of the raintight type.* There are a great variety of connectors and couplings available, but regardless of the type used, care should be taken to make up the connection tightly. It will be recalled that EMT will, in most cases, be serving as the equipment ground. Loose connections will not provide proper grounding and could be the cause of a fire or injury.

Where permitted in concrete, couplings and fittings might be damaged during the installation of the concrete, and once buried, repairs are very costly. Care should be taken to make sure that such damage does not occur.

348-9. Bends—How Made—*Bends in the tubing shall be so made that the tubing will not be injured and that the internal diameter of the tubing will not be effectively reduced. The radius of the curve of the inner edge of any field bend shall not be less than shown in* **Table 346-10.** These are the same requirements as for rigid metal conduit. In making field bends, the proper equipment should always be used. Also see **Table 346-10(b).**

348-10. Bends—Number in One Run—These requirements are the same as for rigid metal conduit—a maximum of the equivalent of four 90° bends, or a total of 360° between outlet and outlet, between fitting and fitting, or between outlet and fitting.

348-11. Reaming—*All cut ends of electrical metallic tubing shall be reamed to remove rough edges.* EMT cuts easily and thus there is a tendency not to worry too much about reaming. Reaming is very important, however, to keep from damaging the insulation of the conductors.

348-12. Supports—Prior to the 1965 Code, there was nothing specific about supporting EMT. This has been taken care of as follows: *Electrical metallic tubing shall be installed as a complete system as provided in* **Article 300** *and shall be securely fastened in place at least every 10 feet and within 3 feet of each outlet box, junction box, cabinet, or fitting.*

This ruling is a definite asset as there has always been much question as to what constituted properly secured EMT in an installation. As required in **Article 300,** raceways shall be installed complete before installing the conductors.

348-13. Boxes and Fittings—See **Article 370.**

B. Construction Specifications

348-14. General—See NEC.

ARTICLE 350—FLEXIBLE METAL CONDUIT

350-1. Other Articles—Not only are the Sections of this Article applicable to flexible metal conduit, but any appropriate provisions of **Article 300** (General Wiring Methods), **Article 334** (Metal-Clad Cable), and **Article 346** (Rigid Metal Conduit) also apply.

350-2. Use—*Flexible metal conduit shall not be used:*

(1) *In wet locations, unless conductors are of the lead-covered type or of other type specially approved for the conditions.* Out-of-doors where subject to rains would be classified as a wet location.

(2) *In hoistways, except as provided in* **Section 620-21.** In Exception No. 2, it states that short runs of flexible conduit may be used on cars where so located as to be free from oil and if securely fastened in place.

(3) *In storage-battery rooms.*

(4) In any hazardous location except as permitted in **Sections 501-4(b), 502-4** and **503-3.**

(5) *Where rubber-covered conductors are exposed to oil, gasoline, or other materials having a deteriorating effect on rubber.*

Flexible metal conduit offers a high impedance, having 3 to 4 times the impedance of AC cable. Therefore, many inspectors will require bonding or the use of an equipment grounding conductor when using flexible metal conduit.

350-3. Minimum Size—For practical purposes, the minimum metal conduit is 1/2-inch electrical trade size. There are a few exceptions which will permit 3/8-inch electrical trade size to be used. There is sometimes a tendency to use 3/8-inch conduit in the wrong places and for the wrong purposes.

Exceptions:

(1) *As permitted for underplaster extensions by* **Section 344-2.**

(2) *As permitted for motors by* **Section 430-145(b).**

(3) *Flexible metal conduit of ⅜ inch nominal trade size may be used in lengths not in excess of 72 inches as a part of an approved assembly for lighting fixtures.* **Table 350-3,** *gives us fill for ⅜ inch flexible metal conduit.*

350-4. Supports—Flexible metal conduit is a wiring method and may be used to wire buildings, etc., unless prohibited in certain locations, such as in most hazardous locations. It shall be supported by approved means at least every 4½ feet and within 12 inches on each side of every outlet box or fitting. There, however, are a few exceptions to this:

Exception No. 1. Where flexible metal conduit is fished. Here of course it would be impossible to support it within walls, etc.

Exception No. 2. Lengths of not more than 3 feet at terminals where flexibility is necessary.

Exception No. 3. Lengths of not more than 6 feet from a fixture terminal connection for tap connections to lighting fixtures as re-

quired in **Sections 410-65(b) (2).** I am certain that most any inspection authority would require that the flexible metal conduit not be draped in such a manner as to lay or drop in ceilings, etc.

350-5. Grounding—*Flexible metal conduit may be used as a grounding means where both the conduit and the fittings are approved for the purpose.* A this writing the author knows of no flexible metal conduit and fittings approved for this purpose. However, the way this section is written, it will leave the door open in the event such are approved.

Exception: Flexible metal conduit may be used for grounding if the length is 6 feet or less, it is terminated in fittings approved for the purpose, and the circuit conductors contained therein are protected by overcurrent devices rated at 20 amperes or less.

Basically, flexible metal conduit is not to be used as an equipment grounding conductor. This exception was put in the Code since there is no way of knowing the problems resulting from the resistance of the conduit in these lengths.

ARTICLE 351—LIQUIDTIGHT FLEXIBLE METAL CONDUIT

351-1. Scope—*The provisions of this Article shall apply to a type of flexible metal conduit having an outer liquidtight nonmetallic sunlight-resistant jacket.*

Liquidtight flexible metal conduit is not intended as a cure-all, but has a very definite purpose. However, when it is used, care must be taken that only approved terminal fittings are employed. When conventional fittings are used, the grounding that is normally provided by the conduit is often destroyed. The following **Section 351-8** will cover grounding.

351-2. Use—

(a) *Liquidtight flexible metal conduit may be used in exposed or concealed locations:*

(1) Where conditions of installation, operation, or maintenance require flexibility or protection from liquids, vapors or solids. One very practical use for this material might be where there is a service pole located close to a pump house. The movement of the pole might prohibit the use of a rigid wiring method. The installation is exposed to the elements, so wiring with liquidtight flexible conduit would be very practical providing that all of the requirements of proper grounding continuity are met.

(2) As permitted by **Sections 501-4(b), 502-4** *and* **503-3,** *and*

in other hazardous locations where specifically approved. The aforementioned Sections do not give a complete release to use flexible liquidtight conduit in all hazardous places, but there still are some places it is permitted.

(b) *Liquidtight flexible metal conduit shall not be used:*

(1) Where subject to physical damage.
(2) Where any combination of ambient and/or conductor temperature will produce an operating temperature in excess of that for which the material is approved. The ambient temperature (operating) of the conductors is very important in deciding whether liquidtight flexible metal conduit may be used or not.

Section 501-4(b) allows flexible metal conduit in Class I, Division 2 areas where limited flexibility is required, such as at motor terminals.

Section 502-4 permits flexible metal conduit to be used to a limited degree in Class II, Division 1 areas where approved fittings are used, but never where there is dust of an electrical conducting nature.

Section 503-3 allows flexible metal conduit to be used in Class III, Division 1 areas where flexible connections are necessary. This type of conduit may be used provided that it meets the provisions of **Section 502-4(a-2).**

351-3. Size.—*The sizes of liquidtight flexible metal conduit shall be electrical trade sizes ½- to 4-inch inclusive.*

Exception. ⅜-inch size may be used as permitted in **Section 350-3.**

351-4. Number of Conductors—

(a) The number of conductors in liquidtight flexible metal conduit will be the same as for rigid metal conduit; see **Section 346-6** and the **Tables** in Chapter 9.

(b) *See* **Table 350-3** *for maximum number of conductors in ⅜ inch liquidtight flexible metal conduit.*

351-5. Fittings—*Liquidtight flexible metal conduit shall be used only with terminal fittings approved for the purpose.* This wiring method has connectors, etc., which are approved for liquidtight flexible metal conduit only and substitutions shall not be made.

351-6. Supports—Where liquidtight flexible metal conduit is used as a fixed raceway, it shall be secured:

(1) By approved methods.
(2) At intervals not to exceed 4½ feet.

(3) Within 12 inches of outlet boxes and fittings.

(4) Except where the conduit is fished.

351-7. Grounding—Liquidtight flexible metal conduit that is 1½-inch diameter or larger is required to have an equipment grounding conductor installed regardless of the length of conduilt used and sized to **Table 250-95,** but 6-foot or less of 1¼-inch size or smaller will not be required to have an equipment grounding conductor pulled in.

All sizes of this conduit and any length need not have an equipment grounding conductor pulled in, if; the conduit and fittings are both approved for the purpose. At this writing, I do not know of any that has been approved for grounding, so check your UL books.

ARTICLE 352—SURFACE RACEWAYS
Metal Raceways

Surface metal raceways provide a wiring method that has many advantages. This wiring method is not intended for new construction, but is quite valuable in additions to existing wiring systems that must be expanded without cutting into the existing building to add conduit and other components. Surface metal raceways have been used for many years and have been found quite satisfactory for the purpose for which they are intended.

352-1. Use—Surface metal raceways may be installed in dry locations, in most any case, except as follows:

(1) Where concealed. As the name indicates, this method is for surface mounting only, except that it may be used for underplaster extensions when approved for that purpose. Refer to **Article 344.**

(2) Where exposed to severe physical damage unless approved for that purpose.

(3) Where the voltage between conductors exceeds 300 volts, unless the metal used in the raceway has a thickness of at least 0.040 inch.

(4) Where subject to corrosive vapors.

(5) In hoistways.

(6) In hazardous areas. See Chapter 5.

(7) *Exception: Where accessible, surface metal raceways may be used in nonair-handling plenum chamber areas.*
See definition of Exposed—(As applied to wiring methods) in **Article 100.**

352-2. Other Articles—The provisions of **Article 300** (General Wiring Methods) shall be used in addition to this Article, where applicable.

A. Installation

352-3. Size of Conductors—Prior to the 1965 Code, No. 6 was the largest conductor permitted to be used. This ruling was changed as follows: *No conductor larger than that for which the raceway is designed shall be installed in surface metal raceway.* This will make necessary knowing what size conductor the raceway was designed for.

352-4. Number of Conductors in Raceways—*The number of conductors installed in any raceway shall be no greater than the number for which the raceway is designed.* Here, again, the specifications for the raceway should be checked.

352-5. Extension Through Walls and Floors—Multioutlet assemblies are not to be extended through floors and walls. Surface metal raceways may be extended through dry walls, dry partitions, and dry floors. However, they shall be in unbroken lengths where they pass through, so that no joint will be hidden.

352-6. Combination Raceways—Take special note of this Section as it is quite different from conduit systems. *Where combination metal raceways are used both for signal and for lighting and power circuits, the different systems shall be run in separate compartments, identified by sharply constrasting colors of the interior finish, and the same relative position of compartments shall be maintained through the premises.*

352-7. Splices and Taps—*Splices and taps shall be made only in junction boxes except that they may be made in surface metal raceway having a removable cover which is accessible after installation. The conductors, including splices and taps, shall not fill the raceway to more than 75 percent of its area at this point. All splices and taps shall be made by approved methods.*

B. Construction Specifications

352-8. General—*Surface metal raceways shall be of such construction as will distinguish them from other raceways. Surface metal raceways and their elbows, couplings, and similar fittings shall be so designed that the sections can be electrically and mechanically coupled together, while protecting the wires from abrasion. Holes for screws or bolts inside the raceway shall be so designed that when the screws or bolts are in place their heads will be flush with the metal surface.* See Figs. 352-1 and 2.

Nonmetallic Raceways

352-21. Description—*The provisions of the following Sections of this Article shall apply to a type of surface nonmetallic raceway and fittings of suitable nonmetallic material which is resistant to moisture and chemical atmospheres. It shall be flame retardant, resistant to impact and crushing, shall resist distortion due to heat under conditions likely to be encountered in service and shall be resistant to low temperature effects.*

352-22. Use—*Surface nonmetallic raceways may be installed in dry locations.*

They shall not be used as follows:
(1) Where concealed.
(2) Where subject to severe physical damage.
(3) Where the voltage is 300 volts or more between conductors.
(4) In hoistways.
(5) In any hazardous location.
(6) Where subject to ambient temperatures exceeding 50°C.
(7) For conductors whose insulation temperatures exceed 75°C.

352-23. Other Articles—The provisions of **Article 300** shall be applicable.

A. Installation

352-24. Size of Conductors—The design of the surface nonmetallic raceways will govern the conductor sizes that may be used.

352-25. Number of Conductors in Raceways—The design of the nonmetallic surface raceways and the size of the conductors will govern.

352-26. Combination Raceways—See NEC.

B. Construction Specifications

352-27. General—See NEC.

ARTICLE 353—MULTIOUTLET ASSEMBLY

Multioutlet assemblies consist of either a flush or surface raceway which has been designed to hold receptacle outlets and has either been factory assembled or assembled in the field. They are used especially where there are a number of outlets required in a relatively short space, such as in show rooms where the connections for appliances for demonstration, for outlets along a workbench, etc., are necessary.

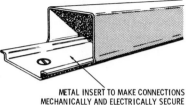

Fig. 352-1. Connections shall be electrically and mechanically secure.

METAL INSERT TO MAKE CONNECTIONS
MECHANICALLY AND ELECTRICALLY SECURE

SCREW HOLE COUNTERSUNK

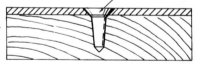

Fig. 352-2. Holes for screws shall be countersunk to protect wire from damage.

Some multioutlet assemblies have receptacles that are movable. They make connection with some type of bus and may be slid along to obtain different spacings. Other assemblies are designed with outlets at fixed intervals so as to facilitate the connection of appliances, tools, etc. There are many different makes available, so care should be taken to pick a multioutlet assembly that is approved and to properly install it.

353-1. Other Articles—The use and installation of multioutlet assemblies is governed not only by this Article but also by **Article 300** (General Wiring Methods).

353-2. Use—Multioutlet assemblies are to be installed only in dry locations. They are not to be installed:

(1) Where concealed, except that the back and sides of metal multioutlet assemblies may be surrounded by the building finish, and nonmetallic multioutlet assemblies may be recessed in the baseboard. See Fig. 353-1 and 2.
(2) Where subject to severe physical damage, unless approved for that purpose.
(3) Where the voltage is 300 volts or more between conductors, un-

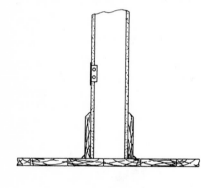

Fig. 353-1. Metal multioutlet assemblies may be installed in building finishes.

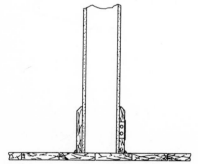

Fig. 353-2. Nonmetallic assemblies may be installed in baseboards.

less the assembly is of metal having a thickness of at least 0.040 inch.

(4) Where subject to corrosive vapors.

(5) In hoistways.

(6) In any hazardous area.

353-3. Metal Multioutlet Assembly Through Dry Partitions—Metal multioutlet assemblies shall not be run in partitions, but may be run through dry partitions providing that the covers outside of the partition are arranged so that they may be removed, and providing that there are no outlets inside the partition. See Fig. 353-3.

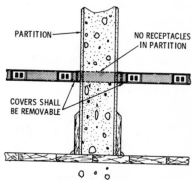

Fig. 353-3. Multioutlet assemblies may pass through dry partitions, provided there are no outlets in the partition and the covers are removable.

PARTITION

NO RECEPTACLES IN PARTITION

COVERS SHALL BE REMOVABLE

ARTICLE 354—UNDERFLOOR RACEWAYS

Underfloor raceways are extensively used in larger buildings, especially those with concrete floors. They have a number of advantages that make them convenient to use where a number of floor outlets are required (as in offices), and where more may be needed at some future date.

354-1. Other Articles—The provisions of this Article and of **Article 300** (General Wiring Methods) apply to the installation of underfloor raceways.

354-2. Use—*Underfloor raceways may be installed beneath the surface of concrete or other flooring material* (Fig. 354-1), *or in office occupancies, where laid flush with the concrete floor and covered with linoleum or equivalent floor coverings.* See Fig. 354-2.

Underfloor raceways shall not be installed:

(1) *Where subject to corrosive vapors.*

(2) In any hazardous location, unless made of material judged suitable for the condition.

Unless corrosion protection approved for the condition is provided, ferrous or nonferrous metallic underfloor raceways, junction boxes, and

225

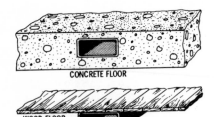

Fig. 354-1. Underfloor raceways may be installed in concrete floors or under other floors.

fittings shall not be installed in concrete or in direct contact with the earth or in areas subject to severe corrosive influences. Formerly, open-bottom type raceways were permitted where they were installed in a concrete fill. This has now been deleted (Fig. 354-3). These raceways shall be corrosion protected and approved for the purpose where installed in concrete or in contact with the earth. This is the same requirement as for rigid metallic conduit.

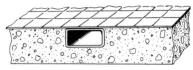

Fig. 354-2. Underfloor raceways may be laid flush with the surface of the concrete in office occupancies, if covered by linoleum or the equivalent.

354-3. Covering—*Raceway coverings shall conform to the following:*

(a) Raceways Not Over 4 Inches Wide. *Half-round raceways not over 4 inches in width, and, except as permitted in* **(c)** *flat-top raceways not over 4 inches in width, shall have not less than 3/4 inch of concrete or wood above the raceway.* See Fig. 354-4.

Fig. 354-3. Open-bottom raceways are no longer permitted.

(b) Raceways Over 4 Inches Wide but Not Over 8 Inches Wide. *Flat top raceways over 4 but not over 8 inches wide with a minimum of 1 inch spacing between raceways shall be covered with concrete to a depth of not less than 1 inch. Raceways spaced less than 1 inch apart shall be covered with concrete to a depth of 1½ inches.* See Fig. 354-5.

(c) Raceways Flush with Concrete. *Approved flush raceways with removable covers may be laid flush with the floor surface. Such*

226

approved raceways shall be so designed that the cover plates will provide adequate mechanical protection and rigidity equivalent to junction covers. This part has also been changed in the 1965 Code. Please note that the 4-inch limitation has been deleted and that the rigidity of the covers has been changed. In addition, the 1/8-inch thickness of the linoleum or equivalent covering has been deleted from the former ruling.

354-4. Size of Conductors—The design of the raceway shall govern the maximum conductor size.

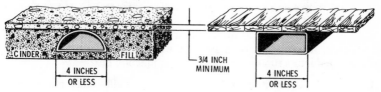

Fig. 354-4. Minimum covering over 4-inch raceways.

354-5. Number of Conductors in Raceway—To figure the number of conductors for underfloor raceways, the total cross-sectional area of all the conductors is calculated. This total area shall not exceed 40% of the cross-sectional area of the interior of the raceway. In arriving at the cross-sectional area of the conductors, use the appropriate Tables in Chapter 9. An exception to this 40% ruling is when nonmetallic sheathed cable or armored cable is used for the conductors.

354-6. Splices and Taps—Splices and taps are not to be made in the raceway itself but only in junction boxes. *For purposes of this Section,*

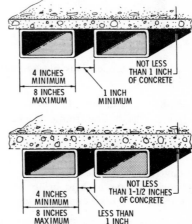

Fig. 354-5. Minimum covering over 4- to 8-inch raceways.

227

so-called loop wiring (continuous, unbroken conductor connecting the individual outlets) is not considered to be a splice or tap. See Fig. 354-6. Attention is also called to the next section.

354-7. Discontinued Outlets—*When an outlet is abandoned, discontinued, or removed, the sections of circuit conductors supplying the outlet shall be removed from the raceway. No splices or reinsulated conductors such as would be the case with abandoned outlets on loop wiring, shall be allowed in raceways.*

To illustrate the essential parts of this ruling, refer to Fig. 354-6. Should outlet No. 2B in Run B of the raceway be removed, the wires that served it shall be removed back to the junction box. Should outlet No. 1A also be removed, the conductors to No. 2A would also have to be removed and new conductors run to No. 2A from the junction box.

Old 354-8. Open Bottom Raceways—How Laid—This old **Section 354-8** is entirely deleted as open bottom raceways are no longer per-

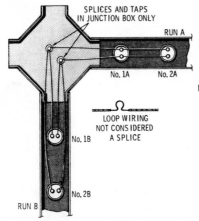

Fig. 354-6. Splices and taps are to be made in junction boxes only.

mitted by the Code. This old **Section 354-8** has been replaced by new **Section 354-8.**

354-8. Laid in Straight Lines—It is necessary to lay underfloor raceways in a straight line from one junction box to the next, with the centerlines of the two junction boxes coinciding with the centerline of the raceway. This is essential so that the raceways may be located in the event that additional outlets are required later and so that the end markers covered by the next section have some meaning. It is also required that the raceways be held firmly in place by appropriate means to prevent disturbing the alignment during construction.

354-9. Markers at Ends—A suitable number of markers that extend through the floor shall be installed at the end of line raceways, and at other places where the location of the raceway is not apparent, so that future location of the raceway is made possible. It is recommended that these identification markers be indicated on any blue prints of the building for future reference to assist in the locating of the raceways.

354-10. Dead Ends—All dead ends of raceways shall be closed by suitable means that are approved by the inspection authority.

354-11. Low Points—Any raceway is subject to condensation. Therefore, in the installation of underfloor raceways, they shall be laid (insofar as practical) so that there will be no low points for the accumulation of moisture.

354-12. Fittings at Angles—*Where raceways are run at other than right angles, special fittings shall be provided.* It also requires that suitable markers, as described in **Section 354-9**, be installed to facilitate in the location of the raceways at a future date.

354-13. Junction Boxes—*Junction boxes shall be leveled to the floor grade and sealed against the entrance of water. Junction boxes used with metal raceways shall be metal and shall be electrically continuous with the raceways.* Metal underfloor raceways, junction boxes, etc., are to be electrically continuous, the same as metallic conduit and electrical metallic tubing. This is one of the most important parts of the installation.

354-14. Inserts—*Inserts shall be leveled to the floor grade and sealed against the entrance of water. Inserts used with metal raceways shall be metal and shall be electrically continuous with the raceway. Inserts set in or on fiber raceways before the floor is laid shall be mechancially secured to the raceway. Inserts set in fiber raceways after the floor is laid shall be screwed into the raceway. In cutting through the raceway wall and setting inserts, chips and other dirt shall not be allowed to fall into the raceway, and tools shall be used which are so designed as to prevent the tool from entering the raceway and injuring conductors that may be in place.* All of this merely means good workmanship. It might be well to mention here that if fiber raceways are used, it will be necessary to install a separate conductor to be used as a grounding conductor, the same as required with nonmetallic rigid conduit.

354-15. Connections to Cabinets and Wall Outlets—*Connections between raceways and distribution centers and wall outlets shall be made by means of rigid or flexible metal conduit or by means of fittings approved for the purpose.* This Article concerns only underfloor raceways—this means that it is not intended to be run up walls to outlets and cabinets. Therefore, conduit or other approved means must be used for this purpose.

ARTICLE 356—CELLULAR METAL FLOOR RACEWAYS

This Article is similar in many respects to the preceding Article on Underfloor Raceways.

356-1. Definition—*For the purpose of this Article, a "cellular metal floor raceway" shall be defined as the hollow spaces of cellular metal floors, together with suitable fittings, which may be approved as enclosures for electrical conductors; a "cell" shall be defined as a single, enclosed tubular space in a cellular metal floor member, the axis of the cell being parallel to the axis of the metal floor member; a "header" shall be defined as a transverse raceway for electrical conductors, providing access to pre-determined cells of a cellular metal floor, thereby permitting the installation of electrical conductors from the distribution center to the cells.* In order to gain a better understanding of cellular metal floor raceways, illustrations will be used.

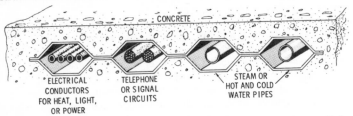

Fig. 356-1. Cross-sectional view of cellular metal floor raceways used for installation of electrical and other systems.

Fig. 356-1 shows a cross section of cellular metal floor raceway. Not only are raceways made for electrical conductors, but also for telephone lines, signal circuits, steam and hot and cold water pipes.

Fig. 356-2 illustrates a cell. Notice that it is just one single enclosed tubular area.

Fig. 356-3 illustrates a header which is transversely connecting two cells. With this arrangement, conductors may be run at right angles to the cells as well as in the cells of the raceway.

Fig. 356-2. Illustration of a cell.

356-2. Use—Conductors are not to be installed in cellular metal floor raceways:

230

(1) Where corrosive vapors are present.
(2) In any hazardous location.
(3) In commercial garages. There is an exception to this in that they may be used where they supply outlets or extensions to the area below the floor but not above.

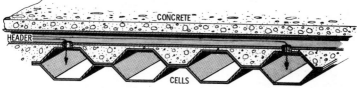

Fig. 356-3. Illustration of a header and cells.

356-3. Other Articles—The provisions of this Article and of **Article 300** (General Wiring Methods) apply to the installation of this wiring method.

A. Installation

356-4. Size of Conductors—*No conductor larger than No. 0 shall be installed, except by special permission.* Your attention is called to the definition of "Special Permission" as it appears in **Article 100**—*The written consent of the authority enforcing this Code.*

365-5. Number of Conductors in Raceway—Attention is called to the fact that no mention is made of new and rewiring work in this Section. Therefore, the same rules apply whether it is new work or rewiring work.

The fill shall be no more than 40% of the cross-sectional area of the raceway. In other words, the total cross-sectional area of all the conductors shall not fill the raceway to over 40% of its capacity. Tables in Chapter 9 of the NEC give the cross-sectional area of various conductors and their insulations. These figures are to be used in the calculation of the total cross-sectional area of the conductors. The requirements just mentioned will not apply where Type AC metal-clad cable or nonmetallic sheathed cables are used in the raceways. The area of the raceway will have to be calculated mathematically unless the specifications are available to the wireman.

356-6. Splices and Taps—*Splices and taps shall be made only in header access units or junction boxes.* These were allowed only in junction boxes with underfloor raceways. With cellular metal floor raceways, they are also permitted in header access boxes. Refer to Fig. 356-3 which shows a header.

356-7. Discontinued Outlets—Conductors that supplied outlets which are being discontinued shall be removed from the raceway back to a junction box. They can not be merely taped up and left in place.

356-8. Markers—Markers are to be extended through the floor for the purpose of locating the cells and the wiring system in the future. There should be enough markers to properly assist in the location of the raceways. It is also recommended that the location of these markers be indicated on the final blue print that is to be given to the owner.

356-9. Junction Boxes—Junction boxes are to be installed level with the floor grade and are to be sealed against the entrance of water and dirt. They shall be made of metal and shall be made electrically continuous with the rest of the system. Although not mentioned at this point, the metal of which the junction boxes are made should be such as to not cause corrosion or electrolysis.

356-10. Inserts—Inserts (such as for outlets) shall be made of metal and made electrically continuous with the rest of the system. They shall be installed level with the floor grade and made water tight. When cutting the raceway for the installation of these inserts, no rough spots shall be left, and the dirt and chips removed, so as not to cause abrasion to the insulation of the conductors. When installing inserts, the tools used when cutting through the raceway shall be such as not to cause damage to the conductors that have been installed.

356-11. Connections to Cabinets and Extensions from Cells—Only approved fittings shall be used for connections going to cabinets or extensions from the cells, and the connections to these approved fittings shall be made by means of rigid or flexible conduit only.

B. Construction Specifications

356-12. General—See NEC.

ARTICLE 357—STRUCTURAL RACEWAYS

This is a new Article added to the 1965 Code. The reason for its addition is that a unique structural system was developed in which raceways were formed for the installation of electrical conductors, with openings provided for the installation of electrical devices.

The vertical members of this system that are used for studs or columns shall be tubes or channels, and the horizontal headers that are used as beams or top plates are to be provided with suitable covers, end closers, and fittings for the installation of conductors. The only place that this system has been approved for use is for single-family dwellings.

Each raceway shall carry no more than 20 conductors in any cross-sectional area nor have more than a 20% fill, with the largest conductor being no larger than No. 6.

In reading this Article, notice that all horizontal members shall be accessible after installation and shall not be obstructed by the wall finish.

232

This system is a new development and could have great possibilities in the construction and wiring of residences. It is recommended that if this type of installation is encountered, that the inspection authority be consulted before any wiring is attempted in order that the proper procedure and Code ruling can be complied with.

ARTICLE 358—CELLULAR CONCRETE FLOOR RACEWAYS

This Article is very similar to **Article 356** (Cellular Metal Floor Raceways). Because of this similarity, only those points that are treated differently will be covered in order to prevent repetition.

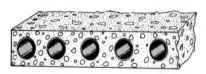

Fig. 358-1. Cross-sectional view of a cellular concrete floor raceway.

Fig. 358-1 shows the construction of cellular concrete floor raceways. They are constructed of precast concrete with cells or openings provided for the wiring conductors. Since this type of raceway is made of concrete, it cannot be made electrically continuous. Therefore, an equipment ground of the proper size must be used in the installation, and all header ducts, junction boxes, and inserts shall be electrically secured to this grounding conductor.

ARTICLE 362—WIREWAYS

362-1. Definition—*Wireways are sheet-metal troughs with hinged or removable covers for housing and protecting electrical wires and cable and in which conductors are laid in place after the wireway has been installed as a complete system.* See Fig. 362-1.

Fig. 362-1. Illustration of a wireway.

COVER MAY BE HINGED
OR ATTACHED WITH SCREWS

362-2. Use—Wireways shall be used only for exposed work, and may be used out-of-doors if of an approved raintight construction. Notice that the cover is hinged or removable to provide for laying conductors.

Wireways shall not be used:

(1) Where subjected to severe physical damage.
(2) Where subjected to corrosive vapors.

(3) In any hazardous location except Class II, Division 2. See **Section 502-4(b).**

362-3. Other Articles—Wireways and the installation therof shall conform to the provisions of **Article 300.**

362-4. Size of Conductors—The design of the wireway shall govern the maximum size conductor that will be permitted.

362-5. Number of Conductors—No more than 20% of the cross-sectional area of a wireway may be used for conductors—this is based on the total cross-sectional area of the conductors. In addition, the total number of current-carrying conductors allowed in a wireway shall not exceed thirty. Exception No. 2 states: *Conductors for signal circuits or controller conductors between a motor and its starter and used only for starting duty shall not be considered as current carrying conductors.*

Exception No. 1 pertains to elevators and dumbwaiters with which it is allowable to use up to 50% of the cross-sectional area of the wireway.

Exception No. 2. See NEC.

Exception No. 3. When the correction factors specified in Note 8 of **Tables 310-12** *through* **310-15** *are applied, no limit on the number of current-carrying conductors is needed, but the sum of the cross sectional areas of all contained conductors at any section of the wireway shall not exceed 20 per cent of the interior cross-sectional area of the wireway.*

Exception No. 4. See **Section 520-5.**

362-6. Splices and Taps—This is one wiring method in which splices and taps are allowed, but with the following restrictions:

(1) They shall be accessible.
(2) They shall be insulated by approved means.
(3) They shall not fill the wireway to more than 75% of its area at that point. If the splices or taps are staggered slightly, more room can be obtained.

362-7. Supports—Wireways may be screwed or bolted to a wall or supported by hangers or any other suitable and acceptable means, but in any case they shall be supported at intervals not to exceed 5 feet. In **Section 620-32** (Elevators and Dumbwaiters), this interval is extended to 15 feet, providing there are no joints between the supports.

Exception: Vertical runs of wireways shall be securely supported at intervals not exceeding 15 feet and shall have not more than one joint between supports. Adjoining wireway sections shall be securely fastened together to provide a rigid joint.

362-8. Extensions Through Walls—*Wireways may extend transversely through walls if in unbroken lengths where passing through.* See Fig. 362-2.

362-9. Dead Ends—Dead ends shall have caps to close the ends of the wireways.

362-10. Extensions From Wireways—Any extensions from wireways shall be made with rigid or flexible metal conduit, EMT, surface metal

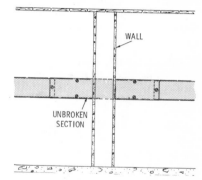

Fig. 362-2. Wireways may extend transversely through a wall in unbroken lengths.

raceways, or metal clad cable. Notice that nonmetallic rigid conduit nonmetallic cable, etc., are not permitted.

In using wireways, they shall be mechanically and electrically secure. This is not mentioned in this part of the Code, but is covered elsewhere.

362-11. Marking—*Wireways shall be marked so that their manufacturer's name or trademark will be visible after installation.*

ARTICLE 363—FLAT CABLE ASSEMBLIES

Type FC

This product is new with the 1971 NEC. As an introduction, it might be well to give some of the submitter's supporting comment as it appears in the 1971 preprint.

This new Article is basically a busway system. In an approved busway system, all of the basic components are factory-assembled. In this proposed wiring system, the basic components are intended to be field assembled.

The conductors are formed into a flat cable assembly of 3 or 4 conductors and are completely encased in an insulating material, properly spaced. Special spacing insulation is extruded integrally with the cable assembly to facilitate the location of the cable within the metal raceway.

Article 362—Wireways, *Chapter 3, more or less completes the requirements for a class of wiring systems intended for use and field assembly of standard components.* **Article 364-1 Busways,** *more or less begins the requirements for wiring systems consisting of completely factory-wired assemblies.*

This proposed **Article 363** *is a transition from the field assembly of standard components to the field of completely wired factory installations.*

363-1. Scope—*This Article covers a field-installed wiring method using Type FC, flat cable assembly, in an approved surface metal raceway.*

363-2. Definition—*Type FC, a flat cable assembly, is an assembly of parallel conductors formed integrally with an insulating material web specifically designed for field installation in surface metal raceway approved for the purpose.*

363-3. Other Articles—*In addition to the provisions of this Article, installation of the Type FC cable shall conform with the applicable provisions of* **Articles 210, 220, 250, 300, 310** *and* **352.**

363-4. Uses Permitted—*Flat cable assemblies may be used only as branch circuits to supply suitable tap devices for lighting, small appliances or small power loads. Flat cable assemblies shall be installed in locations where they will not be subjected to severe physical damage.*

363-5. Uses Not Permitted—FC cable shall not be installed:

(1) Where subjected to corrosive vapors unless specifically approved for the purpose.
(2) In hoistways.
(3) In hazardous locations.
(4) Outdoors unless approved for the purpose.
(5) In damp or wet locations, unless approved for the purpose.

363-6. Installation—*Flat cable assemblies shall be installed in the field only in surface metal raceways approved for the purpose. The surface metal raceway systems shall be installed as complete systems before the flat cable assemblies are pulled into the raceways.*

363-7. Number of Conductors—*The flat cable assemblies may consist of either 3 or 4 conductors.*

236

363-8. Size of Conductors—This comes in only one size, namely No. 10 AWG special stranded copper wires.

363-9. Conductor Insulation—*The entire flat cable assembly shall be formed to provide a suitable insulation covering all of the conductors and using one of the materials recognized in* **Table 310-2(a)** *for general branch-circuit wiring.*

363-10. Splices—*Splices shall be made in approved junction boxes using approved terminal blocks.*

363-11. Taps—*Taps shall be made only between any phase conductor and the neutral by means of devices and fittings approved for the purpose. Tap devices shall be rated at not less than 15 amperes or more than 300 volts, and they shall be color-coded in accordance with the requirements of* **Section 363-21.**

363-12. Dead-Ends—*Each flat cable assembly dead-end shall be terminated in an end-cap device approved for the purpose.*

The dead-end fitting for the enclosing surface metal raceway shall be approved for the purpose.

363-13. Fixture Hangers—*Fixture hangers installed with the flat cable assemblies shall be approved for the purpose.*

363-14. Fittings—*Fittings to be installed with flat cable assemblies shall be designed and installed to prevent physical damage to the cable assemblies.*

363-15. Extensions—*All extensions from flat cable assemblies shall be made from the terminal blocks enclosed within the junction boxes, installed at either end of the flat cable assembly runs.*

363-16. Supports—*The flat cable assemblies shall be supported by means of their special design features, within the metal surface raceways with which they are specifically approved to be used.*

363-17. Rating—*The rating of the branch circuit shall not exceed 30 amperes.*

363-18. Marking—See the NEC.

363-19. Protective Covers—See the NEC.

363-20. Identification—See the NEC.

363-21. Terminal Block Identification—*Terminal blocks approved for the purpose shall have distinctive and durable markings for color or word coding. The neutral section shall have a white marking or other suitable designation. The next adjacent section of the terminal block* *shall have a black marking or other suitable designation. The next section shall have a red marking or other suitable designation. The final or outer section, opposite the neutral section of the terminal block shall have a blue marking or other suitable designation.*

ARTICLE 364—BUSWAYS

364-1. Other Articles—The installation of Busways shall comply with the provisions of **Article 300** as well as with the provisions of this Article.

364-2. Use—*Busways are to be installed only for exposed work.* They shall not be installed in the following locations:

(1) Where they may be subject to severe physical damage.
(2) In hoistways.
(3) In any hazardous location.
(4) Out-of-doors or in any damp or wet locations unless specifically approved for such application (see the following).

According to **Section 230-44**, they may be used for service-entrance conductors. However, they still shall be approved for the location, if out-of-doors, in a damp location, etc.

Whenever there are two or more adjacent conductors with a difference of potential between them, a capacitor effect is created. This section takes this into consideration, as well as other conditions, as follows: *It is recommended that where secondary systems are operated ungrounded, a combination ground detector and potentializer plug be used as an auxiliary fitting for busway systems to establish a definite potential difference between the bus-bars and the grounded casing of the busways. This will serve to drain off any static or other charge from the entire busway system including its connected apparatus, supply and branch circuit conductors.* In designing electrical systems, or in their installation, it is always well to observe recommendations that are made in the NEC. There is always a good reason for these recommendations.

The combination ground detector and potentializer plug mentioned will probably consist of lamps which will indicate a ground, should it occur, and resistors to supply these lamps and to bleed off any charge that accumulates between bus-bars or between the case and the bus-bars.

364-3. Supports—Busways are to be supported at intervals not exceeding 5 feet unless specifically approved for support at greater distances. In no case are they to be supported at intervals greater than 10 feet. Where busways are run vertically, the supports are to be designed for such an installation.

364-4. Through Walls and Floors—Busways may be extended through walls transversely (horizontally), providing that they go through dry walls and are in unbroken lengths. See Fig. 364-1.

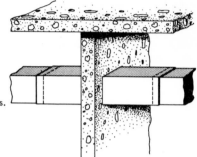

Fig. 364-1. Busways may extend transversely through walls in unbroken lengths.

Busways may be extended vertically through dry floors when totally enclosed, provided this total enclosure extends for a minimum distance of 6 feet above the floor through which they pass and are adequately protected from physical damage. See Fig. 364-2.

364-5.   Dead Ends—Any dead ends of busways shall be closed.

364-7.   Branches from Busways—Branches from busways shall be made with busways, rigid or flexible conduit (metal), electric metallic tubing, surface metal raceways, metal-clad cable, or with suitable cord assemblies approved for hard usage with portable equipment or to facilitate the connection of stationary equipment to aid in interchanging said equipment.

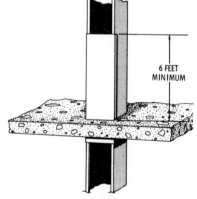

Fig. 364-2. Busways may extend vertically through floors (dry), if not ventilated, for a minimum height of 6 feet.

6 FEET
MINIMUM

364-8.   Overcurrent Protection—It is necessary to provide overcurrent protection with busways in accordance with **Section 364-9** through **364-13.**

364-9.   Rating of Overcurrent Protection–Feeders and Subfeeders—

If the overcurrent protection device does not correspond to the rating of the busway, the next larger size of overcurrent protection may be used.

364-10. Reduction in Size of Busway —Busways may be reduced in size without the use of overcurrent protection at the point of reduction providing that the following condition or conditions are met:

(1) The smaller busway does not extend over 50 feet.

(2) The smaller busway has a current rating of at least one-third that of the larger busway.

(3) The smaller busway is protected by overcurrent capacity of not over three times the rating of the smaller busway.

(4) The smaller busway shall not come in contact with combustible material.

364-11. Branch Circuits—Busways may be used as feeders if the device or plug-in connections for the tapping off of branch circuits contain overcurrent devices for the protection of the branch circuits. There are three exceptions:

Exception No. 1. For the overcurrent protection of taps, refer to **Section 240-15,** which allows placing the overcurrent protection at various distances from the busway, depending upon conditions.

Exception No. 2. On cord-connected fixtures of the fixed or semi-fixed type, the overcurrent device may be a part of the fixture cord plug.

Exception No. 3. The overcurrent protection may be mounted on cordless fixtures that are plugged directly into the busway.

364-12. Rating of Overcurrent Protection–Branch Circuits—There is nothing prohibiting the use of busways as branch circuits. The overcurrent protection shall determine the ampere rating of the busway branch circuit and the installation shall meet the requirements of **Article 210** that apply to branch circuits of that particular rating.

364-13. Length of Busways Used as Branch Circuits—A general rule for the length of busway branch circuits is that they shall not exceed three times the ampere rating of the branch circuit—for example, a 30-ampere branch circuit shall not exceed 90 feet in length.

364-14. Marking—See NEC.

ARTICLE 365—CABLEBUS

See NEC.

ARTICLE 370—OUTLET, SWITCH AND JUNCTION BOXES, AND FITTINGS

This is one of the most important Articles in Chapter 3, so should be carefully examined.

A. Scope and General

370-1. Scope—The intent of this Article is to cover the specific installation of outlets, switch and junction boxes, and fittings. Requirements of **Section 300-15** also apply. Installations in hazardous locations shall comply with requirements of **Articles 500** to **517** inclusive.

The provisions contained in this Section for boxes shall also apply to those conduit fittings with covers which serve to enclose the conductors in that conduit system. This may be interpreted to mean conduits, or any other conduit fitting with covers. The fill of these devices will come under this Article.

370-2. Round Boxes—Round boxes create a problem with the use of locknuts, bushings, and connectors. There are usually knockouts in the bottom of the boxes, so where these types of connections are used, they shall not be connected to the sides of the box. Round boxes are usually found on existing jobs. Boxes that are now manufactured are in accordance with the NEC or else they are not approved.

370-3. Nonmetallic Boxes — Nonmetallic boxes are approved for specific purposes—they may be used only with open wiring on insulators, concealed knob-and-tube work, nonmetallic sheathed cable (NM cable), and with approved nonmetallic conduit. Nonmetallic boxes have advantages and disadvantages which the wireman must consider and make the decision as to when to use them.

370-4. Metallic Boxes—The use of metallic boxes with knob-and-tube work or metallic sheathed cable (NM cable), and where mounted on metal or metal lath ceilings or walls, or where they contact insulation with metallic covering, requires that they shall be insulated from their supports or from any metal with which they come into contact, or else they shall be grounded. This is not a problem when NM cable with a grounding conductor is used. Boxes are now being manufactured with tapped screw holes for grounding purposes.

B. Installation

370-5. Damp or Wet Locations—When used in damp or wet locations, boxes and fittings shall be so installed as to prevent the accumulation of moisture or to prevent water from entering the boxes or fittings. All boxes and fittings that are installed in wet locations shall be weatherproof.

Where boxes are mounted in floors, they shall be approved for this purpose. The reason for this is that, in scrubbing floors, for example, water may enter these boxes and be a source of trouble. **Section 370-17** covers boxes in floors.

370-6. Number of Conductors in a Box—*Boxes shall be of sufficient size to provide free space for all conductors enclosed in the box.* This is a basic and broad statement which, in itself, is quite sufficient; however, a complete analysis of this will be made as it is in the Code. The main point is that in the installation of conductors in boxes, it should be unnecessary to force the conductors into the box as this is a potential source of trouble. The Code spells out what is good practice as well as the minimum requirements. The installer should, however, always bear in mind the intent and, if necessary to do a good job, go even further than the minimum requirements.

The limitations imposed by **Sections 370-6 (a** and **b)** are not intended to apply to terminal housings supplied with motors, nor to those types of boxes or fittings without knockouts that have hubs or recessed parts for terminal bushings and locknuts.

Section 370-6 (a and **b)** *does not apply to conductors used for rewiring existing raceways as referred to in* **Table 1,** *Chapter 9.* The intent here is that, when rewiring takes place, there may be more conductors than before. The exemption is intended not to make rewiring prohibitive, although the wireman and inspector are still responsible for a safe rewiring job.

(a) **Tables 370-6 (a-1** and **a-2)** cover the maximum number of conductors that will be permitted in outlet and junction boxes. There has been no allowance in these Tables for fittings or devices, such as studs, cable clamps, hickeys, switches, or receptacles that are contained in the box. These must be taken into consideration and deductions made for them. A deduction of one conductor shall be made for each of the following:

(1) One or more fixture studs.

(2) Cable clamps.

(3) Hickeys.

There shall be a further deduction of one conductor for one or several flush devices mounted on the same strap. A conductor that runs through a box is counted as only one conductor. A conductor originating out of the box and terminating in the box is counted as one conductor. Conductors of which no part leaves the box will not be counted, such as wires to fixtures that are spliced onto the other wires in the box.

Boxes are often ganged together with more than one device per strap mounted in these ganged boxes. In these cases, the same limitations will apply as if they were individual boxes.

Please refer to Figs. 370-1 through 370-4 for illustrations concerning this Section. This was clarified in the 1968 Code. Caution shall be taken to use boxes large enough to accommodate the counting of these grounding conductors. This was interpreted in various ways in the past, but it is now very clear. **Table 370-6(a-1)** now has the cubic content listed for the popular sizes of boxes, and has also been expanded.

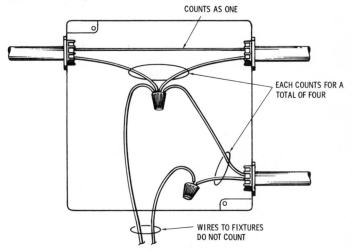

COUNTS AS ONE

EACH COUNTS FOR A
TOTAL OF FOUR

WIRES TO FIXTURES
DO NOT COUNT

Fig. 370-1. Which conductors to count in junction box.

(b) There will be numerous occasions where **Tables 370-6 (a-1 and a-2)** will not be applicable. In such cases, refer to **Table 360-6 (b)** from which the number of conductors that will be permitted in the box can be calculated. The various wire sizes and the space that will be allowed per conductor are given. It is only necessary to calculate the cubic space in the box, and multiply by the free space within the box for each conductor. If the calculation exceeds the cubic size of the box, the next larger box will have to be used or an extension added.

The question concerning plaster rings and the effect that they have on the conductors permitted in the box is always arising. This does not seem to be specifically covered in the Code. Although the plaster ring is meant for another purpose, most any inspector will agree that extra space is provided by the plaster ring and, based on the cubic inches that it adds, he makes allowances for this by using a larger box should more room be needed. The entire intent is not to crowd the conductors and cause failure of the insulation in so doing.

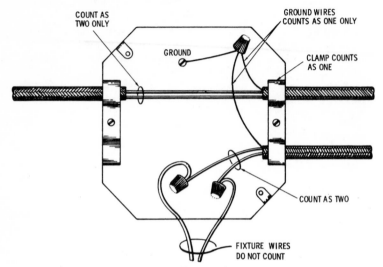

Fig. 370-2. Grounding wire does not count.

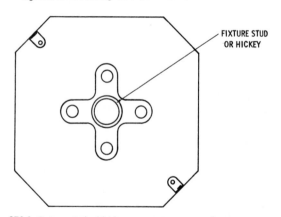

Fig. 370-3. Fixture stud or hickey counts as one conductor.

(c) *Boxes, other than those described in* **Tables 370-6(a) (1)** *and* **370-6(a) (2),** *shall be durably and legibly marked by the manufacturer with their cubic inch content. All boxes shall be durably and legibly marked with the manufacturer's name or trademark.* This will be quite advantageous to the trade, in that they will not have to calculate the cubic inch space of boxes which do not appear in the Tables.

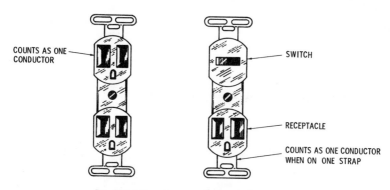

Fig. 370-4. How to count devices in figuring fill.

370-7.   Conductors Entering Boxes or Fittings—Care shall be exercised in protection of the conductors from abrasion where they enter the boxes or fittings. With conduit, this is accomplished by bushings or other approved devices. With NM Cable, as may be seen in Fig. 370-5, the outer covering of the cable should protrude from the clamp to provide this protection. With armored cable, fiber bushings are to be inserted between the conductors and the armor to prevent any abrasion. The following shall be complied with:

(a) Openings to Be Closed. *Openings through which conductors enter shall be adequately closed.* Where single conductors enter the boxes, loom covering is to be provided; with cable, cable clamps shall be used or the boxes provided with built-in cable clamps; with conduit, the locknuts and bushings will adequately close the openings.

(b) Metal Boxes and Fittings. When metal boxes or fittings are used with open wiring, proper bushings shall be used. In dry places, a flexible tubing may be used and extended from the last conductor support into the box and secured. See Fig. 370-6.

Where a raceway or cable enters the box or fitting, the raceway or cable is to be properly secured to the box or fitting. With conduit, two locknuts and a bushing should be used. With armored cable, approved connectors shall be used. With NM cable, a connector or built-in clamps shall be used.

(c) Nonmetallic Boxes. Where nonmetallic boxes are used with either concealed knob-and-tube work or open wiring, the conductors shall pass through individual holes in the box. If flexible

245

tubing is used over the conductor, it shall extend from the last conductor support into the hole in the box.

Where nonmetallic cable is used, it shall extend through the opening in the box. It is not required that individual conductors or cables be clamped if the individual conductors or cables are supported within 8 inches of the box. When nonmetallic

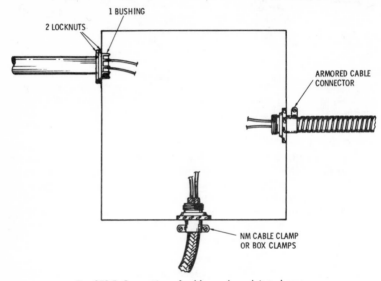

Fig. 370-5. Connection of cables and conduit to boxes.

conduit is used with nonmetallic boxes, the conduit shall be connected to the box by approved means.

370-8. Unused Openings—Any unused openings of boxes or fittings, where the knockout has been removed, shall be effectively closed by an approved means which will afford equal protection to that of the original. Metal plugs or plates used to close the holes in nonmetallic boxes shall be recessed at least 1/4 inch from the outer surface of the box.

370-9. Boxes Enclosing Flush Devices—See NEC.

370-10. In Wall or Ceiling—This Section is much abused in the field. It is recommended that close attention be paid to this part to prevent fires from starting in walls and ceilings.

In walls and ceiling of concrete, tile, or other noncombustible materials, boxes and fittings are to be so installed that the front or outer edge of the box or fitting is not set back more than 1/4 inch from the finished surface.

In walls or ceilings constructed of wood or other combustible materials, the outer or front edge of the box or fitting shall be flush with the finished surface or project therefrom. In the event of a short circuit or any arcing, the box or fitting will afford protection to the combustible materials. See Fig. 370-7.

370-11. Repairing Plaster—See NEC.

370-12. Exposed Extensions—Exposed extensions from boxes or fit-

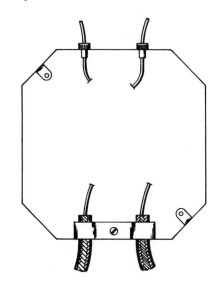

Fig. 370-6. Open wiring into boxes.

tings are very often desirable or necessary. In making these extensions, there are a number of approved wiring methods which may be used, but a box extension ring or blank cover shall be used for attaching to the concealed wiring and shall be electrically and mechanically secured to the original box and extensions therefrom and shall be in accordance with the regulations as provided in other Articles of Chapter 3.

370-13. Supports—*Boxes shall be securely and rigidly fastened to the surface upon which they are mounted, or securely and rigidly embedded in concrete or masonry. Except as otherwise provided in this Section, boxes shall be supported from a structural member of the building either directly or by using a substantial and approved metallic or wooden brace. If of wood the brace shall not be less than nominal 1 inch thickness. If of metal it shall be corrosion resistant and shall be not less than 0.0239 inch thick (No. 24 MSG).*

Where mounted in new walls in which no structural members are provided or in existing walls in previously occupied buildings, boxes less

247

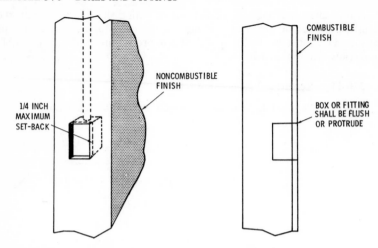

Fig. 370-7. Setback of boxes in walls and ceilings.

than 100 cubic inches in size, specifically approved for the purpose, shall be affixed with approved anchors or clamps so as to provide a rigid and secure installation.

Threaded boxes or fittings less than 100 cubic inches in size, which do not contain devices or support fixtures may be considered adequately supported if two or more conduits are threaded into the box wrench-tight and are supported within three feet of the box on two or more sides as is required by this Section.

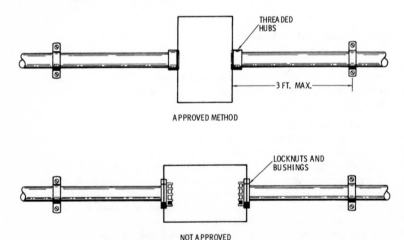

Fig. 370-8. Method of attaching conduit to junction or control boxes.

Many times we find boxes of less than 100 cubic inches that are used as pull boxes or junction boxes and which are held in place by the conduit, with the box itself not fastened to the wall. Please note the last paragraph which states that these boxes are to be without devices and are not to support fixtures. We also find that threaded boxes are to be used and the conduits supported within three feet of the box. Note that it *does not say locknuts and bushings,* but states the conduit is to be threaded into the box. See Fig. 370-8.

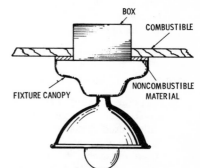

Fig. 370-9. Noncombustible material shall be installed between a canopy and a combustible ceiling.

370-14. Depth of Boxes for Concealed Work—Certain rules for a minimum depth of boxes are necessary for a safe installation. Therefore, outlet boxes for concealed work shall have a minimum internal depth of 1-1/2 inches, the exception to this being where is is impossible or impractical to use such a box, in which case a box of no less then 1/2 inch internal depth may be used.

370-15. Covers and Canopies—*In completed installations each outlet box shall be provided with a cover unless a fixture canopy is used.*

(a) Either nonmetallic or metallic plates and covers may be used with nonmetallic boxes, but when metallic plates or covers are used, the grounding provisions of **Section 250-42** will appply—it will be necessary to see that they are properly grounded.

A reference is made to **Section 410-95.** This Section states: *Ungrounded metal lighting fixtures, lampholders and face plates shall not be installed in contact with conducting surfaces nor within 8 feet vertically or 5 feet horizontally of laundry tubs, bath tubs, plumbing fixtures, steam pipes, or other grounded metal work or grounded surfaces.* As always, the Code is concerned with the practical side of things. Any metal part of a wiring system is subject to becoming energized, so should therefore be grounded whenever there is a possibility of anyone touching the device and a grounded surface at the same time. Concrete floors and walls are, as a rule, considered to be grounded surfaces, even if covered with block tile.

(b) This paragraph is one that is often overlooked. *Where a fixture canopy or pan is used, any combustible wall or ceiling finish exposed between the edge of the canopy or pan and the outlet box shall be covered with noncombustible material.* See Fig. 370-9.

(c) *Covers of outlet boxes having holes through which flexible cord pendants pass, shall be provided with bushings designed for the purpose or shall have smooth, well-rounded surfaces on which the cords may bear. So-called hard-rubber or composition bushings shall not be used.*

370-16. Fastening to Gas Pipe—See NEC.

370-17. Outlet Boxes—

(a) Boxes at Lighting Fixture Outlets. Any boxes used for lighting fixture outlets are to be designed for that purpose and all outlets used exclusively for lighting fixtures shall have the boxes designed or installed so that the lighting fixture may be attached. Attention should be given to the weight of the fixture. The provisions of **Article 410** pertaining to the hanging of fixtures shall be complied with.

(b) Floor Boxes. *Floor boxes especially approved for the purpose shall be used for receptacles located in the floor.*

Exception. The standard approved type of flush receptacle box may be used where receptacles are located in elevated floors of show windows or other locations when the authority enforcing this Code judges them to be free from physical damage, moisture and dirt.

This part **(b)** of **Section 370-17,** should be adhered to and the jurisdiction to rule as to the approval of standard receptacle boxes, etc.

370-18. Pull and Junction Boxes—Pull and junction boxes shall conform to the following:

(a) Minimum Size. For the purpose of this Section, the minimum size of raceway taken into consideration is 1 inch and the minimum size of conductor is No. 6. This also covers cables containing conductors of No. 6 or larger. For transposing the cable into conduit size, **Table 1** of Chapter 9 shall be used. For example, a cable with three No. 6 conductors is treated the same as three No. 6 single conductors—the minimum size of conduit for three No. 6 conductors is 1 inch. The following will give the minimum dimensions of pull or junction boxes to be used with conductors No. 6 or larger and raceways of 1 inch or larger:

(1) Straight Pulls. The width of a box for straight pulls is governed by the size of conduits used and the space required for the locknuts and bushings. The length, however, will not be less than 8 times the trade size of the largest race-

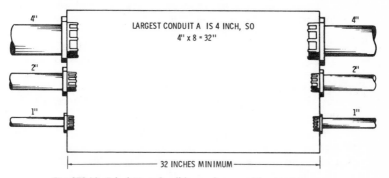

Fig. 370-10. Calculation of pull boxes for use without splices or taps.

way. In Fig. 370-10, for example, there is a 4-inch conduit, a 2-inch conduit, and a 1-inch conduit. Therefore, the length will be 4 × 8, or a minimum of 32 inches in length, and the width will be approximately 12 inches to accommodate the locknuts and bushings without crowding.

(2) Angle or U Pulls. *Where angle or U pulls are made, the distance between each raceway entry inside the box and the opposite wall of the box shall not be less than 6 times the trade diameter of the largest raceway. This distance will be increased for additional entries by the amount of the sum of the diameters of all other raceway entries on the same wall of the box. The distance between raceway entries enclosing the same conductor shall not be less than 6 times the trade diameter of the larger raceway.* In Fig. 370-11, the dimensions shown are minimum. It is very possible that the 30-inch figure will not agree with the diagonal figures—this will depend upon the actual locations of the conduits. Nevertheless, the figures are minimum and, if necessary, a larger box will be required.

(3) *Boxes of lesser dimensions than those required in sub-sections* **(1)** *and* **(2)** *of this Section may be used for installations*

251

of combinations of conductors which are less than the maximum conduit fill (of conduits being used) permitted in **Table 1,** *Chapter 9, provided the box has been approved for and is permanently marked with the maximum number of conductors and the maximum AWG size permitted.*

Exception: Terminal housings supplied with motors which shall comply with the provisions of **Section 430-12.**

(b) Conductors in Pull or Junction Boxes—In pull or junction boxes having any dimension over 6 feet, it is necessary to either rack or cable the conductors. This is required not only to maintain some sort of support for the conductors, but it will also tend to keep the conductors of the same circuit together and, in this way, to keep magnetic induction to a minimum. This is especially important in circuits that carry heavy currents where magnetic induction may affect the voltage balance between phase. See Fig. 370-12.

Reference is made to **Section 370-6(b)** that requires insulated bushings or an equivalent insulation at terminations where No. 4 or larger conductors are used. See Fig. 370-13. These bush-

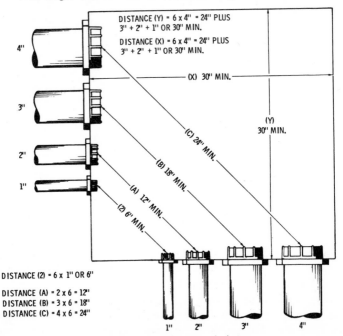

DISTANCE (Y) = 6 x 4" = 24" PLUS 3" + 2" + 1" OR 30" MIN.
DISTANCE (X) = 6 x 4" = 24" PLUS 3" + 2" + 1" OR 30" MIN.

(X) 30" MIN.

(Y) 30" MIN.

(C) 24" MIN.
(B) 18" MIN.
(A) 12" MIN.
(Z) 6" MIN.

DISTANCE (Z) = 6 x 1" OR 6"
DISTANCE (A) = 2 x 6 = 12"
DISTANCE (B) = 3 x 6 = 18"
DISTANCE (C) = 4 x 6 = 24"

Fig. 370-11. Junction box calculations.

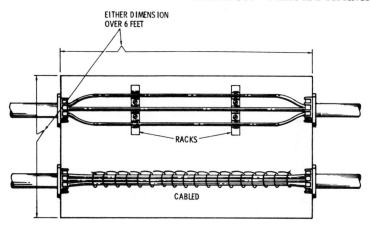

Fig. 370-12. Cabling or racking conductors in large boxes.

ings may be fiber or plastic, a combination metal and plastic (where a grounding-type bushing is required), or fiber inserts.

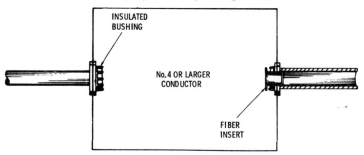

Fig. 370-13. Use of insulation at bushings.

(c) **Covers.** *All pull boxes, junction boxes and fittings shall be provided with covers approved for the purpose. Where metallic covers are used, they shall comply with the grounding requirements of* **Section 250-42.** In other words, where metal covers are used, the covers shall be effectively grounded. Covering is essential, in case a short or ground should occur, to contain the sparks in the box or fitting.

370-19.   Junction, Pull and Outlet Boxes Be Accessible—All junction, pull, or outlet boxes shall be accessible without the necessity of removing any part of the building structure, paving, or sidewalk. It can be certain that an inspector will not consider a box buried in the ground and cov-

253

ered over as accessible. Junction, pull, and outlet boxes are there for a specific purpose—either for pulling in of conductors, for junctioning conductors, or for the connection of a device. Should it ever be necessary to rework the system, these boxes must be accessible. Boxes in accessible attics or crawl spaces are considered as accessible, as are boxes in drop ceilings with removable panels.

C. Construction Specifications

The wireman is not too concerned in most cases with the construction specifications of boxes. He purchases approved boxes which will, of course, meet specifications. However, it sometimes becomes necessary to build or assemble a box to meet a certain purpose. Therefore, it is well to be aware of what these specifications are.

370-20. Metallic Outlet, Switch and Junction Boxes and Fittings— *Outlet, switch and junction boxes and fittings, when of metal, shall conform to the following:*

(a) **Corrosion-Resistant.** The covering of metallic boxes, of course, shall be suitable for the conditions that prevail in the area in which they are used. They shall be protected by one of the following means (the one to be chosen shall be applicable for the conditions):

   (1) Corrosion-resistant metal.
   (2) Well-galvanized.
   (3) Enameled.
   (4) Otherwise properly coated.

Reference is made to **Section 300-5** which prohibits the use of enamel in certain places. Also, coating with a conductive material is recommended, such as cadmium, tin, or zinc, since these will secure a better electrical connection.

(b) **Thickness of Metal.** See NEC.

(c) **Boxes over 100 Cubic Inches.** See NEC.

370-21. Covers—See NEC.

370-22. Bushings—See NEC.

370-23. Nonmetallic Boxes—See NEC.

ARTICLE 373—CABINETS AND CUTOUT BOXES

373-1. Scope—This Article covers the installation of cabinets and cutout boxes with the exception of those used in hazardous areas which are covered in **Articles 500** through **517.**

A. Installation

373-2.   Damp or Wet Locations—Cabinets and cutout boxes used in wet or damp locations shall be suitable for the location and installed in such a manner that moisture is not likely to enter or accumulate in the enclosure. They shall be mounted with a minimum air space of 1/4 inch between the enclosure and the wall or other supporting members. Cabinets and cutout boxes used in wet places shall be weatherproof.

A recommendation that would be well to follow is: *It is recommended that boxes of nonconductive material be used with nonmetallic sheathed cable when such cable is used in locations where moisture is likely to be present.*

An interesting case involving this sort of installation concerned a 2-inch service mast which ran straight down to a service-entrance cabinet with branch circuit breakers included. The location was a turkey brooder house which had high humidity, was warm, and the outside temperature was below zero. The mast acted as a chimney drawing the warm moist air up and out of the interior. The moisture in the air condensed on the interior of the cold mast and continually dripped into the service-entrance equipment, causing a short which could have possibly developed into a fire. An inspector found the condition and required a seal-off next to the service-entrance equipment. This is mentioned because such an area might be overlooked as a damp location.

373-3.   Position in Wall—The requirements here are the same as for outlet boxes, namely that, in concrete, tile, or other noncombustible walls, the boxes or cabinets may be set back not to exceed 1/4 inch from the finished surface, and on walls of combustible materials, they shall be flush with or project from the finished surface.

373-4.   Unused Openings—See NEC.

373-5.   Conductors Entering Cabinets or Cutout Boxes—All conductors entering cabinets or cutout boxes shall be protected from abrasion and shall meet the following requirements:

(a) Openings to Be Closed.   *Openings through which conductors enter shall be adequately closed.* In other words, where conduit is used, the hole in the cabinet or box shall be the proper size for the trade size of conduit used.

(b) Metal Cabinets and Cutout Boxes.   *Where metal cabinets or cutout boxes are installed with open wiring or concealed knob-and-*

255

tube work, conductors shall enter through insulated bushings or, in dry places, through flexible tubing extending from the last insulating support and firmly secured to the cabinet or cutout box.

373-6. Deflection of Conductors—This covers the deflection of conductors in cabinets and cutout boxes at terminals, or conductors entering or leaving cabinets and cutout boxes.

(a) Width of Wiring Gutters. *Conductors shall not be deflected within a cabinet or cutout box unless a gutter having the width in accordance with* **Table 373-6(a)** *is provided. Conductors in multiple in accordance with* **Section 310-10** *are judged on the basis of the number of conductors in multiple.*

Table 373-6(a), gives us the: **Minimum Wire Bending Space at Terminals and Minimum Width of Wiring Gutters in Inches.** Unless we have these minimums specified, the radius of bending is too short and the conductor strands will tend to pull out from the terminations.

(1) Wire Bending Space at Terminals. This covers the minimums specified in **Table 373-6(a),** See the NEC.

The fine print note after **Table 373-6,** tells us how the bends are measured. See NEC.

(b) Insulation at Bushings. *Where ungrounded conductors of No. 4 or larger enter a raceway in a cabinet, pullbox, junction box, or auxiliary gutter, the conductors shall be protected by a substantial bushing providing a smoothly rounded insulating surface, unless the conductors are separated from the raceway fitting by substantial insulating material securely fastened in place. Where conduit bushings are constructed wholly of insulating material, a locknut shall be installed both inside and outside the enclosure to which the conduit is attached.*

Insulating bushings and inserts are made in various forms. A metal bushing with a fiber insert which will lock into place may be used; an insulating bushing of insulating material in entirety may be used but a locknut installed ahead of it is a must; or bushings that are metal and have insulation incorporated as a part of the bushing may be used. See Fig. 373-1.

373-7. Space in Enclosures—See NEC.

373-8. Enclosures for Switches or Overcurrent Devices—

This Section has caused much discussion in the field and left much on the shoulders of the authority having jurisdiction, to make the judgment as to adequate spaces within enclosures. See NEC. The enclosures for overcurrent devices and switches, may not be used as junction boxes, auxiliary gutters or raceways, for conductors tapping off, or feeding through to other switches or overcurrent devices unless the space is:

(1) There is adequate wiring space so that conductors feeding through or tapping off do not fill the wiring space to more than 4 percent.

(2) Conductors, splices, and taps do not fill the cross-sectional area of the wiring space to more than 75 percent. See Figs. 373-2, -3 and 4.

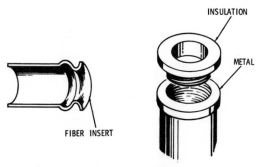

INSULATION

METAL

FIBER INSERT

Fig. 373-1. Bushing insulation for conductors No. 4 or larger.

373-9.   Side or Back Wiring Spaces or Gutters—Cabinets and cutout boxes are required to be furnished with adequate wiring space, auxiliary gutters, or special compartments for wiring as required by **Section 373-11 (c and d).**

B. Construction Specifications

373-10.   Material—*Cabinets and cutout boxes shall conform to the following:*

(a) Metal Cabinets and Boxes. Metal cabinets and cutout boxes shall be coated inside and outside by one of the following:

(1) Galvanized.
(2) Plated with cadmium.
(3) Tin plated.
(4) Other approved metallic finish.
(5) Enameled.
(6) Otherwise properly coated.

It is recommended that a conductive material such as cadmium, tin, or zinc be used to give better electrical contact.

(b) Strength. The design and construction of cabinets and cutout boxes shall be such as to secure ample strength and rigidity. If

257

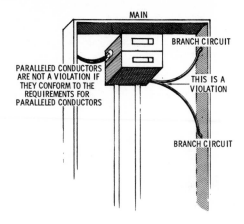

Fig. 373-2. Cabinets and cutout boxes shall not be used as junction boxes.

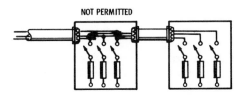

Fig. 373-3. Improper method of connecting more than one switch enclosure.

constructed of sheet metal, the metal shall be of not less than No. 16 USS gauge (0.0598 inch) in thickness.

(c) Composition Cabinets. Composition cabinets shall be submitted for approval prior to installation.

373-11. Spacing—Author's Note. The mere fact that a switch enclosure is rated at X number of amperes does not mean that the space inside is adequate for the job. For instance, the enclosure might be designed for single-conductor installation but would be overcrowded if conductors were paralleled. Thus, the engineer, installer, and inspector must analyze the use to which it is to be put and see that the bending space conforms to **Table 373-6(a).**

ARTICLE 374—AUXILIARY GUTTERS

374-1. Purpose—For all appearances, auxiliary gutters could, in a sense, be termed wireways (**Article 362**) or busways (**Article 364**). The

AUXILIARY GUTTER

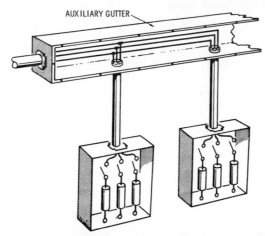

Fig. 373-4. Proper manner of connecting more than one switch enclosure.

main difference is the purpose for which they are to be used and some of the installation requirements. Auxiliary gutters are a supplemental wiring method to be used at meter centers, distribution centers, switchboards, and similar points of wiring systems. They may enclose conductors or bus-bars, but are never to be used for the following:

(1) To enclose switches.
(2) For overcurrent devices.
(3) For other appliances.
(4) For other apparatus.

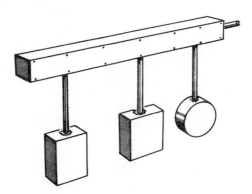

Fig. 374-1. Purpose of auxiliary gutters.

374-2.   Extension Beyond Equipment—The only place where auxiliary

259

gutters may be extended beyond a distance of 30 feet is for elevator work. Whenever they extend beyond this 30-foot distance, they fall in the

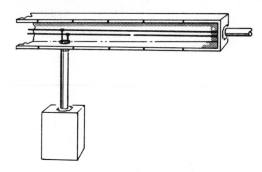

Fig. 374-2. Interior and construction of auxiliary gutters.

category of wireways or busways and come under the provisions of wireways (**Article 362**) and busways (**Article 364**). See Fig. 374-1.

Auxiliary gutters are troughs with a removable lid, and may be purchased in most any length. The lid is usually fastened to the trough with screws (Fig. 374-2).

374-3.   Supports—Auxiliary gutters shall be securely fastened at intervals not to exceed 5 feet.

374-4.   Covers—The covers shall be securely fastened to the gutter—this is usually done by means of screws.

374-5. Number of Conductors—The ruling is that auxiliary gutters shall contain no more than 30 current-carrying conductors at any cross-section. However, there is no limit on the number of conductors used only for signal circuits or the number of controller conductors between a motor and its starter if these control wires are used only for starting duty. In addition, the number of conductors that may be installed in a gutter shall not exceed 20% fill, regardless of the use of the conductors.

374-6.   Ampacity of Conductors—The ampacity of insulated aluminum and copper conductors is listed in **Tables 310-12** and **310-14,** respectively. Conductors in auxiliary gutters are not subject to Note 8 that accompanies these tables for derating.

When copper bars are used in gutters, their ampacity is limited to 1000 amperes per square inch of the cross-section of the bar. Aluminum is limited to 700 amperes per square inch cross-section.

374-7.   Clearance of Bare Live Parts—Bare conductors shall be securely and rigidly fastened, with adequate allowance made for contraction and expansion. This expansion and contraction may be provided for by various means, as long as the bars or bare conductors are mechanically secured.

The minimum clearance between bare current-carrying parts that are mounted on the same surface, but of opposite polarity, shall be 2 inches. There shall also be a minimum of 1 inch clearance between bare metal conductors (current-carrying) and the metal surfaces of the gutters.

374-8. Splices and Taps—

(a) Splices and taps are permitted in gutters, but shall be made and insulated by approved methods only. They must be accessible by means of removable covers or doors. Not more than 75% of the area of the gutter shall be taken up by the conductors plus the taps and splices.

(b) Taps that are made from bare conductors (such as buses) shall leave the gutter opposite their point of terminal connection to the bus and the taps shall not come into contact with any bare current-carrying parts of opposite polarity.

(c) *All taps from gutters shall be suitably identified as to the circuit or the equipment which they supply.* The Code does not spell out exactly how to do this, but the means of identifying the circuits or equipment supplied must meet the approval of the inspection authority. This could be done by tagging the leads in the gutter, but a very practical method is to mark the circuits served on the gutter lid. See Fig. 374-3.

(d) Taps from conductors in a gutter are all subject to the provisions outlined in **Section 240-15.** In brief, **Section 240-15** states that tap conductors not over ten feet in length shall have an ampacity of not less than the ampacity of the one or more circuits or loads that they supply. Taps not over 25 feet in length shall have an ampacity of at least 1/3 of the ampacity of the conductors to which they are tapped, and they shall terminate in a single set of fuses or circuit breakers which will limit the current to that of the tap conductors or less. There is considerably more to this "tap rule" in **Article 240,** but it will not be repeated here.

374-9. Construction and Installation—*Auxiliary gutters shall be constructed in accordance with the following:*

(a) *Gutters shall be so constructed and installed that adequate electrical and mechanical continuity of the complete system will be secured.* Mechanical and electrical security are two important

261

points that are ever present in electrical wiring and must never be overlooked.

(b) *Gutters shall be of substantial construction and shall provide a complete enclosure for the contained conductors. All surfaces, both interior and exterior, shall be suitably protected from corrosion. Corner joints shall be made tight and where the assembly is held together by rivets or bolts, these shall be spaced not more than 12 inches apart.*

(c) Protective means shall be applied any place where conductors may be subject to abrasion. In other words, bushings, shields, or other fittings necessary to protect the conductors, shall be used

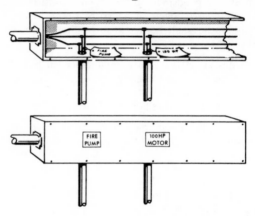

Fig. 374-3. Identifying circuits or loads from gutters.

at all joints, around bends, between gutters and cabinets or junction boxes, or at any other possible location where abrasion might occur. Insulation laying on the edge of metal may eventually cut through to the conductor because of weight, temperature, or vibration.

(d) Gutters shall be constructed of sheet metal the thickness of which is not less than that listed in **Table 374-9(d).**

(e) **Section 373-6** and **Table 373-6(a)** will apply wherever insulated conductors are deflected within the auxiliary gutter, at the ends, or where conduit, fittings, or other raceways enter or leave the gutter, or at any point where the gutter is deflected more than 30°.

(f) *Auxiliary gutters intended for use outdoors shall be approved for the purpose.*

ARTICLE 380—SWITCHES

A. Installation

380-1. Grounded Conductors—A grounding conductor should never be opened unless all other conductors associated with it are opened at the same time or before disconnecting the neutral or grounding conductor. In most instances, the grounded conductor is not disconnected, but with circuits going to or passing through gasoline dispensing islands, it is required that the neutral also be disconnected at the same time as the ungrounded conductor.

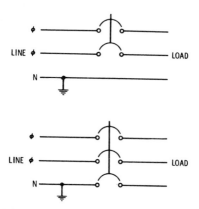

Fig. 380-1. A switch that opens the neutral shall simultaneously open the phase wires.

Fig. 380-1 illustrates two circuits; in one the grounded conductor is not disconnected and in the other the grounded conductor is disconnected simultaneously with the ungrounded conductors. Note that the ground is on the supply side in each case so that the system is still grounded.

380-2. Three-way and Four-way Switches—With three-way and four-way switches, the connections shall be so made that the neutral or grounded conductor is not switched. If a metallic raceway is used, the conductors shall be run so that both polarities are in the raceway in order to counteract inductance. See Fig. 380-2.

380-3. Enclosures—It is required that all switches and circuit breakers be enclosed in metal cabinets with externally operable handles, and the enclosure marked to indicate the position of the switch whether OFF or ON. Exceptions to this are:

(1) Pendant switches.
(2) Surface-type snap switches.
(3) Open knife switches mounted on an open-face switchboard or panelboard.

380-4. Wet Locations—Section 373-2 covered cabinets and cutout boxes in damp or wet locations, and required a 1/4-inch spacing between the cabinet and the mounting surface. The same applies to switches in wet

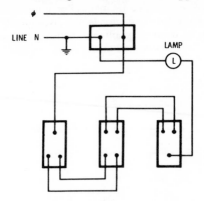

Fig. 380-2. The neutral on three- and four-way switching shall not be opened.

locations and, if mounted out-of-doors, they are required to be in a weatherproof enclosure. Raintight is commonly acceptable if prevailing weather conditions are not such that they are endangered by the elements.

380-5. **Time Switches, Flashers, and Similar Devices**—Time switches, flashers, and similar devices are not required to be externally operable, but they shall be mounted in metal boxes or cabinets, except as follows:

Exception No. 1. Where mounted on switchboards or control panels.

Exception No. 2. Where enclosed in approved individual housings.

Where mounted in the open (Exception No. 1), they must meet all requirements of safety.

380-6. **Position of Knife Switches**—Single-throw knife switches shall be mounted in a position so that gravity will not tend to close the switch, but preferably so that they will tend to open. This ruling does not apply to double-throw switches, which may be mounted either vertically or horizontally as required.

380-7. **Connection of Knife Switches**—Knife switches, except those of the double-throw type, shall be so connected that when open the blades are dead. See Fig. 380-3. (Author's Note: If this is a fusible switch, the fuses shall also be dead when the switch is open. This is not a problem with modern switches as they would not be approved unless containing this feature. However, some older switches are not arranged in this manner.)

380-8. **Accessibility and Grouping**—Switches and circuit breakers shall be mounted where accessible and shall be grouped. There may be some instances where this is not practical, in which case the inspection

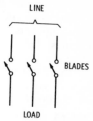

LINE

Fig. 380-3. Position of knife switches.

BLADES

LOAD

authorities ruling will apply. Snap switches in outlet boxes are permitted to be ganged only when the voltage between live metal parts of adjacent switches does not exceed 300 volts, or unless they are installed in boxes equipped with permanently installed barriers between adjacent switches.

380-9. Faceplates for Flush-Mounted Snap Switches—Whenever flush snap switches are mounted on ungrounded boxes, the plates shall be of a nonconducting material in any location where they may be touched at the same time that contact can be made with grounded surfaces or any other conductive surface. Ferrous faceplates shall be at least 0.030-inch thick while nonferrous faceplates shall be at least 0.040-inch thick. Insulated faceplates shall be noncombustible and shall be at least 0.10-inch thick. If they are less than 0.10-inch thick, they shall be reinforced or formed to provide additional strength. In other words, be certain that approved plates are used.

380-10. Mounting of Snap Switches—

(a) Surface Type. (Use present material in the Guide.)

(b) Box Mounted. Flush-type snap switches mounted in boxes which are set back of the wall surface as permitted in **Section 370-10** shall be installed so that the extension plaster ears are seated against the surface of the wall. Flush-type snap switches mounted in boxes which are flush with the wall surface or projection therefrom shall be so installed that the mounting yoke or strap of the switch is seated against the box.

This is quite plain, but it might be well to go back to **Section 370-10.** In walls of non-combustible materials, the boxes may be set back not to exceed ¼ inch, but on walls that are of combustible material, the boxes are to be set flush.

380-11. Circuit Breakers as Switches—A circuit breaker may be used as a switch provided that it has the same number of poles required by the switch to do the job. Thus, a single-pole breaker with a switched neutral may be used as a switch for simultaneously opening the hot and the neutral conductor feeding or passing through a gasoline dispensing island.

380-12. Grounding of Enclosures—It is mandatory that enclosures for switches or circuit breakers be grounded, except where accessible to qualified operators only. **Article 250** sets forth the manner of grounding enclosures. This does not imply that enclosures for switches or circuit breakers of less than 150 volts to ground are not grounded, as in most cases this has been taken care of elsewhere. But it does make it mandatory to ground the enclosures of switches or circuit breakers on circuits of more than 150 volts to ground.

380-13. Knife switches—The following sets forth the requirements of knife switches and the interrupting capacities as to sizes for amperages and voltages. Notice that nothing is stated about interrupting currents larger than the amperage of the switch. Unless marked, a knife switch is not intended to interrupt more than the rating of the switch. For example, a 200-ampere switch will interrupt 200 amperes, but a 200-ampere switch might be purchased that has an interrupting capacity of 8000 amperes. The intent is to show that there is a difference between the current-carrying ratings and the interrupting ratings of switches. Therefore, a switch that will interrupt more than the normal current-carrying rating of the switch will be so marked.

(a) *Knife switches rated for more than 1200 amperes at 250 volts or less, and for more than 600 amperes at 251 to 600 volts, shall be used only as isolating switches and shall not be opened under load.*

(b) *To interrupt currents greater than 1200 amperes at 250 volts or less, or 600 amperes at 251 to 600 volts, a circuit breaker or a switch of special design approved for such purpose shall be used.*

(c) Knife switches rated lower than 1200 amperes at 250 volts or less, and 600 amperes at 251 to 600 volts, may be used as general-purpose switches and may be opened under load. Nothing, however, is mentioned of opening under fault currents.

(d) Reference is made to Article 100 for the definition of motor-circuit switches in which percentages of load and horsepower ratings are mentioned. *Motor-circuit switches may be of the knife-switch type.*

380-14. Rating and Use of Snap Switches—*Snap switches shall be used within their ratings and as follows:*

(a) **AC General-Use Snap Switch.** *A form of general-use snap switch suitable only for use on alternating-current circuits for controlling the following:*

266

(1) Resistive and inductive loads, including electric-discharge lamps, not exceeding the ampere rating of the switch at the voltage applied.

(2) Tungsten-filament lamp loads not exceeding the ampere rating of the switch at 120 volts.

(3) Motor loads not exceeding 80 percent of the ampere rating of the switch at its rated voltage.

General-use snap switches means the switches such as are general purpose switches in wall boxes or handy boxes.

(b) AC-DC General-Use Snap Switch. *A form of general-use snap switch suitable for use on either AC or DC circuits for controlling the following:*

(1) Resistive loads not exceeding the ampere rating of the switch at the voltage applied. Resistive loads are similar to DC loads and do not have an inductive kick-back, which will cause the arcing which are common with inductive loads.

(2) Inductive loads not exceeding 50 percent of the ampere rating of the switch, at the applied voltage. Switches rated in horsepower are suitable for controlling motor loads within their rating at voltage applied. Note the percentage and the restrictions because of the inductive loads.

(3) Tungsten-filament lamp loads not exceeding the ampere rating of the switch at the applied voltage, when "T" rated.

For noninductive loads other than tungsten-filament lamps, switches shall have an ampere rating not less than the ampere rating of the load.

Noninductive loads are loads that have a 100% power factor. Induction is basically a load with a lagging power factor. However, the same effect would result when a capacitive load presented itself, but this would be a rather unusual case. Tungsten-filament lamps draw a heavy current on start.

Tungsten filaments draw a heavy initial current for energizing the tungsten filament. Inductive loads includes discharge lighting and all other inductive loads. Switches controlling signs and outline lighting should be selected according to the requirements of **Section 600-2,** and for controlling motors, **Sections 430-83, 430-109** and **430-110.**

Inductive loads, when opened, create a high-voltage kick caused by the collapsing flux with a resultant tendency to burn the contacts. High-amperage switches are the answer to this problem.

B. Construction Specifications.

380-15.   Marking—*Switches shall be marked with*:

(1) Current rating.

(2) Voltage rating.

(3) Maximum horsepower rating (if so rated).

380-16. 600-Volt Knife Switches—This is fundamentally a design factor, but is important. *Auxiliary contacts of a renewable or quick-break type or the equivalent, shall be provided on all 600-volt knife switches designed for use in breaking currents over 200 amperes.* It is recommended that such auxiliary contacts be provided on all direct-current switches rated at over 250 volts.

380-17. Fused Switches—*A fused switch shall not have fuses in parallel.*

ARTICLE 384—SWITCHBOARDS AND PANELBOARDS

384-1. Scope—This is one of the more important Articles in the NEC and one which gives the most trouble in the field. It applies to all switchboards, panelboards, and distribution boards installed for the control of light and power circuits. Remember that utilities are exempt from the NEC rulings in operation as distributors and manufacturers of electrical power. Therefore, any switchboard pertaining to utility company operated central stations or substations, which directly control energy derived from generating and transforming devices, are exempted from this Article. The ordinary wiring of the building is not exempted, however. Switchboards, or portions thereof, that are operated by batteries or for signal circuits only are also exempted. This does not imply that panelboards, switchboards, etc., that take power from lighting or power circuits for charging of batteries is exempt. Such devices do come under the rulings of this Article.

384-2. Application of Other Articles—There are many Articles in the NEC that also pertain to switches, circuit breakers, and overcurrent devices that are used on switchboards, panelboards, distribution boards, and their enclosures. These devices shall conform to these Articles as well as this one. This Article clarifies many general requirements and is therefore supplemental to **Articles 240, 250, 370, 380,** and any other Article which may apply. Also, switchboards and panelboards in hazardous locations shall comply with **Articles 500** to **517** inclusive.

It is impossible to include all of these rulings in one Article, but many facts have been incorporated here as a matter of clarification and intent. Therefore, it is highly recommended that this Article be thoroughly examined and understood.

384-3. Support and Arrangement of Bus-Bars and Conductors—

(a) See NEC.

(b) See NEC.

(c) *Each switchboard, switchboard section or panelboard, if used as* *service equipment, shall be provided with an equipment ground-ing means placed within the service disconnect section for con-necting the grounded circuit conductor on its supply side to the switchboard or panelboard frame. The equipment grounding means shall not be smaller than called for in* **Table 250-95** *nor smaller than No. 8 AWG copper conductor or approved equiva-lent.*

(d) *Load terminals in switchboards and panelboards shall be so located that it will be unnecessary to reach across or behind a line bus in order to make load connections.*

A. Switchboards

384-4. Location of Switchboards—Switchboards which have any ex-posed live parts shall be installed in dry locations and accessible only to qualified persons and under the supervision of competent persons.

384-5. Wet Locations—Wherever switchboards are in a wet location, in or outside a building, they are required to be in a weatherproof en-closure and, if necessary, shall conform to **Section 373-2** which requires a 1/4-inch spacing from the surface on which they are mounted.

384-6. Location Relative to Easily Ignitible Material—All switch and panelboards shall be mounted away from readily ignitible materials. This brings up the question that so often arises about mounting service-entrance panels in clothes closets. Most certainly, clothes are considered as readily ignitible, and most inspection authorities will rule out such locations. While this applies to switchboards in this instance, it might be practical to think of panelboards also.

384-7. Clearance from Ceiling—Unless there is an adequate fireproof ceiling, a switchboard shall not be installed closer than 3 feet from the ceiling.

384-8. Clearances Around Switchboards—A change in clearances was made in the 1965 NEC. Refer to **Section 110-16.**

384-9. Conductor Covering—The wiring of switchboards requires the close grouping of conductors. Therefore, conductors shall have a flame-retardant outer covering. Insulated conductors used for instrument or control wiring may be of the following types, or of other types that are specifically approved for this purpose—Types R, RH, RW, RHH, RHW, V, ALS, AVA, AVB, SIS, T, TA, TBS, TW, THW, and MI.

384-11. Grounding Switchboard Frames—The grounding of all switchboard frames is mandatory except on frames of direct-current, single-polarity switchboards that are effectively insulated.

384-12. Grounding of Instruments, Relays, Meters and Instrument

Transformers on Switchboards—This is covered in **Section 250-121** to **Section 250-125**. In addition to other facts concerning grounding, the grounding conductor shall be no smaller than No. 12 copper.

B. Panelboards

384-13. General—**Article 220** gives the facts necessary for computing the feeder loads to panelboards. After arriving at the feeder load, the panelboard shall have a rating not less than the minimum feeder size as calculated. All of the facts as to voltages, phase, capacity, etc., shall be plainly visible after installation. Most inspection authorities will also require the UL label. However, a UL label on an enclosure should not be construed to mean that it also applies to the devices installed therein. Each must have their own UL label.

384-14. Lighting and Appliance Branch Circuit Panelboard—It is necessary that a distinction be made between lighting and appliance panelboards and power panelboards. Therefore, in this Section, a lighting and appliance branch-circuit panelboard is defined as a panelboard which has more than 10% of its overcurrent devices rated at 30 amperes or less and for which neutral connections are provided.

384-15. Number of Overcurrent Devices on One Panelboard—The Code limits the number of overcurrent devices that are permitted in a lighting and appliance branch-circuit panelboard to 42. This number does not include the devices used as a main. In counting the devices, a double-pole overcurrent device is counted as two, and a three-pole overcurrent unit is counted as three. Each of these units is often counted as only one, which defeats the intent of this Section. Older equipment often were made up with wafer-thin and piggyback breakers which made it possible to increase or even double the number of overcurrent devices in a panelboard. Thus, it might have been possible to install 84 breakers in a 42-breaker panel. The 1965 NEC took care of this possibility—*A lighting and appliance branch circuit panelboard shall be provided with physical means to prevent the installation of more overcurrent devices than the number for which the panelboard was designed, rated and approved.* The newer panels have ratings, such as 12-24, which means it is designed for 12 full-size breakers or 24 piggyback breakers with provisions made for a bus ample to supply these. In this way, the number can be limited to the 42 requirement.

A case of interest was where someone wanted to weld two 42-circuit panels together and run buses between them. The decision made, and rightly so, was that the UL label on the panelboard was for the panelboard as originally built, and that welding them together and the addition of the buses was not approved.

384-16. Overcurrent Protection—

(a) *Each lighting and appliance branch circuit panelboard shall be individually protected on the supply side by not more than two main circuit breakers or two sets of fuses having a combined rating not greater than that of the panelboard.* This pertains to a feeder panel. As an example, a 100-ampere panel (one with 100-ampere buses) is fed by 200-ampere conductors and protected by 200-ampere overcurrent devices. In this case, the feeder panel is required to have a 100-ampere maximum main in it in order to give the proper protection.

A similar case involves a feeder panel with 100-ampere buses. The conductors feeding the panel are of 100-ampere capacity or larger, and are protected by a 100-ampere or smaller overcurrent protection at the source. In this case, it is not required to have a main in the feeder panel.

Exception No. 2. Please note that this exception applies to an individual residential occupancy only. *Individual protection for lighting and appliance branch circuit panelboards is not required where such panelboards are used as service equipment in supplying an individual residential occupancy and where any bus supplying 15 or 20 ampere circuits is protected on the supply by an overcurrent device.* Thus, a split-bus panel is permissible on service equipment in a single dwelling occupancy as long as it is limited to 6 operations and the 15- or 20-ampere branch circuit bus is protected by an overcurrent device that will adequately protect these buses.

There is controversy on split-bus panels as to the size of the service entrance conductors to be used. In a residence, and this is the only place split-bus panels are permitted, we might have a 2-pole, 50-ampere service for the range; a 2-pole, 40-ampere service for the dryer; a 2-pole, 30-ampere service for the water heater; and a 2-pole, 50-ampere service for the 15- and 20-ampere branch circuits. This would give us a total of 170 ampere as mains with the use of 100-ampere service-entrance conductors. Would the Code be met where there was a total of 170-ampere mains? It would be our interpretation that we have not met the Code requirements . Refer to **Section 230-90.**

Sometimes a conventional panelboard is installed which has lugs on the buses and a breaker is fed backwards as a main and the lugs are still intact. Inspection authorities will probably turn this down as there is a chance that the panelboard may be converted back to one without a main. They will probably accept it if the lugs are sawed off or otherwise fixed so that they may not be used later, but this will void the UL approval.

(b) See NEC.

(c) See NEC.

384-17. Panelboards in Damp or Wet Locations—Reference is made to **Section 373-2** which requires that panelboards in wet places shall be weatherproof, in damp locations shall be arranged to drain, and in both locations shall be installed with a 1/4-inch air space back of them.

384-18. Enclosure—*Panelboards shall be mounted in cabinets or cut-out boxes.* Panelboards not enclosed will, in most cases, come under the classification of a switchboard.

384-19. Relative Arrangement of Switches and Fuses—*Panelboards having switches on the load side of any type of fuses shall not be installed except for use as service equipment as provided in* **Section 250-94.** With fuses ahead of the switch, they would have to be replaced while still energized. Refer to **Section 250-94** for any exceptions.

384-27. Grounding of Panelboards—*Panelboard cabinets shall be grounded in the manner specified in* **Article 250** *or* **Section 384-3(c).** *An approved terminal bar for equipment grounding conductors shall be provided and secured inside of the cabinet for the attachment of all feeder and branch circuit equipment grounding conductors, when the panelboard is used with nonmetallic raceway, cable wiring or where separate grounding conductors are provided. The terminal bar shall be bonded to the cabinet or panelboard frame and shall not be connected to the neutral bar except at service equipment as permitted in* **Section 250-52.** See Fig. 384-1.

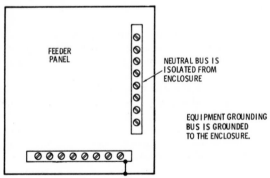

Fig. 384-1. Illustrating grounding terminals on **feeder panel.**

C. Construction Specifications

See NEC.

ARTICLE 390—PREFABRICATED BUILDINGS

See NEC.

Chapter 4. Equipment for General Use

ARTICLE 400—FLEXIBLE CORDS AND CABLES

A. General and Types

Considerable information on flexible cords is included in this chapter of the NEC, a greater part being in the form of Tables. Flexible cords are essential to the full utilization of electrical energy but are probably the most abused item in use today. A large part of the abuse comes from the use to which they are put by the general public and not by the electrical contractor or wireman.

400-1. General—*Flexible cords shall be suitable for the conditions of use and location.*

400-2. Types—*Cords of the several types shall conform to the descriptions of* **Table 400-11.** *Types of flexible cords other than those listed in* **Table 400-11** *and uses for types listed in the Table, shall be the subject of special investigation and shall not be used before being approved.* This is rather plain in that it is recognized that flexible cords are subject to many and varied usages, and that the responsibility of usages other than those specified by the NEC is given to the inspection authority involved. It would be impossible for a book such as the NEC to cover any and all usages to which flexible cords are put.

B. Use and Installation

400-3. Use—Flexible cords may be used only for the following:

(1) Pendants.
(2) Wiring of fixtures.
(3) Connection of portable lamps or appliances.
(4) Elevator cables.
(5) Wiring of cranes and hoists.
(6) Connection of stationary equipment to facilitate their frequent change.
(7) Prevention of the transmission of noise or vibration.
(8) Facilitating the removal or disconnection of fixed appliances for maintenance or repair.

In reference to the above, a few cases will be cited to give a general idea of the intent or uses that will be left up to the inspection authority.

273

These are the author's opinions, and some inspection authorities will no doubt disagree.

In (7) might be included the use of portable shop equipment. Such equipment is essentially stationary but, by necessity, might have to be moved to other locations at times.

In (8) could be included a disposal unit, which so often is sold and installed by a plumber who will usually be called upon to repair it. If a flexible cord and plug is installed, the unit may be readily removed and any chance of reconnecting it to the wrong wires or mixing the equipment grounding conductor with the current-carrying conductors will be cut to a minimum. This, plus the fact that much time will be saved. The same is also true of ranges, dryers, washers, etc.

400-4. Prohibited Uses—The following usages of flexible cords are prohibited by the NEC:

(1) As a substitute for the fixed wiring of a structure.
(2) Where run through holes in walls, ceilings, or floors.
(3) Where run through doorways, windows, or similar openings.
(4) Where attached to building surfaces.
(5) Where concealed between building walls, ceilings, or floors.

400-5. Splices—This is important—*Flexible cord shall be used only in continuous lengths* and shall not be spliced or tapped.

400-6. Cords in Show-Windows and Show-Cases—*Flexible cords used in show-windows and show-cases shall be of types S, SO, SJ, SJO, ST, SJT, or AFS,* which are all heavy-duty types. Where used for the wiring of chain-supported fixtures, and for supplying current to portable lamps and other merchandise for exhibition purposes, the cord may be of other than those listed, but care should be exercised to secure a safe cord of the proper type.

400-7. Minimum Size—The minimum size of flexible cord conductors is covered in **Table 400-11.**

400-8. Insulation—Over 300 Volts—See NEC.

400-9. Overcurrent Protection and Ampacities of Flexible Cords—

Overcurrent Protection. Flexible cords that are not smaller than No. 18, or tinsel cords (or cords having similar characteristics), shall be considered to be properly protected by a 20-ampere overcurrent protective device, as covered in **Section 240-5.**

Table 400-9(b) lists the current-carrying capacity of cords. The current rating of the connected equipment shall not exceed this rating. If the cord has four to six current-carrying conductors, the ampacity of each conductor must be derated to 80% of the capacity listed in the Table. Note that this Table is based on a room temperature of 86°F. See the three notes in the NEC which follow **Table 400-9(b).**

400-10.   Pull at Joints and Terminals—Flexible cords are not designed to handle tensions at devices and at terminations. In each case, the cord must have supplemental protection to keep the tension from being transmitted to the joints or terminal screws. This may be accomplished by:

(1) A knot in the cord.
(2) Winding with tape.
(3) By special fittings designed for the purpose, such as clamps that are built into some attachment plugs.

Table 400-11 is a very important table which covers trade names, type letters, size, number of conductors, insulation, braid on each conductor, outer covering, and the use for which the particular cord is designed. The Notes accompanying this table are also important.

C.   Construction Specifications

400-12.   Labels—*Flexible cords shall be examined and tested at the factory and shall be labeled before shipment.* The public very often interprets the UL label on a flexible cord as meaning that the appliance they are purchasing is UL approved. This is not the case. The appliance will also have a UL label attached, if it is approved.

400-13.   Grounded Conductor Identification—See NEC.

400-14.   Grounding-Conductor Identification—The aim of this Section is to point out the coloring methods used for the grounding conductor in flexible cords. The grounding conductor shall be identified by a continuous green covering, or by a green braid with a yellow stripe, so as to not mistake its purpose as being for grounding only. This conductor is never to be used as a current-carrying conductor.

400-15.   Insulation Thickness—See NEC.

400-16.   Attachment to Receptacle Plugs—When a flexible cord is provided with a grounding conductor, this grounding conductor shall be attached to a terminal that is for grounding purposes only, as provided for in **Section 250-59** (**a** and **b**).

ARTICLE 402—FIXTURE WIRES

Fixture wires are identified by the letter F as part of the type designation and are to be used only for the wiring of the fixture itself. They are not to be used as branch-circuit wires.

402-1.   Use—*Fixture wires are designed for installation in lighting fix-*

275

tures and in similar equipment where enclosed or protected and not subject to bending or twisting in use. Also, they are used for connecting lighting fixtures to the conductors of the circuit that supplies the fixture. Their application in lighting fixtures is covered in **Article 410.** They are not intended for general use, such as the connection of portable appliances or stationary appliances, nor for branch circuits. TF is allowable in some instances for remote control wiring, as mentioned in **Section 725-15. Table 310-2(a)** lists the specifications of fixture wires, their usage temperature ratings, etc. *Fixture wires are not intended for installation as branch circuit conductors, except as permitted in* **Article 725.**

402-2. Minimum Size—*Fixture wires shall not be smaller than No. 18.*

402-3. Insulation—The main point of this Section is both the high and low temperature limits of the insulation. Flexible cords should be selected for both the job and temperatures to be expected.

402-5. Overcurrent Protection—In **Exception 3** of **Section 240-5** it states that No. 16 or No. 18 fixture wire shall be considered as protected by 20-ampere overcurrent devices, except in some cases of elevator and dumbwaiter wiring. Also, **Section 210-19 (c-2)** covers taps of fixture wires.

Table 402-6 covers trade names, type letters, type of insulation, thickness of insulation, and the type of outer coverings for fixture wires. Use this Table in conjunction with **Table 310-2(a)**, remembering that fixture wires have an F in the Letter Type designation.

ARTICLE 410—LIGHTING FIXTURES, LAMPHOLDERS, LAMPS, RECEPTACLES AND ROSETTES

A. General

410-1. Scope—*Lighting fixtures, lampholders, pendants, receptacles, and rosettes, incandescent filament lamps, arc lamps, electric discharge lamps, the wiring and equipment forming a part of such lamps, fixtures, and lighting installations shall conform to the provisions of this Article, except as otherwise provided in this Code.*

410-2. Application to Other Articles—**Articles 500** through **517** cover hazardous locations, and all equipment with, and pertaining to, the fixtures used in such locations shall meet the requirements of these Articles.

410-3. Live Parts—There shall be no live parts normally exposed on any fixture, lampholder, lamp, rosette, or receptacle, with the exception of cleat-type lampholders, rosettes, and receptacles which may have exposed live parts if they are at least 8 feet above the floor. Lampholders, receptacles, and switches that have live terminals exposed and accessible shall not be installed in metal canopies or in the open bases of portable table or floor lamps.

B. Provisions for Fixture Locations

410-4. Fixtures in Specific Locations—

(a) The installation of fixtures in all damp or wet locations shall be so done that water cannot enter or accumulate in the lampholders, wireways, or any other electrical parts of the installation. Fixtures that are to be installed out of doors in damp or wet locations shall be marked SUITABLE FOR WET LOCATIONS. This should eliminate any haphazard installations that are exposed to moisture. *All fixtures installed in damp locations shall be marked, "Suitable for Wet Locations" or "Suitable for Damp Locations."* Fine print tells us the difference between Wet and Damp Locations. Wet Locations:

(1) Installations underground.
(2) In concrete slabs or masonry in direct contact with the earth.
(3) Unprotected and exposed to weather.
(4) Vehicle washing areas.
(5) Similar locations.

Damp Locations:

(1) Interior locations protected from weather, but with moderate degrees of moisture.
(2) Basements.
(3) Some barns.
(4) Some cold-storage warehouses.
(5) Under canopies, marquees, roofed open porches, etc.

(b) *Fixtures installed in corrosive locations shall be of a type approved for the purpose.* This will, of course, include any installation in atmospheres with corrosive ducts, gases, or liquids.

(c) According to the 1971 preprint, (c) was added; For correlation with NFPA 96, **Article 9-H.** Also to take care of any possible problems in correlation with residential installations.

Fixtures in nonresidential occupancies shall not be installed in ducts, or hoods used for removal of cooking smoke or grease-laden vapors or located in the path of travel of such exhaust products unless specifically approved for such use.

Fixtures installed where grease-laden fumes can accumulate deposits on the fixture are a fire hazard. Look to your UL book for approval of fixtures in these locations.

Fixtures in nonresidential occupancies having approved metallic

277

enclosures mounted on the outer surface of the hood and separated from exhaust products by tight fitting glass may be used. Fixtures on hoods in nonresidential occupancies shall not be located in concealed spaces unless part of an approved grease extractor.

410-5. Fixtures near Combustible Material—The construction of fixtures shall be such, or they shall be so installed or equipped with shades or guards, so that any combustible materials in the immediate vicinity of the fixture will not be subject to a temperature more than 90°C (194°F). Combustible materials that are subject to higher temperatures will change in composition to a substance that ignites very readily.

410-6. Fixtures over Combustible Material—Lampholders that are installed over highly combustible materials shall not have a switch as a part of the lampholder, but shall be switched elsewhere and, unless an individual switch (located elsewhere) is used for each fixture, the lampholder shall be located at least 8 feet above the floor or otherwise located or guarded so the lamp may not be readily removed or damaged. See Figs. 410-1 and 2.

410-7. Fixtures in Show Windows—See NEC.

410-8. Fixtures in Clothes Closets—

(a) *A fixture in a clothes closet shall be installed:*

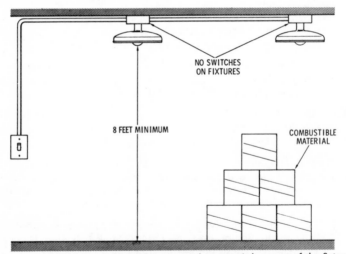

NO SWITCHES
ON FIXTURES

8 FEET MINIMUM

COMBUSTIBLE
MATERIAL

Fig. 410-1. Fixtures over combustibles must not have a switch as part of the fixture. but must be switched elsewhere.

(1) *On the wall above the closet door, provided the clearance from the fixture to a storage area where combustible material may be stored within the closet is not less than 18 inches, or*

(2) *On the ceiling or wall over an area which is unobstructed to the floor, maintaining an 18-inch clearance upward and horizontally from the fixture to a storage area where combustible material may be stored within the closet.*

Note: *A flush recessed fixture equipped with a solid lens is considered to be outside the closet area.*

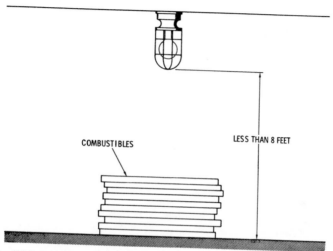

COMBUSTIBLES

LESS THAN 8 FEET

Fig. 410-2. Guarding and switching of fixtures over combustibles when the fixture is less than 8 feet from the floor.

This Section has been considerably clarified in the 1965 NEC. The main point to consider is that the lamp must not come into contact with any combustible material.

(b) *Pendants shall not be installed in clothes closets.* This means that fixtures supported by cords, chains, or other devices to lower them, are not permitted in clothes closets.

410-9. Space for Cove Lighting—See NEC.

C. Provisions at Fixture Outlet Boxes, Canopies and Pans

410-10. Space for Conductors—Basically, this Section refers to **Article 370** which provides for the proper capacity in outlet boxes, canopies, and pans. The fundamental idea is that an adequate space must be provided so as not to crowd the fixture wires, the branch circuit conductors, and their connecting devices.

410-11. Temperature of Conductors in Outlet Boxes—A great many fixtures are of the enclosed type which will trap considerable heat. This Section provides that the fixtures be so constructed that the conductors are not subjected to a temperature higher than their rating. Often an outlet box is separated from the fixture proper by a short piece of flexible tubing through which high-temperature wire is run. This is done so that the wire with ordinary temperature insulation may be connected to the fixture conductors and not be overheated.

A common violation of the Code is in the use of an outlet box, which is an integral part of an incandescent lighting fixture, for the purpose of passing branch-circuit conductors through this outlet box. The only time that this is permissible is if the fixture and outlet box has been approved for this purpose. Look for the UL label.

410-12. Outlet Boxes to be Covered—When an installation is complete, all outlet boxes shall be covered by a:

(1) Fixture Canopy.
(2) Lampholder.
(3) Receptacle.
(4) Rosette.
(5) Similar device.

410-13. Covering of Combustible Material at Outlet Boxes—Whenever a combustible wall or ceiling is exposed between the outlet box to which a fixture is connected and the canopy or pan of the fixture, the exposed part of the combustible material shall be covered with a noncombustible material. See Fig. 410-3.

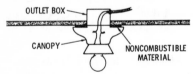

Fig. 410-3. Method of installing a canopy larger than the outlet box.

410-14. Connection of Electric Discharge Lighting Fixtures—As a general rule, fluorescent fixtures that are supported independently of the outlet box are to be connected to the outlet box by metal raceways, metal-clad cable, or nonmetallic sheathed cable, not by flexible cords. When supported directly below the outlet box, however, this ruling may be waived and flexible cord used if there is no strain on the cord and if it will not be subjected to physical damage. When thus connected, the outer end of the cord shall terminate in an approved grounding-type plug or busway plug.

Electric-discharge lighting fixtures provided with mogul-base screw-shell lampholders may be connected to branch circuits of 50 amperes or less by cords complying with **Exception No. 2** *of* **Section 240-5(a).** *Receptacles and caps may be lower ampere rating but not less than 125 percent of the fixture full-load current.*

Fixtures may be connected in accordance with **Section 364-11.**

It would be well to give the supporting comment as it appears in the 1971 preprint:

Mercury vapor fixtures in large wattages (400 and above) are often connected by cord and plug to facilitate maintenance. The only load connected to the receptacle is the fixture. The receptacle serves no other purpose and should not have to meet the requirements of **Section 210-21(b)** *and* **Table 210-25.**

Section 240-5(a), *Exception No. 2,* tells us the size cord which must be used on different ampere branch circuits.

D. Fixture Supports

410-15. Supports—General—*Fixtures, lampholders, rosettes and receptacles shall be securely supported. A fixture which weighs more than 6 lbs. or exceeds 16 inches in any dimension shall not be supported by the screw shell of a lampholder.* This section might cause some discussion, but the final decision is left up to the inspection authority. The one point that must be satisfied is that the fixture must be secure and not subject to a failure of the supporting device.

410-16. Means of Support—**Section 370-13** covers the support and methods of supporting outlet boxes. When a box is properly supported, it may be used to support fixtures weighing up to 50 pounds. Where not supported adequately, or where the fixture exceeds 50 pounds, the fixture shall be supported independently from the box.

E. Wiring of Fixtures

410-17. Fixture Wiring—General—See NEC.

410-18. Conductor Size—See NEC.

410-19. Conductor Insulation—See NEC.

410-20. Conductors for Certain Conditions—The information given in this Section is basically for use in manufacturing of fixtures. However, it may be necessary to know what type of conductors to use as a replacement in repair work or to construct a special fixture that is not available commercially. Refer to the NEC.

410-21.   Conductors for Movable Parts—

(a) *Stranded conductor shall be used for wiring on fixture chains and on other movable or flexible parts.*

(b) It is not the intent of the NEC that the weight of a fixture or a movable part be placed upon the conductors. Other means shall be supplied for this purpose.

410-22.   Pendant Conductors for Incandescent Filament Lamps—

(a) Pendant lampholders with permanently attached leads (commonly termed pigtail sockets) that are used for other than festoon wiring are to be hung by separate stranded rubber-covered conductors which are separately soldered to the circuit conductors. These rubber-covered conductors are not to support the lampholder; other means of support shall be used. See Fig. 410-4.

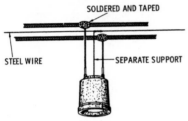

SOLDERED AND TAPED

STEEL WIRE — SEPARATE SUPPORT

Fig. 410-4. Method of attaching pigtail sockets.

(b) *Such pendant conductors shall be not smaller than No. 14 AWG for heavy-duty or medium-base-screw-shell lampholders, nor, except for approved Christmas tree and decorative lighting outfits, smaller than No. 18 AWG for intermediate or candelabra-base lampholders.*

(c) When pendant conductors are longer than 3 feet, they shall;
   (1) Be twisted together, or
   (2) Cabled in an approved assembly.

410-23.   Protection of Conductors and Insulation—

(a) *Conductors shall be secured in a manner that will not tend to cut or abrade the insulation.*

(b) *Conductor insulation shall be protected from abrasion where it passes through metal.*

(c) *Individual showcases, other than fixed, may be connected by flexible cord to permanently installed receptacles, and groups of not more than six such showcases may be coupled together by flexible cord and separable locking-type connectors with one* *of the group connected by flexible cord to a permanently installed receptacle.*

The installation shall comply with the following requirements:

(1) *Flexible cord shall be hardservice type, having conductors not smaller than the branch circuit conductors, having ampacity at least equal to the branch circuit overcurrent device, and having an equipment grounding-conductor. See* **Table 250-95.**

(2) *Receptacles, connectors and plugs (caps) shall be of an approved grounding type rated 15 to 20 amperes.*

(3) *Flexible cords shall be secured to the undersides of showcases so that:*

    (a) *Wiring will not be exposed to mechanical damage.*

    (b) *Will allow a separation between cases not in excess of two inches, nor more than 12 inches between the first case and the supply receptacle.*

    (c) *The free lead at the end of a group of showcases will have a female fitting not extending beyond the case.*

(4) *Equipment other than showcases shall not be electrically connect to showcases.*

(5) *Standpipes of floor receptacles shall allow floor cleaning equipment to be operated without damage to the receptacles.*

410-24. Conductor Protection at Lampholders—See NEC.

410-25. Connections, Splices and Taps—

(a) *Fixtures shall be so installed that the connections between the fixture conductors and the circuit conductors may be inspected without requiring the disconnection of any part of the wiring, unless the fixture is connected by means of a plug and receptacle.*

(b) There shall be no splices or taps in the stems or fixture arms. If trouble develops, the conductor shall be replaced and not spliced.

(c) Splices and taps shall be held to a minimum in fixtures. Any splices or taps are potential sources of trouble.

(d) Connections may be made according to the requirements in Section 110-14. Approved pressure connectors or soldering may be used, but the joints shall be electrically and mechanically secure. If solder is used, approved flux shall be used for the purpose. When connections are made between copper and aluminum, only approved connectors shall be used.

410-26. Fixture Raceways—Fixtures in general are not intended to be used as raceways for circuit conductors unless they are specifically designed and approved for that purpose. There are two exceptions to this, but it must be remembered that the exceptions cover only the conductors of a single branch circuit supplying these fixtures.

Exception No. 1. An installation of fixtures approved for end to end assembly to form a continuous raceway, or

Exception No. 2. Fixtures which are connected together by approved wiring methods.

Any branch circuit conductor which runs within 3 inches of the ballast compartment shall have an insulation temperature rating of not less than 90°C(194°F). Such types of insulation as Type RHH, THHN, FEP, FEPB, SA, XHHW, and AVA. **See Table 310-2(a)** for Type THW.

410-27. Polarization of Fixtures—Screw-shells of lampholders shall all be wired to the same fixture conductor, circuit conductor, or terminal. **Section 200-8** states that the screw-shells of lampholders are to be connected to the identified conductor (neutral).

F. Construction of Fixtures

See NEC.

G. Installation of Lampholders

410-41. Screw-Shell Type—It has long been a common practice to use screw-shell type lampholders for other purposes than for lamps, such as the female end of an attachment plug, or a pigtail socket as a fuse holder, etc. These uses are all prohibited by the NEC. Screw-shell sockets are to be used as lampholders only.

410-42. Double-Pole Switched Lampholders—Where a lampholder is connected to the unidentified, or hot, conductors of a multiwire circuit, the switching device of the lampholder shall simultaneously disconnect both conductors of the circuit. This can be readily understood considering that, whenever hot wires feed a circuit, if only one is opened it leaves one hot. The Code has provided for this dangerous condition by requiring that both hot conductors be opened simultaneously. See **Section 200.5.**

410-43. Lampholders in Damp or Wet Locations—See NEC.

H. Construction of Lampholders

See NEC.

J. Lamps

410-49. Bases, Incandescent Lamps—Incandescent lamps for general use on lighting branch circuits are limited to not over 300 watts when used in medium-base lampholders. Mogul-base lampholders are limited to 1500-watt incandescent lamps. Special bases or other devices shall be used for incandescent lamps above 1500 watts.

410-50. Enclosures, Mercury-Vapor Lamp Auxiliary Equipment— Resistors and regulators used with mercury-vapor lamps are sources of heat and shall be so treated by being installed in noncombustible cases and wired accordingly.

410-51. Arc Lamps—See NEC.

K. Receptacles, Cord Connectors and Attachment Plugs (Caps)

410-52. Rating and Type—

(a) *Receptacles installed for the attachment of portable cords shall be rated at not less than 15 amperes, 125 volts, or 10 amperes, 250 volts, and shall be of a type not suitable for use as lampholders.* Notice that receptacles shall be of such a type that lamps cannot be screwed into them.

(b) See NEC.

(c) See NEC.

(d) See NEC.

410-54. Receptacles in Damp or Wet Locations—

(a) Damp Location. *A receptacle outlet installed outdoors in a location protected from the weather or in other damp locations shall have an enclosure for the receptacle which is weatherproof when the receptacle is covered (attachment plug cap not inserted and receptacle covers closed.)* This clarifies receptacles on open porches, etc.

An installation suitable where exposed to wet locations is also suitable for damp locations.

A receptacle outlet may be considered to be in a location protected from the weather when located under roofed open porches, canopies, marquees, and the like, so as not to be subjected to a beating rain or water run-off.

(b) Wet Locations. *A receptacle installed outdoors where exposed to weather or in wet locations shall be a weatherproof enclosure, the integrity of which is not affected when the receptacle is in use (attachment plug cap inserted).*

Exception: An enclosure which is weatherproof only when a self-closing receptacle cover is closed may be used for a receptacle installed outdoors where the receptacle is not likely to be used with other than portable tools or other portable equipment not usually left connected to the outlet indefinitely.

(c) **Flush Mounting With Faceplate.** *The enclosure for a receptacle installed in an outlet box flush-mounted on a wall surface may be weatherproof when the faceplate assembly for use in the weatherproof installation is used and the connection between the plate and the wall surface has been made watertight.*

(d) **Installation Height.** *A receptacle outlet installed outdoors shall be located above the ground or floor such that water accumulation is not likely to touch the outlet cover or plate.*

410-55. Grounding-Type Receptacles, Adapters, Cord Connectors and Attachment Plugs—see NEC.

L. Rosettes

410-57. Approved Types—

(a) At one time rosettes contained fuse wire. This is prohibited by the NEC.

(b) Rosettes that have the cap and base separable may be used provided that they may be joined together in only one way so that the polarity will not be reversed.

410-58. Rosettes in Damp or Wet Locations—See NEC.

410-59. Rating—See NEC.

410-60. Rosettes for Exposed Wiring—See NEC.

410-61. Rosettes for Use with Boxes or Raceways—See NEC.

M. Special Provisions for Flush and Recessed Fixtures

410-62. Approved Type—All fixtures installed in recessed spaces of walls or ceilings are required to be of an approved type. The approval will, in most cases, be by the use of UL approved fixtures, or as designated by the authority enforcing the NEC. The provisions of **Sections 410-63** through **410-70** shall be followed.

410-63. Temperature—

(a) Fixtures installed adjacent to any combustible materials will not subject the combustible material to a temperature in excess of 90°C (194°F). Hotter temperatures may change the composition of the combustible materials to where they will reach a low flash point.

(b) See NEC.

410-64. Clearance—Recessed fixtures shall have a minimum clearance from combustible materials of at least 1/2 inch, except at the points of support. Too often in installing recessed fixtures, the proper clearance is given, but the fact that combustible insulation may be added is overlooked, making for a very dangerous condition. Care should be taken to see that any insulation of a combustible nature is kept clear of the fixture. Insulation, even though noncombustible, around the fixture will not allow the heat to dissipate as rapidly as it should, and will cause a rise in temperature that has not been provided for.

410-65. Wiring—

(a) See NEC.

(b) See NEC.

(1) If the branch circuit conductors have insulation suitable for the temperature that will be encountered in the fixture, they may be run directly into the fixture for making the connections. By checking specifications of the temperature of the fixture and then checking the conductor insulation temperature in **Table 310-2(a),** the proper type of insulation required may be determined.

(2) Tap connection conductors which have a temperature rating for that which will be encountered shall be run from the fixture terminal connection to an outlet or junction box placed at least one foot away from the fixture. Take note of the *one foot away* and don't forget the part which says: *Such a tap shall extend for at least four feet but not more than six feet and shall be in a suitable metal raceway.* This means that the box may be not less than one foot away from the fixture, but that a raceway shall be run to it that is not less than 4 feet nor more than 6 feet long. A suitable metal raceway may be flexible metallic conduit. The reason for the four-foot minimum length is to prevent the heat from traveling through too short a raceway. Type AF wire is not allowed as a branch-circuit conductor, but would be allowed for the tap from a branch circuit into the fixture where the above method of connection is used.

N. Construction, Flush and Recessed Fixtures

These Sections pertain mostly to the manufacturing of flush and recessed fixtures. However, attention is called to **Section 410-68** which requires marking the fixture in 1/4-inch letters or larger to indicate the maximum wattage bulb that may be used. Larger wattage lamps will produce a higher temperature than the fixture is designed for. Also refer to **Section 410-69** which prohibits the use of solder.

P. Special Provisions for Electric Discharge Lighting Systems of 1,000 Volts or Less

410-71. General—See NEC.

410-72. Direct-Current Equipment—All discharge lighting equipment in this class that is designed for use on direct-current shall be so marked and the resistors and other equipment used shall be designed for direct-current operation. A fluorescent fixture designed for alternating current will not work on direct current.

410-73. Voltages–Dwelling Occupancies—

(a) Lighting equipment for dwelling occupancies is limited to an open-circuit voltage of not more than 1000 volts. Sometimes a request is made to use neon lighting in a residence. According to the Code, this type of lighting would be prohibited because the voltage will exceed 1000 volts in practically all cases.

(b) See NEC.

410-74. Fixture Mounting—

(a) **Exposed Ballasts.** There are times when exposed ballasts or transformers are used. In such installations they shall be so mounted that they do not come in contact with any combustible material.

(b) **Combustible Low-Density Cellulose Fiberboard.** *Where a fixture containing a ballast is to be installed on combustible low-density cellulose fiberboard it shall, where surface mounted:*

(1) *Be approved for this condition,* that is, marked as being approved for direct mounting on this type of combustible material, *or*

(2) If not approved for mounting directly on low-density cellulose fiberboard, it shall *be spaced not less than 1-1/2 inches from the surface of the fiberboard.*

(3) Where such a fixture is partially or wholly recessed, the provisions of **M** and **N** of this Article **(Sections 410-62** through **410-70)** shall apply.

Combustible low-density cellulose fiberboard is considered to include sheets, panels and tiles which have a density of 20 pounds per cubic foot or less, and which are formed of bonded plant fiber material; but does not include solid or laminated wood, nor fiberboard which has a density in excess of 20 pounds per cubic foot or is an approved material which has been integrally treated with fire retarding chemicals to the degree that the flame spread in any plane of the material will not exceed twenty-five as determined by the method of NFPA No. 225, ASTM Designation E-84 or U.L. No. 723.

410-75.   Auxiliary Equipment Not Integral with Fixture—See NEC.

410-76.   Auto-transformers—This Section is very similar to the requirements for autotransformers supplying branch circuit as covered in **Section 200-4,** except that this covers lighting. Autotransformers that are used as a part of a ballast for supplying lighting units and which raises the voltage to more than 300 volts shall be supplied only from a grounded system.

410-77.   Switches—See NEC.

Q.   Special Provisions for Electric Discharge Lighting Systems of More Than 1,000 Volts

410-78.   General—

(a) Only equipment that is approved for the type service shall be used on electric discharge lighting systems with an open-circuit voltage in excess of 1000 volts.

(b) *The terminal of an electric discharge lamp shall be considered as alive when any lamp terminal is connected to a potential of more than 300 volts.*

(c) Not only the general requirements for lighting fixtures apply but also **Sections 410-78** through **410-90.**
Signs and outline lighting will be covered in **Article 600.**

410-79.   Control—

(a) Fixtures and lamp installations may be controlled individually by switches or circuit breakers, but either shall open all of the ungrounded conductors of the primary circuit (the branch circuit supplying the fixtures or lamps).

(b) For protection, the switches or circuit breakers shall be located within sight of the fixtures or lamps, or shall be capable of being locked in an open position.

410-80.   Lamp Terminals and Lampholders—Any fixture parts that must be removed for lamp replacement shall be hinged or fastened in an approved manner, and the lamps and lampholders, or both, shall be so designed that there will be no exposed live parts when lamps are being removed or replaced.

410-81.   Transformer Ratings—The open-circuit rating of ballasts and transformers shall not exceed 15,000 volts, with an allowable 1000 volts on test in addition. The secondary current rating shall not exceed 120 milliamperes (0.120 amp) when the open-circuit voltage to the ballast or transformer exceeds 7500 volts, and the secondary current shall not exceed 240 milliamperes (0.240 ampere) when the open-circuit voltage is 7500 watts or less.

410-82. **Transformer Type**—All transformers shall be enclosed and approved. Transformers other than dry types or askarel-insulated types shall not be used.

410-83. **Transformer Secondary Connections**—

  (a) The high-voltage windings of transformers shall not be connected in parallel or series, with the exception that two transformers, each of which has one end of the high-voltage winding grounded and attached to the enclosure, may have the high-voltage windings connected in series to form the equivalent of a mid-point grounded transformer. See Figs. 410-5 and 6.

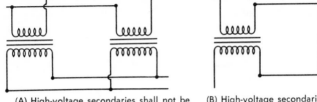

(A) High-voltage secondaries shall not be paralleled.

(B) High-voltage secondaries shall not be connected in series.

Fig. 410-5. These connections are prohibited on high-voltage lighting transformers.

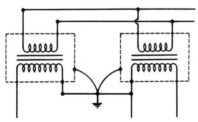

Fig. 410-6. A connection that is permissible on high-voltage lighting transformers.

  (b) *The grounded ends shall be connected by an insulating conductor not smaller than No. 14 AWG.*

410-84. **Transformer Locations**—See NEC.

410-85. **Transformer Loading**—The loading of the transformer should be such that there will not be a continuous over-voltage condition. At first glance this sounds odd, but these transformers are of the high-leakage reactance type and as the load increases the voltage increases to maintain the proper current. The lamp load should be properly balanced for the the transformer being used.

410-86. **Wiring Method. Secondary Conductors**—See NEC.

410-87. **Lamp Supports**— See **Section 600-31.**

410-88. Exposure to Damage—See NEC.

410-89. Marking—See NEC.

410-90. Switches—See **Section 380-14.**

R. Grounding

410-91. General—Grounding will follow the requirements set forth in **Sections 410-92** through **410-96.**

410-92. Metallic Wiring Systems—Metal fixtures that are installed on metallic wiring systems—that is, grounded metal raceways or grounded AC metal-clad cables, or grounded Type MI, AC, or ALS cable—shall be grounded. The metallic system, if properly installed, will provide the grounding source.

410-93. Nonmetallic Wiring Systems—All metal fixtures installed on outlets that are wired with knob-and-tube or nonmetallic sheathed cable, and operating at 150 volts or less to ground, shall be grounded. This may be done by the equipment grounding conductor in NM cable or by running a No. 14 green, or green with yellow stripe, colored conductor.

Exception: Fixtures and their outlet boxes mounted on electrically nonconducting ceilings or walls need not be grounded where located not less than 8 feet vertically or 5 feet horizontally from grounded surfaces. (See **Section 410-95).**

A recommendation in the NEC states: *Fixtures made of insulating materials, and lampholders with shells of insulating material, are recommended for use with wiring systems that do not afford a ready means for grounding the exposed noncurrent-carrying parts of fixtures and lampholders.*

410-94. Equipment of More Than 150 Volts to Ground—See NEC.

410-95. Equipment Near Grounded Surfaces—This was mentioned in **Section 410-93.**

(a) Metal lighting fixtures, lampholders, and face plates shall not be installed on conducting surfaces nor within 8 feet vertically or 5 feet horizontally from:

(1) Laundry tubs.
(2) Bath tubs.
(3) Shower baths.
(4) Plumbing fixtures.
(5) Steam pipes.
(6) Other grounded metal work or grounded surfaces. It will be

found that inspection authorities will, in most cases, classify concrete, earth, concrete with floor covering, and similar conditions as grounded surfaces. A tiled concrete floor will become conductive when wet or damp. Also, the metal ducts of air-conditioning systems and heating systems will also be considered as conducting surfaces.

410-96. Methods of Grounding—As in Article 250, equipment will be considered as grounded where mechanically and electrically connected in a permanent and effective manner to metal raceways, the armor Type AC, MI, and ALS metal-clad cable, the grounding conductor of nonmetallic sheathed cable, or to a separate grounding conductor (either bare or green colored, or green with a yellow stripe) that is not smaller than No. 14 AWG.

ARTICLE 422—APPLIANCES

A. General

422-1. Scope—*This Article shall apply to electric appliances used in* any occupancy. Four definitions of appliances are given in **Article 100.**

Equipment shall be of a type approved for the purpose and location where installed.

422-2. Live Parts—The live parts of appliances shall be normally enclosed to avoid exposure to contact. This, however, cannot always be done, as in the case of toasters, grills, and the like.

422-3. Other Articles—**Article 430** covers Motors. The requirements of this Article will amend and supersede portions of **Article 430.**

All requirements of this Code shall apply when applicable. Appliances for use in hazardous locations shall be installed to conform to **Articles 500** *through* **517.**

B. Branch Circuit Requirements

422-5. Branch Circuit Sizing— This Section is not intended to apply to the conductors which are an integral part of an appliance. This Section applies to the sizes of branch circuit conductors which may be used without heating under the conditions specified in **Article 210.**

(a) *The rating of an individual branch circuit shall not be less than the marked rating of the appliance or the marked rating of an appliance having combined loads (see* **Section 422-32).**

Exception No. 1. For household cooking Appliances, see **Table 220-5.** You will recall that this gave us demand factors for cooking equipment.

Exception No. 2. Motor-operated appliances which do not have the ampacity of the branch circuit marked on the appliance shall be treated according to Part B of **Article 430,** covering this type of operation.

Exception No. 3. Except as noted in **Section 210-23(b), Exception No. 1,** *an appliance, other than a motor-operated appliance, which is continuously loaded, the branch circuit ampacity shall not be less than 125 per cent of the marked rating.*

(b) Section 210-24 gives us percentages to use on branch circuit loading. So branch circuits supplying appliances and other loads shall conform to **Section 210-24.**

422-6. Branch Circuit Overcurrent Protection—Section 240-5 gives us the necessary information for protecting branch circuits.

When there is a protective device rating marked on an appliance, the branch-circuit overcurrent device rating shall not exceed the protective device rating marked on the appliance.

C. Installation of Appliances

422-7. General. *All appliances shall be installed in an approved manner.*

422-8. Flexible Cords. *Flexible cords used to connect heating appliances shall comply with the following:*

(a) Heater Cords Required. This part defines the types of cords required for all smoothing irons and portable electrically-heated appliances rated at more than 50 watts and that produce temperatures in excess of 121°C (250°F) on surfaces that the cord is likely to come in contact with. **Table 400-11** lists cords for heating appliances, along with their temperature ranges and usages.

(b) Other Heating Appliances. All other portable heating appliances shall have cords that are listed in **Table 400-11** and meet the requirements for the use to which they are put.

(c) Other Appliances. Flexible cord may be used for the following purposes:
(1) Connection of portable appliances.
(2) Connection of stationary appliances to facilitate their frequent interchange or prevention of the transmission of noise or vibration. This could be electric cooking equipment, etc.
(3) Facilitate the removal or disconnection of fixed appliances for maintenance or repair. A good example of this is a garbage disposal. With a flexible cord connection, it merely has to

293

be unplugged and thus the danger of a wrong connection upon reinstallation are largely avoided.

422-9. Portable Immersion Heaters—Portable immersion heaters are to be constructed and installed so that the current-carrying parts shall not come into contact with the substance into which they are immersed. This prohibits the type of immersion heaters which have open coils in contact with the liquid. The inspection authority may make exceptions where it is deemed advisable.

422-10. Protection of Combustible Material.—All electrically-heated appliances that, because of size, weight, or service, and that are intended to be used in fixed position, shall provide for ample protection from combustibles.

422-11. Stands for Portable Appliances—All portable heating appliances, such as irons, that are intended to be used by applying them to combustible substances shall be provided with stands for support when actually not being used. These stands may be a part of the appliance or a separate item.

422-12. Signals for Heated Appliances—This does not apply to appliances intended for residential use, but other electrically-heated appliances that are applied to combustible articles shall have a signaling device unless the appliance has a temperature-limiting device.

422-13. Flatirons—All electrically-heated smoothing irons shall be equipped with an approved temperature-limiting means, such as a thermostat.

422-14. Water Heaters–Storage and Immersion Types—*Each storage or instantaneous-type water heater shall be equipped with temperature limiting means in addition to the control thermostat to disconnect all ungrounded conductors, and such means shall be:*

(1) *Installed to sense maximum water temperature;*
(2) *Trip-free, manually reset, or it shall use a replacement element;*
(3) Such water heaters shall be marked to require the installation of a temperature and pressure relief valve;
(4) See ANSI Standard Z-21.22-1971.

Exception: Each water heater with supply water temperature of 180°F or above and capacity of 60 kw or above, and water heaters with a capacity of one gallon or less, approved for the purpose.

It is almost universally a Code that there is to be a pressure and temperature relief valve installed on water heaters. The requirement in (1) and (2) above are in addition to this requirement. Some heaters in the past have provisions for opening only one ungrounded conductor by means of a thermostat. It is now required that all ungrounded conductors be opened by the thermostat. Often, if an element is shorted to ground, one side will open but the other side of the circuit will stay energized. Thus, current will go to ground, still producing heating of the water. By opening all ungrounded conductors, this problem will be eliminated.

422-15.   Infrared Lamp Industrial Heating Appliances—See NEC.

422-16.   Grounding—*Metal frames of portable, stationary and fixed electrically heated appliances, operating on circuits above 150 volts to ground, shall be grounded in the manner specified in* **Article 250;** *provided, however, that where this is impracticable, grounding may be omitted by special permission, in which case the frames shall be permanently and effectively insulated from the ground.*

In rural areas especially, grounding the water heater frame to the same ground as the service entrance will save many burnouts due to lightning. This provision of grounding that requires the cold-water pipe to be bonded to a made electrode (when a made electrode is required) will automatically do much to prevent troubles that used to develop. Even when (by special permission) the equipment is not required to be grounded, the Code recommends that the frames be grounded in all cases. It will be recalled that the frames of ranges and dryers may be grounded to the neutral if the neutral is No. 10 or larger. These are two cases in which this type of grounding is permitted. It does not apply to Mobile Homes or Travel Trailers.

422-17.   Wall-mounted Ovens and Counter-mounted Cooking Units—

(a) Wall-mounted ovens and counter-mounted cooking units are considered to be fixed appliances, and this includes the provisions for mounting and connection of the wiring.

(b) A separable connector or plug and receptacle combination in the supply line to a wall-mounted oven or a counter-mounted cooking top shall not be considered as a disconnecting means, but only to be used as a means for ease of servicing. This means that it is not to be used as a disconnecting means as covered in **Section 422-20.** Also, it shall be approved for the temperature to which it might be subjected, especially since the space is limited in most cases.

422-18.   Other Installation Methods—*Appliances employing methods of installation other than covered by this Article may be used only by special permission.* Remember, *Special Permission* means permission in writing by the authority having jurisdiction.

D. Control and Protection of Appliances

422-20.   Disconnecting Means—Each appliance shall have some means for disconnecting all ungrounded conductors. These means for fixed, portable, and stationary appliances will be covered in the next few sections.

295

422-21.   Disconnection of Fixed Appliances—

(a) *For fixed appliances rated at not over 300 volt amperes or 1/8 hp. the branch circuit overcurrent device may serve as the disconnecting means.*

(b) *For fixed appliances of greater rating the branch circuit switch or circuit breaker may, where readily accessible to the user of the appliance, serve as the disconnecting means.*

The above should not prevent the addition of a separable connection or a plug and receptacle approved for conditions as being installed as a means of serving the fixed appliance. They are not intended merely to be the disconnecting means.

422-22.   Disconnection of Portable Appliances—See NEC.

422-23.   Disconnection of Stationary Appliances—See NEC.

422-24.   Unit Switches as Disconnecting Means—See NEC.

422-25.   Switch and Circuit Breaker to Be Indicating—Switches or circuit breakers used as disconnecting means for appliances shall indicate whether they are in the open or closed position.

422-26.   Disconnecting Means for Motor-Driven Appliances—
When a switch or circuit breaker serves as the disconnecting means for a stationary or fixed motor-driven appliance of more than 1/8 horsepower, it shall be located within sight of the motor controller or shall be capable of being locked in the open position. It will be found that most inspection authorities will consider any distance over 50 feet as being out of sight. The intent of this part is to give safety on motor-driven appliances of over 1/8 horsepower during service work.

422-27.   Overcurrent Protection—

(a) *Appliances shall be considered as protected against overcurrent when supplied by branch circuits as specified in **Sections 422-5** and **422-6,** and* (e) *below.*

  Exception: Motors of motor-operated appliances shall be provided with overload protection in accordance with Part C of **Article 430.** *Sealed (hermetic-type) motor-compressors in air conditioning or refrigeration equipment shall be provided with overload protection in accordance with Part F of* **Article 440.** *When appliance protective devices separate from the appliance are required, data for selection of these devices shall be marked on the appliance. The minimum marking shall be marked on the appliance. The minimum marking shall be that specified in* **Section 430-7** *and* **440-3.**

(b) **Table 220-5** lists the demand factors for residential ranges. Any residential range that has a demand factor of over 60 amperes (as calculated from this Table) must have its power supply divided into two or more circuits, each of which is provided with overcurrent protection of not more than 50 amperes.

(c) Infrared heating appliances shall be protected by overcurrent protection of not more than 50 amperes.

(d) *Open coil or exposed sheathed-coil types of surface heating elements in commercial type heating appliances shall be protected by overcurrent protection devices which are rated at not more than 50 amperes.*

(e) *When the branch circuit supplies a single nonmotor-operated appliance, rated at 10 amperes or more, the overcurrent device rating shall not exceed 150 percent of the appliance rating.*

E. Marking of Appliances

See NEC.

F. Provisions for Room Air-Conditioning Units

422-40. General—

The following provisions in the balance of this Article, **Sections 422-41** through **422-44,** inclusive, apply to electrically energized room air-conditioning units which control temperature and humidity. A definition for these Sections of an air conditioner is as follows:

An AC hermetic type air-cooled window, console, or in-wall air-conditioner, including equipment not rated over 250 volts, and also one which has provisions for heating and which is installed in the conditioned room.

Room air conditioning rated at 3-phase or above 250 volts shall be directly connected to a wiring method recognized in Chapter 3. See Part **H** *of* **Article 430** *for disconnecting means.* Note the *directly connected*—this would indicate that it could not be a plug-in type of connection.

422-41. Grounding—See **Sections 250-42, 43,** and **45.**

422-42. Branch Circuit Requirements—This should be carefully studied.

(a) If no light or other appliances are supplied from the branch circuit, the total load of a motor-operated air-conditioning unit shall not exceed 80% of the rating of the branch circuit.

(b) If there are any lighting or other appliances on the branch circuit, the total air-conditioning load shall not exceed 50% of the branch-circuit rating. This is not meant to be a blanket rule, as lighting or other appliance loads might exceed 50%, in which case the branch circuit could not handle the air conditioning if it also imposed a load of 50% of the branch-circuit rating.

(c) Section 430-53(c) shall apply to air-conditioning units that employ two or more motors.

422-43. Disconnecting Means—For a single-phase, 250 volt or less, room air conditioner, the disconnecting means may be an attachment plug and receptacle, when:

(1) *The manual controls on the air conditioner units are readily accessible and located within 6 feet of the floor; or*

(2) *An approved manually operable switch is installed in a readily accessible location within sight of the air-conditioning unit.*

422-44. Supply Cords—When supply cords are used with air-conditioning equipment, the cords shall not exceed 10 feet in length for nominal 125-volt ratings, and not more than 6 feet in length for nominal 250-volt ratings.

ARTICLE 424—FIXED ELECTRICAL SPACE HEATING EQUIPMENT

A. General

424-1. Scope—This Article covers fixed equipment for space heating. The equipment may be heating cables, unit heaters, boilers, central systems, or other approved fixed heating equipment. Not covered in this Article is process heating and room air-conditioning.

424-2. Application to Other Articles—This is basically the same requirements as appear in other Articles of the Code to primarily indicate that heating equipment intended for use in hazardous locations must also comply with **Articles 500** through **517.** It also indicates that heating equipment employing motors must comply with **Article 430.**

Fixed electric space heating equipment incorporating a sealed (hermetic-type) motor-compressor shall comply with **Article 440.**

424-3(a) Branch Circuit Requirements—Branch circuits to fixed heating equipment is limited to 15, 20, or 30 amperes. An individual branch circuit may supply any load.

There is an exception which refers us to **Section 424-22** and says that branch circuits for fixed infra-red heating equipment shall not be rated at more than 50 amperes.

(b) **Branch Circuit Sizing.** For the sizing of overcurrent devices and branch-circuit conductors, for electrical space heating equipment (fixed), they shall be calculated on the basis of 125% of the total load of the heaters and motors if equipped with motors. Contactors, relays, thermostats, etc., that are rated at continuous load ratings of 100% may be used to supply the full rated load. *See* **Section 210-23(b),** *Exception No. 1 and 2.*

The ampacity of the branch circuit conductors supplying fixed space heating equipment consisting of mechanical refrigeration with or without resistance units shall be calculated as provided for in **Section 430-25.** This would be what is commonly termed "a heat pump".

The size of the branch-circuit conductors and overcurrent protective devices supplying fixed electric space heating equipment consisting of mechanical refrigeration with or without resistance units shall be calculated as provided in **Sections 440-34** *and* **440-35.**

The provisions of this Section are not intended to apply to conductors, which form an integral part of approved fixed electric space heating equipment.

B. Installation

424-9. General—*All heating equipment shall be installed in an approved manner.*

424-10. Special Type Heaters—Special permission shall be secured from the inspection authority to install fixed space-heating systems employing methods of installation other than covered in this Article.

424-11. Supply Conductors—Some heating equipment will require high-temperature wiring for the connections. Any equipment which is not suitable for connection to conductors with 60°C insulation shall be *clearly and permanently marked* and this marking shall be plainly visible after installation.

424-12. Locations—

(a) *Fixed electric space heating equipment shall not be used where exposed to severe physical damage unless adequately protected.*

(b) *Heaters and related equipment installed in damp or wet locations shall be approved for such locations and shall be constructed and installed so that water cannot enter or accumulate in wireways, electrical components or duct work:*

A Note calls attention to **Section 110-11.** This is where equipment shall be covered during installation for protection.

424-13. Spacing from Combustible Materials—All fixed electrically heated appliances (heating equipment) that because of size, weight, or service, are intended to be used in a fixed position shall be amply protected from combustibles. That is, unless they have been approved when installed in direct contact with combustible materials.

424-14. Grounding.—Metal parts that are exposed and are a part of fixed electrical heating equipment shall be grounded as required in **Article 250.**

299

C. Control and Protection of Fixed Electric Space Heating Equipment

424-19. Disconnection Means—All fixed electric space heating equipment shall be provided with a means for disconnection from all ungrounded conductors. Where heating equipment is supplied by more than one source, the disconnecting means shall be grouped and identified.

(a) The branch circuit overcurrent device may be used as a disconnecting means where the equipment is not rated at over 300 volt-amperes, or over 1/8 horsepower.

(b) Where branch circuit overcurrent devices are readily accessible to the user, these devices may be used as the disconnecting means if the ratings are larger than (a) above.

(c) Motor Driven Heating Equipment. The disconnection means shall conform to the requirement for motors as covered in Part H of **Article 430.**

(d) Unit Switches as Disconnecting Means. *Unit switches with a marked "off" position, which are a part of a fixed heater, that disconnect all ungrounded conductors may be used as the disconnecting means required by this Article when other means for disconnection are provided in the following types of occupancies:*

(1) Multi-Family Dwellings. *In multi-family (more than two) dwellings, the other disconnecting means shall be within the apartment, or on the same floor as the apartment in which the fixed heater is installed, and may also control lamps and appliances.*

(2) Two-Family Dwellings. *In two-family dwellings, the other disconnecting means may be located either inside or outside of the apartment in which the fixed heater is installed.*

(3) Single-Family Dwellings. *In single-family dwellings, the service disconnecting means may be the other disconnecting means.*

(4) Other Occupancies. *In other occupancies, the branch circuit switch or circuit breaker, where readily accessible to the user of the fixed heater, may be used for the other disconnecting means.*

424-20. Controllers and Disconnecting Means—

(a) *Thermostats and thermostatically controlled switching devices which indicate an off position and which interrupt line current shall open all ungrounded conductors when the control device is in this off position.* The reason for this is that the leads to 230 volts are red and for 115 volts are yellow, so that the neutral connection is not identified. If the thermostat has an "off" position, it would naturally be considered that the circuit was disconnected when it is not if only one conductor was disconnected.

(b) *Thermostats and thermostatically controlled switching devices which do not have an off position are not required to open all ungrounded conductors.* In this instance, devices without "on" and "off" positions will not give the impression that they were meant to be a disconnecting means.

(c) *Remote control thermostats do not meet the requirements of paragraphs* **(a)** *and* **(b)***. These devices shall not serve as the disconnecting means.*

(d) *Switching devices consisting of combined thermostats and manually controlled switches which serve both as controllers and disconnecting means shall:*

  (1) *Open all ungrounded conductors when manually placed in the off position.*

  (2) *Be so designed that the circuit cannot be energized automatically after the device has been manually placed in the off position.*

424-21. Switch and Circuit Breaker to be Indicating:—Switches or circuit breakers used for disconnecting means for heating equipment shall indicate whether they are in the open or closed position.

424-22. Overcurrent Protection. (a) Article 210, covering Branch Circuits, goes into considerable detail on overcurrent protection. Heating equipment will generally be considered to have overcurrent protection when the conditions of **Article 210** are met, with the exception of motor-driven heating equipment which comes under **Article 430.**

(b) Infrared heating equipment shall be protected by overcurrent protection of not more than 50 amperes.

(c) Any space heating equipment which draws a total of more than 48 amperes shall have the heating units subdivided so that each subdivided section will not draw more than 48 amperes; if it draws 48 amperes, it shall be protected by not more than 60 amperes.

Where protection is within or on the heater enclosure, overcurrent protection shall be suitable for branch circuit protection meeting accessibility requirements of **Section 424-65** *but not meeting readily accessibility requirements of branch circuit protection.*

D. Marking of Heating Equipment

424-28. Nameplate. See NEC.

424-29. Marking of Heating Elements—Heating elements that are replaceable in the field shall have the following markings on each heating element:

(1) Volts and amperes, or
(2) Volts and watts.

E. Electric Space Heating Cables and Panels

424-34. Heating Cable Construction—Heating cables are supplied by the manufacturer in a complete unit with 7-foot nonheating leads made up of conductors and wiring approved for general use, or other wiring approved for the purpose. The nonheating leads shall not be cut off or shortened in any manner. See next Section. Also see Fig. 424-1.

Fig. 424-1. Nonheating leads shall be a minimum of 7 feet.

424-35. Marking of Heating Cables and Panels—*Each unit shall be marked with the identifying name or identification symbol, catalog number, ratings in volts and watts or amperes.*

(a) Heating Cables   Within 3 inches of the terminal end of the heating cable, legible markings shall be marked on the non-heating leads. This is why these shall not be shortened as it would eliminate the markings.

The non-heating leads shall have color identification as follows:

120-volt nominal—yellow
208-volt nominal—blue
240-volt nominal—red
227-volt nominal—brown.

(b) Heating Panels. *Permanent marking in a location that is readily visible prior to building finishing shall be provided.*

424-36. Clearances of Wiring in Ceilings—Wiring located above heated ceilings and in thermal insulation must be sized according to the temperature that it might be exposed to. Therefore, wiring above heated ceilings shall be located not less than 2 inches above the heated ceiling and, if it is in thermal insulation at this height, it shall be considered as being operated at an ambient temperature of 50°C. It will be necessary to refer to the correction factors that are in Note 13 that accompanies **Tables 310-12** through **310-15** to find the correction factors for the

302

ampacity of conductors at 50°C. Wiring above heated ceilings and located above thermal insulation having a minimum thickness of 2 inches will require no correction factor.

424-37. Clearances of Branch Circuit Wiring in Walls—

(a) Wiring in exterior walls shall be located between the exterior wall and the insulation. This applies if the walls are heated.

(b) Wiring in interior walls shall be located on the side away from the heat and is to be derated as if subjected to 40°C ambient temperature. See **Note 13** with **Tables 310-12** through **310-15.**

424-38. Area Restrictions—

(a) *Heating cables and panels shall not extend beyond the room or area in which they originate.* See Fig. 424-2.

(b) *Cables and panels shall not be installed in closets, over walls or partitions that extend to the ceiling, or over cabinets whose clearance from the ceiling is less than the minimum horizontal dimension of the cabinet to the nearest cabinet edge that is open to the room or area.*

Exception: Isolated single runs of cable may pass over partitions where they are embedded.

(c) There are climates where humidity control is required in closets, but the prohibition of cables in closets is not intended to prohibit the use of low-temperature humidity controls in closets.

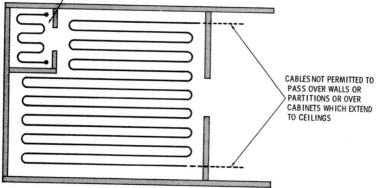

Fig. 424-2. Illustration showing where heating cables may and may not be installed in ceilings.

424-39. Clearance from Other Objects and Openings—*Panels and cables shall be separated at least 8 inches from the edge of outlet boxes and junction boxes that are to be used for mounting surface lighting fix-*

tures. Two inches shall be provided from recessed lighting fixtures and their trims, ventilating openings and other such openings in room surfaces. Sufficient area shall be provided to assure that no heating cable or panel will be covered by other surface mounted lighting units. The temperature limits and overheating of the cable are involved in this instance. Therefore, the requirements of this Section should be very carefully followed and, if in doubt, a little extra clearance should be given.

424-40. Splices—Splicing of cables is prohibited except where necessary due to breaks. Even then the length of the cable should not be altered as this will change the characteristics of the cable and the heat. It will be necessary to occasionally splice a break, but only approved methods shall be used.

424-41. Installation of Heating Cables on Dry Board, in Plaster and on Concrete Ceilings—

(a) Heating cable shall not be installed in walls. It is not designed for this purpose and is strictly forbidden, with the exception that isolated runs of cable may run down a vertical surface to reach a drop ceiling.

(b) Adjacent runs of heating cable shall be spaced not closer than 1½ inches on centers and have a wattage not to exceed 2¾ watts per square foot. See Fig. 424-3.

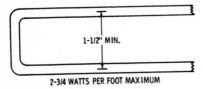

1-1/2" MIN.

2-3/4 WATTS PER FOOT MAXIMUM

Fig. 424-3. Heating cable installed in ceilings shall be spaced at least 1½ inches apart.

(c) Heating cables shall be applied only to gypsum board, plaster lath, or similar fire-resistant materials. If applied to the surface of metal lath or any other conducting material, there shall be a coat of plaster commonly known as a brown or scratch coat applied before the cable is installed. This coating of plaster shall entirely cover the metal lath or conducting surface. See also **Section 424-41(f).**

(d) *All the heating cables, the splice between the heating cable and nonheating leads, and 3 inch minimum of nonheating lead at the splice shall be embedded in plaster or dry board in the same manner as the heating cable.*

(e) On plastered ceilings, the entire surface shall have a finish coat of thermally noninsulating sand plaster or other approved coating which shall have a nominal thickness of ½ inch. Insulation (thermal) plaster shall not be used.

(f) The cable shall be fastened at intervals not to exceed 16 inches by means of taping, stapling, or plaster. Staples or metal fasteners which straddle the cable shall not be used with metal lath or other conducting surfaces. The fastening devices shall be of an approved type.

(g) When dry-board ceilings are used, the cable shall be installed and the entire ceiling below the cable shall be covered with gypsum board not exceeding ½ inch in thickness, but the voids between the two layers and around the cable shall be filled with a conducting plaster or other approved thermal conducting material so that the heat will readily transfer.

(h) Heating cables shall not come in contact with metal or other conducting materials.

(i) *In dry board applications, cable shall be installed parallel to the joist, leaving a clear space centered under the joist of 2½ inches (width) between centers of adjacent runs of cable. Crossing of joist by cable shall be kept to a minimum and should be at the ends of the room. Surface layer of gypsum board shall be mounted so that the nails or other fastenings do not pierce the heating cable.*

424-42. Finished Ceilings—The question often arises as to whether wallpaper or paint may be used over a ceiling that has heating cable. These materials have been used as finishes over heating cable since cables first were used in the late 1940's. This Section gives formal recognition to painting or papering ceilings.

424-43. Installation of Nonheating Leads of Cables and Panels—

(a) Only approved wiring methods shall be used for installing the nonheating leads of cables and panels from junction boxes to the underside of the ceiling. In these installations, single leads in raceways (conductors) or single or multiconductors Type UF, Type NMC, Type MI, or other approved conductors. Please note the absence of Type NM.

(b) Where the nonheating leads terminate in a junction box, there shall be not less than 6 inches of the nonheating leads free within the junction box. Also, the markings of the leads shall be visible in the junction box. This is highly important so that the heating cable can be identified.

(c) *Excess leads shall not be cut but shall be secured to the underside of the ceiling and embedded in plaster or other approved material, leaving only a length sufficient to reach the junction box with not less than 6 inches of free lead within the box.*

305

424-44. Installation of Panels or Cables in Concrete or poured Masonry Floors.—This Section is for fixed indoor space heating and is not to be confused with ice and snow melting, which is covered in **Part G.**

(a) *Panels or heating units shall not exceed 33 watts per square foot of heated area or 16½ watts per linear foot of cable.*

(b) *The spacing between adjacent runs of cable shall not be less than 1 inch on centers.*

(c) Cables have to be secured in place while concrete or other finish material is being applied. Approved means, such as nonmetallic spreaders or frames, shall be used. Concrete floors often have expansion joints in them. Cables, units, and panels shall be so installed that they do not bridge an expansion joint unless they are protected so as to prevent damage to the cables, units, or panels due to expansion or contraction of the floor.

(d) *Spacings shall be maintained between the heating cable and metal embedded in the floor.*

Exception: Grounded metal-clad cable may be in contact with metal embedded in the floor. This includes MI heating cable which is being extensively used.

(e) Sleeving of the leads by means of conduit or EMT shall be used for protection where the leads leave the floor.

(f) The sleeves mentioned in (e) shall have bushings or other approved means used where the leads emerge within the floor slab to prevent damage to the cable.

424-45. Tests During and After Installation—

(a) Great care shall be exercised in the installation of embedded heating cables to prevent any damage thereto. In addition, the installation *shall be inspected and approved before cables are covered or concealed.*

(b) After plastering ceilings or pouring floors, the cables shall be tested to see that the insulation resistance is within safe limits.

424-46. Panels-General—Sections 424-46 *to* **48** *cover only heating panels of less than 25 watts per square foot assembled together in the field to form a heating installation in one room or area using approved methods of interconnection. Such an installation shall be connected by a recognized wiring method.*

424-47. Panels to be Complete Units—*Panels shall be installed as complete units unless approved for field cutting in a recognized manner.*

424-48. Installation—*Panels shall be installed in an approved manner. Nails, staples, or other electrically conducting fasteners shall not be used where they penetrate current-carrying parts.*

Exception: Insulated fasteners may be used with systems for which they are recognized.

F. Duct Heaters

424-57. General—*The provisions in* **Part F** *shall apply to any heater mounted in the air stream of a forced air system where the air moving unit is not provided as an integral part of the equipment.*

424-58. Approval—*Heaters installed in an air duct shall be approved for the purpose and installed in the approved manner.* Look for the UL Label and check the installation instructions closely.

424-59. Air Flow—Air flow over the face of the heater must be adequate and uniform in order to be assured of no hot spots, etc. If the heaters are mounted within 4 feet of a fan outlet, elbow, baffle plate, or other obstruction that might be present in the duct work and which might interfere with adequate and uniform air flow, it may be required to use turning vanes, pressure plates, or some other device on the inlet side of the duct heater to assure that the air flow will be uniform over the face of the heater.

424-60. Elevated Inlet Temperature—Many duct heaters are used with heat pumps or other sources of air that are above room temperature. The operation of the heater may not be the same with an elevated air temperature at the inlet as it would be with the inlet temperature at room temperature. Therefore, the heater shall be approved for operation at higher inlet temperatures and shall be so marked.

424-61. Installation of Duct Heaters with Heat Pumps and Air Conditioners—A duct heater installed immediately adjacent to an air conditioner or heat pump under abnormal operating conditions could adversely affect electrical equipment in the heat pump or air conditioner. It has been found that the duct heater shall be mounted not less than 4 feet from such equipment, unless the duct heater has been approved for closer mounting and is so marked.

424-62. Condensation—*Duct heaters used with air conditioners or other air cooling equipment which may result in condensation of moisture shall be approved for use with air conditioners.*

424-63. Fan Circuit Interlock—A duct heater that operates in such a manner that the fan circuit is not energized with the first heating element might cycle on the high limit. This can cause an undue number of operations with the high limit to occur. Conceivably, in the course of years, the high limit might operate enough times to exceed the 100,000-cycle requirement and become erratic in its operation. By causing the fan motor to be energized with the first heater circuit, we eliminate this potential problem.

424-64. Limit Controls—In order to prevent overheating, each duct heater is required to be provided with an integral approved automatic-reset temperature limiting control or controllers to de-energize the circuits if the temperature rises too high.

In addition, an integral independent supplementary control or controllers shall be provided in each duct heater which will disconnect a sufficient number of conductors to interrupt current flow. This device shall be manually resettable or replaceable.

424-65. Location of Disconnecting Means—All control equipment for duct heaters shall be accessible and a disconnecting means provided which shall be installed at or within sight of the controllers for the heating units.

424-66. Installation—*See NFPA Pamphlets Nos. 90A and 90B.*

ARTICLE 426—FIXED OUTDOOR ELECTRIC DE-ICING AND SNOW MELTING EQUIPMENT

A. General

426-1. Scope—*The requirements of this Article shall apply to electrically energized heating units, panels, and cables where embedded in driveways, walks, steps, and other areas.*

426-2. Application of Other Articles—*All requirements of this Code shall apply where applicable.*

426-3. Branch-Circuit Requirements—*Fixed outdoor electric de-icing and snow melting equipment shall be:*

(1) *considered as a continuous load for sizing branch-circuits and subject to the 80% loading,*
(2) *installed according to* **Section 210-24.**

B. Installation

426.9. General—Equipment and materials used for installing fixed outdoor electric de-icing and snow melting systems may be subject to many troubles and possible hazards, so extreme care should be taken in the installation to use approved materials and to install in an approved manner.

426-10. Use—

(a) De-icing and snow melting equipment is approved for use and installation in approved materials.

(b) De-icing and snow melting units shall not be used where exposed to severe physical damage, unless adequately protected.

426-11. Complete Units—

(a) *Units, panels, and cables shall be installed in their complete sizes or lengths as supplied from the manufacturer, except—*

Nonheating leads are required to be marked. They may be shortened if the marking, which will be specified a little later in **Section 426-26,** is retained. No units that do not bear nameplates are permitted to be installed.

(b) *Units shall be suitable for use with approved wiring system.*

426-12.   Special-Type   Equipment—If special-types of de-icing or snow melting equipment are to be used which will employ methods of construction or installation other than approved by this Article, they shall not be used or installed unless special permission is granted in writing.

C.   Control and Protection

426-20.   Disconnecting Means—Disconnecting means which opens all ungrounded conductors shall be used for de-icing and snow melting equipment. Branch-circuit switches or circuit breakers may be used for this purpose if readily accessible and marked so as to indicate what position they are in. Never trust any circuit as being de-energized unless proper tests have been performed to assure yourself that they are open.

426-21.   Controllers—

(a) *Thermostats and thermostatically controlled switching devices which indicate an off position and which interrupt line current shall open all ungrounded conductors when the control device is in the off position, and may be used as the disconnecting means.*

(b) *Thermostats and thermostatically controlled switching devices shall be so designed that the circuit cannot be energized automatically after the device has been manually placed in the off position.*

(c) *Thermostats and thermostatically controlled switching devices which do not have an off position are not required to open all ungrounded conductors, but shall not be used as the disconnecting means required in* **Section 426-20.**

426-22.   Overcurrent Protection—**Article 210** covers the overcurrent protection for fixed outdoor de-icing and snow melting equipment. See NEC.

426-23.   Nonheating Leads.—Nonheating leads for panels, cables or units, shall not be installed in the field, but shall be factory assembled and shall consist of approved conductors for the purpose.

426-24.   Installation of Heating Cables, Units, or Panels.

(a) The manufacturers specifications for the installation of embedded assemblies should be followed, as the installation will be governed by the materials in which they are to be embedded. Different materials may require different methods of installation. See NEC.

(b) *Panels or heating units shall not exceed 120 watts per square foot of heated area.*

(c) *The spacing between adjacent cable runs will depend upon the wattage rating of the cable, but in no case shall it be installed less than a 1 inch spacing.*

(d) *Units, panels, and cables shall be installed:*

> *(1) On a substantial asphalt or masonry base at least 2 inches thick and have at least 1½ inches of asphalt or masonry applied over the units, panels, or cables, or*
> *(2) They may be installed over other approved bases and embedded within 3½ inches of masonry or asphalt but not less than 1½ inches from the top surface, or*
> *(3) Equipment which has been specially investigated for other forms of installation shall be installed only in a manner for which it has been investigated.*

(e) *Cables shall be secured in place by frames or spreaders, or other approved means, while the masonry or asphalt is being applied.*

(f) *Cables, units and panels shall not be installed where they bridge expansion joints unless adequately protected from expansion and contraction.*

426-25.   Installation of Nonheating Leads—

(a) If the non-heating leads have a grounding sheath or braid, they may be embedded in masonry or asphalt in the same manner as heating cable without the need of additional protection.

(b) All but 1 to 6 inches of non-heating leads of type TW, or cables with other approved types of insulation which do not have a grounding sheath or braid, shall be installed in conduit, EMT, or other raceway, and this conduit or other protection shall extend a minimum of 1 inch from the factory splice to the heating part of the cable to not more than 6 inches from the factory splice.

(c) Insulated bushings shall be installed on the conduit, EMT, etc., in the masonry or asphalt where the cable emerges from the conduit.

(d) All leads shall be protected where buried in expansion joints; where they emerge from masonry or asphalt they shall be installed in conduit, EMT, or other raceway.

(e) There shall be a minimum of 6 inches of non-heating leads left in junction boxes.

426-26. Marking—*Each heating unit, panel, and cable shall be legibly marked within 3 inches of each end of the nonheating leads with the identification symbol, catalog number, and ratings in volts and watts or amperes.*

426-27. Junction Boxes—All splices, with the exception of factory made splices, shall be made in approved junction boxes, properly made up, and the junction boxes shall be approved for the location in which they are located.

426-28. Grounding—

(a) All exposed metal parts of fixed outdoor electric de-icing and snow melting equipment, raceway, boxes, etc., liable to become energized shall be grounded as required in **Article 250.**

(b) The heating section of the cable, panel, or unit shall have a means for grounding, such as copper braid, lead, copper sheath, or other approved means. Cables, panels, or units that are approved for the purpose will come with this grounding means built-in.

(c) All noncurrent-carrying parts which are liable to become energized shall be bonded together by a continuous (without splice) copper conductor of No. 14 AWG or larger, which shall be carried back to the distribution panel. If the grounding conductor is liable to damage, it shall not be smaller than No. 10 copper. Copper is the only approved material for use in grounding. See **Table 250-95.**

426-29. Tests—Embedded heating installations shall be tested, inspected, and approved before covering. An insulation test should be made.

ARTICLE 430—MOTORS, MOTOR CIRCUITS AND CONTROLLERS

A. General

430-1. (a). Motor Feeder and Branch Circuits—The Articles in the NEC are divided into parts A, B, C, etc., each having a specific heading.

This materially aids in finding the desired information. Once this key to the Code has been mastered, it will seldom be necessary to refer to the index. A very thorough and fine job has been done in setting up the Code structure. *See* **Article 440** *for air-conditioning and refrigeration equipment.*

Diagram 430-1 (a) is an important key to finding the correct Parts and what they cover in this Article. Notice that the Parts are indicated in the right-hand column. Thus, if the concern is with *Motor Running Overcurrent Protection,* notice that it refers to *Part C, Motor Disconnecting Means* in *Part H,* and so on for each part of the circuit. This diagram is extremely helpful and is a prime example of the lengths taken to make the Code easy to use.

(b) General—This part covers general requirement for motors, motor circuits, and controllers which do not properly fall into the remaining Parts of the Article. It might be termed the stepping stone to the rest of the Article.

430-3. Part Winding Motors—This Section has a very complete decription of a part-winding motor. *A part-winding-start induction or synchronous motor is one arranged for starting by first energizing part of its primary (armature) winding and, subsequently, energizing the remainder of this winding in one or more steps. The purpose is to reduce the initial values of the starting current drawn or the starting torque developed by the motor. A standard part-winding-start induction motor is arranged so that one-half of its primary winding can be energized initially and, subsequently, the remaining half can be energized, both halves then carrying the same current. A sealed "hermetic type" refrigeration compressor motor is not to be considered a standard part-winding-start induction motor.*

When separate overcurrent devices are used with a standard part-winding-start induction motor, each half of the motor winding shall be individually protected in accordance with **Sections 430-32** and **430-37,** *except that the trip current shall be one-half that specified.*

Each motor winding connection shall have short circuit and ground fault protection rated not more than one-half that specified in **Section 430-52** *except that a single device having this half rating may be used for both windings if this will allow the motor to start.*

430-4. In Sight From—For some reason this ruling causes trouble. The term *in sight* will be used in this Article at various times, and it means literally that the equipment in question must be capable of being seen from the control point but shall not be more than 50 feet away, even though in sight.

430-5. Other Articles—See NEC.

430-6. **Ampacity Determination**—Ampacities shall be determined as follows:

(a) **General Motor Applications.** This part is very important and should be carefully read. Whenever the current rating of a motor is used for figuring the ampacity of conductors, switches, branch-circuit overcurrent devices, etc., the actual motor nameplate current rating shall not be used. Instead, **Tables 430-147, 430-148, 430-149,** and **430-150,** which give full-load currents for Direct-Current Motors, Single-Phase AC Motors, Two-Phase AC Motors, and Three-Phase AC Motors are used.

Separate motor overcurrent (running) protection is to be figured from the actual nameplate current rating. When a motor is marked in amperes instead of horsepower, the horsepower rating shall be assumed to correspond to the values given in **Tables 430-147, 430-148, 430-149,** and **430-150.** At times, it may be necessary to interpolate to arrive at an intermediate horsepower rating.

Exception: For multispeed motors, see **Sections 430-22(a) and 430-52.**

(b) **Torque Motors.** This sub-section is new. It is required because of the increased usage of torque motors. *For torque motors the rated current shall be locked-rotor current and this nameplate current shall be used to determine the ampacity of the branch-circuit conductors* **(see Section 430-22** *and* **430-24)** *and motor operating overcurrent protection. For motor controllers and disconnecting means, see* **Section 430-83, Exception 4 and Section 430-110.**

The main point is that the current rating of a torque motor is the locked-rotor current. This current will appear on the nameplate and is to be used in ampacity calculations.

430-7. Marking on Motors and Multimotor Equipment—

(a) **Usual Motor Applications.** *A motor shall be marked with the following information:*

(1) *Makers' name.*
(2) *Rated volts and full-load amperes.*
(3) *Rating frequency and number of phase, if an alternating-current motor.*
(4) *Rated full-load speed.*
(5) *Rated temperature rise or the insulation system class and rated ambient temperature.*
(6) *Time rating.*
(7) *Rated horsepower if ⅛ horsepower or more.*

313

(8) *Code letter if an alternating-current motor rated ½ horse-power or more* **(see Section 430-7(b)).**

(9) *Secondary volts and full-load amperes if a wound-rotor induction motor.*

(10) *Winding: Straight Shunt, Stabilized Shunt, Compound or series, if a direct-current motor.*

A multispeed motor, except a shaded-pole or permanent-split capacitor motor, shall be marked with the amperes and horsepower at each speed. A motor provided with a thermal protector complying with **Section 430-32(a-2)** *or* **430-32(c-2)** *shall be marked "Thermally Protected."*

Exception No. 1. On motors of arc welders, the horsepower rating may be omitted.

Exception No. 2. On polyphase wound-rotor motors the code letter shall be omitted.

A very fine editorial job has been done on this as well as many points clarified.

(b) Locked Rotor Indicating Code Letters. The Code letters marked on the motor nameplate show the kilovolt-ampere input per horsepower when the rotor is locked. These code letters are given in **Table 430-7(b)** and also used with **Table 430-152** in determining branch-circuit overcurrent protection.

(1) *Multi-speed motors shall be marked with the code letter designating the locked-rotor KVA per horsepower for the highest speed at which the motor can be started, except constant horsepower motors which shall be marked with the code letter giving the highest locked-rotor KVA per horsepower.*

(2) *Single-speed motors starting on Y connection and running on delta connections shall be marked with a code letter corresponding to the locked-rotor KVA per horsepower for the Y connection.*

(3) *Dual-voltage motors which have a different locked-rotor KVA per horsepower on the two voltages shall be marked with the code letter for the voltage giving the highest locked-rotor KVA per horsepower.*

(4) *Motors with 60- and 50-cycle ratings shall be marked with a code letter designating the locked-rotor KVA per horse-power on 60 cycles.*

(5) *Part-winding-start motors shall be marked with a code letter designating the locked-rotor KVA per horsepower that is based upon the locked-rotor current for the full winding of the motor.*

(c) Torque Motors. Torque motors have a standstill-rated operation, so all of the markings as covered in **(a)** of this Section will apply except that locked-rotor torque shall replace horsepower.

(d) Multimotor and Combination Load Equipment. See the NEC. This marking is needed for multimotor and combination load equipment because often the individual nameplates are not visible after mounting. It may be very difficult for both the inspector and the installing contractor to determine which loads may or may not be in operation at the same time, and this is necessary to determine the minimum circuit ampacity and maximum rating of the circuit protective device required. Such information can best be furnished by the equipment builder who knows the conditions of operation, thereby minimizing the chance of errors in field calculations where the specific conditions may not be known.

Later in **Section 430-52** we will find the next part very useful: *Combination controllers employing adjustable instantaneous circuit breakers (without time delay) shall be clearly marked to indicate the ampere settings of the adjustable trip element.*

Where a controller is built in as an integral part of a motor or of a motor-generator set, the controller need not be individually marked when the necessary data is on the motor nameplate. For controllers which are an integral part of equipment approved as a unit, the above marking may be on the equipment nameplate.

A considerable portion of the above applies to the manufacturer, but it is also very essential that the trade and inspectors know what and where to look.

430-8. Marking on Controllers—Controllers shall be marked as follows:

(1) Manufacturer's name or identification.
(2) Voltage.
(3) The current or horsepower rating.
(4) Any other data which might be necessary to indicate the proper application of the motor.
(5) *A controller which includes motor running overcurrent protection, when suitable for group motor application shall be marked with the motor running overcurrent protection and the maximum branch circuit overcurrent protection for such application.*

Where a controller is built in as an integral part of a motor or of a motor-generator set, the controller need not be individually marked when the necessary data is on the motor nameplate.

430-9. Marking at Terminals—See NEC.

430-10. Wiring Space in Enclosures—In **Article 373** it was stated that switches were not intended to be used as junction boxes or wireways.

315

This ruling also includes enclosures for controllers and disconnecting means for motors. Neither shall they be used as junction boxes or raceways for conductors feeding through or tapping off to other apparatus unless they are specifically designed for this purpose. Other means, such as auxiliary gutters, junction boxes, etc., shall be used instead.

430-11.   Protection Against Liquids—Motors that are mounted directly under or in locations where dripping or spraying oil, water, or other injurious liquids may occur shall be either suitably protected or designed for the existing conditions.

430-12.   Motor Terminal Housings—You are referred to this Section of the NEC, but for the first time, the 1968 NEC gives us usable information as to cover-opening sizes and the volume of terminal housings for motors. In addition, nonmetallic housing are approved in some cases.

Incorporated in this Section is **Table 430-12(b), Terminal Housing— Wire to Wire Connections.** This Table gives us the horsepower, minimum cover opening dimension, and the minimum usable volume. Please note, however, that nothing is stated concerning the voltages of the motors.

In part **(c)** we find two tables. **Table 430-12 (c) (1) Terminal Spacings—Fixed Terminals,** gives us the information necessary for terminal housings. enclosing rigidly-mounted motor terminals, while **Table 430-12(c) (2) lists the usable volumes.** All of this is information pertinent to the manufacturer and to the trade as well.

430-13.   Bushings—All conductors to the motor, including leads, shall be properly bushed to prevent abrasion and deterioration by oils. greases, or other contaminants.

430-14.   Location of Motors—

(a) Ventilation and Maintenance. Motors shall be located so as to give adequate ventilation and provide room for normal maintenance, such as greasing of bearings and changing of brushes.

(b) Open Motors. Open motors that have commutators or slip rings shall be so located that sparks from the brushes will not ignite combustibles. This does not prohibit the mounting of motors on wooden floors or supports.

430-16.   Overheating from Dust Accumulations—Motors in locations where dust or flying materials will accumulate within the motor in such quantities as to interfere with the cooling and thereby cause dangerous temperatures, shall be replaced with types that are suitable for the conditions. There are many types of motors designed to eliminate the accumulation of dusts, dirt, etc. If extremely severe conditions exist, pipe-ventilated motors should be used or the motors located in reasonable dust-free rooms.

430-17. Highest Rated (Largest) Motor—*In determining compliance with* **Sections 430-24, 430-53(b), 430-53(c),** *and* **430-62(a),** *the highest rated (largest) motor shall be considered to be that motor which has the highest rated full-load current. The full-load current used to determine the highest rated motor shall be the equivalent value corresponding to the motor horsepower rating selected from* **Tables 430-147, 430-148, 430-149,** *and* **430-150.**

You are advised that it might be possible in calculations to become fooled by the horsepower rating and find that you should, in fact have taken the full-load currents instead.

B. Motor Circuit Conductors

430-21. General—*The provisions of* **Part B** *specify sizes of conductors capable of carrying the motor current without overheating under the conditions specified.*

(a) The provisions covering Grounding in **Article 250** and Conductors in General in **Article 310** are not intended to apply to conductors which form an integral part of equipment such as motors, motor controllers, etc. See **Sections 300-1(b)** and **310-1(c).**

430-22. Single Motor—

(a) Branch-circuit conductors that supply a single motor shall have an ampacity of not less than 125% of the full-load current of the motor. Remember that the ampacity in **Tables 430-147** through **430-150** will govern the branch-circuit conductor calculations, and not the nameplate amperes.

In case of a multispeed motor, the selection of branch circuit conductors on the line side of the controller shall be based on the highest of the full load current ratings shown on the motor nameplate; selection of branch circuit conductors between the controller and the motor, which are energized for that particular speed, shall be based on the current rating for that speed.

Exception: Conductors for a motor used for short-time, intermittent, periodic, or varying duty shall have an ampacity not less than the percentage of the motor nameplate current rating as shown in **Table 430-22 (a-Exception)** *unless the authority enforcing the Code grants special permission for conductors of smaller size.* Notice that there is a variation of from 85% up to as high as 200% in **Table 430-22.** This is why it is necessary to use this Table instead of the 125% usually used.

(b) *The conductors between a stationary motor rated one horsepower or less, and the separate terminal enclosures permitted in* **Section 430-145(b)** *may be smaller than No. 14 but not smaller than No.*

317

18, provided they have an ampacity as specified in **Table 430-22 (a-Exception)**.

430-23. Wound-Rotor Secondary—

(a) *For continuous duty the conductors connecting the secondary of a wound-rotor alternating-current motor to its controller shall have an ampacity which is not less than 125 per cent of the full-load secondary current of the motor.*

(b) *For other than continuous duty, these conductors shall have an ampacity, in percent of full load secondary current, not less than that specified in* **Table 430-22 (a-Exception)**.

(c) The secondary resistor of a wound-rotor motor is not always a part of the controller and may be located elsewhere. In this case, **Table 430-23(c)** will give the percentage of full-load secondary current from which the ampacity of the conductor that may be used can be figured. Always remember that an oversized conductor is far better than a conductor that is too small.

430-24. Conductors Supplying Several Motors—Conductors that supply several motors sometimes cause confusion. The basic rule is that 125% of the ampacity of the largest motor is taken, plus the ampacity (100%) of the other motors connected. This applies when there are two or more motors. It will be recalled that **Tables 430-147** through **430-150** give the ampacity used for figuring conductor sizes.

Example: For four 3-phase, 220-volt motors, the following ratings would be used to figure the service-entrance conductors:

Motor Size	Ampacity from Table 430-150
25 HP	64
25 HP	64
5 HP	15
10 HP	27
Total amperes	170
Plus 25% of 64	16
Ampacity to use in figuring the conductors	186

The preceding example will not apply when one or more motors are used on short-time, intermittent, periodic, or varying duty. In this case, 125% of the nameplate full-load current of the largest continuous-duty motor, or the highest current obtained by multiplying the applicable percentage of **Table 430-22 (a-Exception)** by the nameplate full-load current of the noncontinuous-duty motor (whichever is the larger), plus the nameplate full-load currents of the other motors, each multiplied by 100% or the applicable percentage of the Table, whichever is smaller.

In using this second part, be certain that the duty cycle of **Table 430-22 (a-Exception)** is properly used.

Exception: When the circuitry is so interlocked as to prevent the starting and running of a second motor or group of motors, the conductor size shall be determined from the larger motor or group of motors that are to be operated at a given time.

Cases of interlocking, where only part of the motors may be operated at a given time, are often encountered. In such a case this is taken into consideration as the conductors will not be called upon to serve all motors at the same time.

430-25. Supply Conductors—

(a) **Combination Load—**When one or more motors is served from a circuit that also has a lighting and appliance load, the lighting and appliance load is computed from **Article 220** or other applicable Sections. The conductors shall have sufficient ampacity to carry this appliance and lighting load as calculated, plus the motor-load ampacity as calculated for a single motor in **Section 430-22** or for two or more motors in accordance with **Section 430-24.**

(b) **Multimotor and Combination Load Equipment.** *The ampacity of the conductors supplying multimotor and combination load equipment shall not be less than the minimum circuit ampacity marked on the equipment in accordance with* **Section 430-7(d).**

430-26. Feeder Demand-Factor—The authority enforcing the Code may grant special permission for feeder conductors to be of less capacity than specified in **Sections 430-24** and **430-25** where motors operate on duty-cycle, intermittently, or where all motors do not operate at the same time.

430-27. Capacitors with Motors—Capacitors are used for power-factor correction and will change the current that the conductor will be required to carry. Figuring loads where capacitors are used on motors is covered in **Sections 460-7, 460-8,** and **460-9.**

C.   Motor and Branch Circuit Running Overcurrent (Overload) Protection

430-31.   General—This Part gives the overcurrent protection that is intended to protect the motors, the motor controllers, and the branch-circuit conductors from overheating due to motor overloads. When a motor controller continually trips, do not merely raise the value of the overcurrent protection—there is something that is causing the trouble, such as low voltage, high voltage, high ambient temperatures, unbalanced

319

voltages, or an overload on the motor. Take time to evaluate the cause and remedy the trouble.

(a) Overload is defined as *an operating overcurrent which, when it persists for a sufficient length of time, would cause damage or dangerous overheating of the apparatus.* This does not include short circuits or ground faults. The Code sets up the maximum overcurrent protection that is permitted for various motors. This is a proven value and should be followed.

(b) NFPA Standard for Centrifugal Pumps (No. 20) sets up provisions for overcurrent protection for equipment such as fire pumps, where the overcurrent would be the less of the hazards. The reference to NFPA No. 20 makes it a part of the NEC.

430-32.   Continuous Duty Motors—

(a) More Than One Horsepower. *Each continuous duty motor rated more than one horsepower shall be protected against overcurrent by one of the following means:* (Please note that it states *over one horsepower*).

   (1) *A separate overcurrent device which is responsive to motor current. This device shall be rated or selected to trip at no more than the following per cent of the motor full-load current rating:*
   Motors with a marked service factor not less than 1.15-125%
   Motors with a marked temperature rise not over 40°C-125%

   All other motors
For a multispeed motor, each winding connection shall be considered separately. This value may be modified as permitted by **Section 430-34.**
When a separate motor running-overcurrent device is so connected that it does not carry the total current designated on the motor nameplate, such as for wye-delta starting, the proper percentage of nameplate current applying to the selection of setting of the overcurrent device shall be clearly designated on the equipment or the manufacturer's selection table shall take this into account.

   (2) An integral thermal protector supplied with the motor and approved for the purpose will be acceptable if it prevents damage or overheating of the motor in case of overload and failure to start. In the case where there is a separate current-interrupting device, apart from the motor, and this device is actuated by the integral thermal device, it shall be arranged so that the interruption of the control circuit will interrupt the current to the windings. An example of this is a thermal protector built into the winding of a motor that interrupts the control current to a magnetic coil.

320

(3) *For motors larger than 1500 horsepower, a protective device employing embedded temperature detectors which cause current to the motor to be interrupted when the motor attains a temperature rise greater than that marked on the nameplate in an ambient of 40°C.* The standards for the application of embedded temperature detectors are covered by the USA standards for Rotating Electrical Machinery, USAS C50.2-1955 and C50.4-1965.

(b) One Horsepower or Less, Manually Started. See NEC.

(1) This gives us the method of overcurrent protection for motors of continuous duty rated at one horsepower or less and the protection required, namely the branch-circuit device that protects the conductors. It is also stated that such a motor may be used at 125 volts or less on a branch circuit protected at 20 amperes.

(2) This portion tells us that any motor located out of sight of the controller, and any motor rated at one horsepower or less which is permanently installed, have to be protected as in the next part **(c)**.

(c) One Horsepower or Less, Automatically Started. *Any motor of one horsepower or less which is started automatically shall be protected against overcurrent by the use of one of the following means:*

(1) *A separate overcurrent device which is responsive to motor current. This device shall be rated or selected to trip at no more than the following percent of the motor full-load current rating:*

Motors with a marked service factor not less than 1.5..125%
Motors with a marked temperature rise not over 40°C..125%
All other motors 125%

(2) An integral thermal protector supplied with a motor and approved for the purpose will be considered as acceptable. This type of protector prevents damage or overheating of the motor in case of overload or failure to start. In the case where a separate current-interrupting device, apart from the motor, is actuated by the integral thermal device, it shall be arranged so that the interruption of the control circuit will interrupt the current to the motor windings.

(3) *The motor shall be considered as being properly protected where it is part of an approved assembly which does not normally subject the motor to overloads and if there is a protective device integral with the motor which will protect the motor against damage due to failure to start, or if the assembly is also equipped with other safety controls* *(such as the safety combustion controls of a domestic oil burner) which protect the motor against damage due to failure to start. Where the assembly has safety controls which protect the motor it shall be so indicated on the nameplate of the assembly where it will be visible after installation.*

(4) Motors that have a winding impedance high enough to prevent overheating due to failure to start will be considered as protected when complying with (b) of this Section if they are manually started.

Many alternating-current motors of less than 1/20 horsepower, such as clock motors, series motor, etc., and also some larger motors, such as torque motors, come within this classification. It does not include split-phase motors having automatic switches to disconnect the starting windings.

(d) **Wound-Rotor Secondaries.** *The secondary circuits of wound-rotor alternating-current motors, including conductors, controllers, resistors, etc., shall be considered as protected against overcurrent by the motor-running overcurrent device.*

430-33. Intermittent and Similar Duty—See NEC.

430-34. Selection or Setting of Protective Device—This Section allows for overcurrent protection where the proper size devices are not available. Where the values specified for the running overcurrent protection for a motor is not built to the standard sizes or ratings of fuses, nonadjustable circuit breakers, thermal cutouts, thermal relays, heating elements of thermal-trip motor switches, or possible settings of adjustable circuit breakers adequate to carry the load, the next higher size, rating, or setting may be used. Other types of motors shall not exceed 130% of their full-load current rating. In cases where the overcurrent protection is not shunted during starting time, it shall have sufficient delay to allow starting and acceleration of the load. See NEC, which gives the percentages allowable for overcurrent protection.

430-35. Shunting During Starting Period—

(a) For manually started motors, which also includes motors using a magnetic starter and push-button start (if approved for this use), it is allowable to shunt or cut out the overcurrent protection during start, providing that the shunting device cannot be left in use after starting and that the fuses or time-delay circuit breakers are rated or set so as not to exceed 400% of the full-load motor current and that these fuses or circuit breakers are so located as to be in the circuit during starting.

(b) It is not permissible to shunt or cut out overcurrent running protection on automatically started motors.

430-36. Fuses–In Which Conductor—*Where fuses are used for motor-running protection, a fuse shall be inserted in each ungrounded conductor.*

Exception: A fuse shall also be inserted in the grounded conductor when the supply is 3-wire, 3-phase AC, one condutor grounded.

In the past there has been much discussion over what is now covered in the Exception. This will clarify the matter. For instance, if the fuse were not in the grounded phase, serious results could occur when one phase opened on a 3-phase irrigation pump motor on a grounded phase Delta system.

430-37. Devices Other Than Fuses – In Which Conductor — The **Table 430-37** and its footnotes have been under discussion for a long time. The 1971 NEC straightens this out and you just as well purchase all 3-phase starters with 3 overload units. See the NEC.

430-38. Number of Conductors Opened by Overcurrent Device—See NEC.

430-39. Motor Controller as Running Overcurrent Protection—Motor controllers may serve as running overcurrent protection for motors under the following conditions:

(1) Where the number of overcurrent devices comply with **Table 430-37.**

(2) Where these overcurrent protective devices are operable both during starting and running when used with direct-current motors.

(3) When in the running position when used with alternating-current motors. When nonautomatic motor controllers serve as the running overcurrent protection for motors, it is recommended that all ungrounded conductors be opened. Always follow Code recommendations.

It is clear that practically all three-phase motor installations shall have three running overcurrent units or other approved means for running overcurrent protection. Many inspection authorities will accept dual-element motor fuses as the other approved means if they are sized properly and the fuse box marked with a warning as to what the replacement is to be. In fact, these dual-element fuses are a very economical form of motor insurance in addition to the three overcurrent units.

430-40. Thermal Cutouts and Overload Relays—*Thermal cutouts, overload relays, and other devices for motor-running protection which are not capable of opening short circuits, shall be protected by fuses or circuit breakers with ratings or settings or by a motor short-circuit protector in accordance with* **Section 430-52,** *unless approved for group* *installation and marked to indicate the maximum size of fuse or time limit circuit breaker by which they must be protected.*

Exception: The fuse or circuit breaker ampere rating may be marked on the nameplate of approved equipment in which thermal cutout or relay is used. For instantaneous circuit breakers or motor short-circuit protectors, see **Section 430-52.**

430-42. Motors on General Purpose Branch Circuits—Article 210 covers the connection of certain motors on general-purpose branch circuits but the overcurrent protection of motors on general purpose branch circuits shall conform to the following:

(a) One or more motors may be connected to general-purpose branch circuits without individual overcurrent protection of the motor or motors provided the requirement of **Section 430-53(a)** are complied with.

(b) Motors rated at over 1 horsepower, as covered in **Section 430-53(a),** may be connected to general-purpose branch-circuits only where each motor has its own running overcurrent protection which meets the overcurrent ratings specified in **Section 430-32.** Both the controller and the motor-running overcurrent device shall be approved for group installation with the protective device of the branch circuit to which they are connected. See **Section 430-53.**

(c) When a motor is connected to a branch circuit by means of a plug and receptacle, and it has no individual overcurrent protection as allowed in **Section 430-42(a),** the rating of the plug and receptacle shall not exceed:

(1) 15 amperes at 125 volts.

(2) 10 amperes at 250 volts.

Where a motor is connected to a branch circuit by means of a plug and receptacle and is used as a motor or motor operated appliance, and also meets the requirements of **Section 430-42(b),** the running overcurrent device shall be an integral part of the motor or appliance. The rating of the plug and receptacle shall be assumed to determine the rating of the circuit to which the motor may be connected. See **Section 210.**

(d) Motors take considerable current on start. Therefore, it is required that branch-circuit overcurrent devices for motors shall have sufficient time delay to allow them to accelerate their load.

430-43. Automatic Restarting—Care shall be taken in installing motors that automatically restart after the overcurrent protection trips. Such a protection device shall not be installed unless it is approved for use with the motor which it protects. When a motor can restart automatically after overcurrent tripping, it shall be so installed that an injury to persons cannot result from its automatic starting.

D. Motor-Branch-Circuit Short Circuit and Ground Fault Protection

430-51. General—This Part is intended to specify protection for branch-circuit conductors that supply motors, motor control apparatus, and the motors against overcurrent due to short circuits and ground faults. These provisions are in addition to or amendatory to the provisions of **Article 240**.

430-52. Rating or Setting for Individual Motor Circuit—The motor branch circuit overcurrent device shall be capable of carrying the starting current of the motor. Short circuit and ground fault current will be considered as being taken care of when the overcurrent protection equals the values in **Tables 430-152**. An instantaneous-trip circuit breaker (without time delay) shall be used only:

(1) If it is adjustable.

(2) If it is a part of a combination controller that has overcurrent protection in each conductor.

(3) If the combination has been approved.

In case the values for branch-circuit protective devices determined by **Table 430-152** *do not correspond to the standard sizes or ratings of fuses, nonadjustable circuit breakers, or thermal devices, or possible settings of adjustable circuit breakers adequate to carry the load, the next higher size, rating or setting may be used. See* **Section 240-5(b)** *for standard ratings.*

There are exceptions where the overcurrent protection as specified in **Table 430-152** will not take care of the starting current of the motor.

Exception: Where the overcurrent protection specified in **Table 430-152** *is not sufficient for the starting current of the motor:*

a. *The rating of a nontime-delay fuse or time-limit circuit breaker may be increased but shall in no case exceed 400 percent of the full-load current.*

b. *The ratings of a time-delay (dual-element) fuse may be increased but shall in no case exceed 225 percent of the full-load current.*

c. *The setting of an instantaneous-trip circuit breaker (without time delay) may be increased over 700 percent but shall in no case exceed 1,300 percent of the motor full-load current.*

325

d. Torque motor branch circuits shall be protected at the motor nameplate current rating. See **Section 240-5(a),** *Exception No. 1.*

Where maximum protective device ratings are shown in the manufacturer's heater table for use with a marked controller or are otherwise marked with the equipment, they shall not be exceeded even if higher values are allowed as shown above. See Example No. 8, Chapter 9, and Diagram 430-1(a) of the NEC.

430-53. Several Motors or Loads on One Branch Circuit—*Two or more motors or a motor(s) and other loads may be connected to the same branch circuit under the following conditions:*

(a) Two or more motors of one horsepower or less, that do not have a full-load rating of more than 6 amperes, may be used on branch circuits that are protected at not more than 20 amperes at 125 volts or less, or on branch circuits rated at not more than 15 amperes at 600 volts or less. Individual running overcurrent protection for these motors is not required unless specifically called for in **Section 430-32.**

(b) If it is determined that the branch-circuit protective device will not open under the most severe normal operating conditions that might be encountered, and the branch-circuit protective device is not larger than allowed in **Section 430-52,** then two or more motors, each having individual running overcurrent protection, may be connected to one branch circuit.

(c) *Two or more motors of any rating or a motor(s) and other load(s), with each motor having individual running overcurrent protection, may be connected to one branch circuit provided all of the following conditions are complied with:*

(1) *Each motor-running overcurrent device must be approved for group installation.* This is an item that is often overlooked.

(2) Each motor controller must also be approved for group installation.

(3) *Each circuit breaker must be of the time limit type and approved for group installation.*
There are two musts in this; (1) the circuit breakers must be of the time-limit type; (2) the breakers shall be approved for group installation. This requires local approval, or preferably, UL approval.

(4) The branch circuit shall be protected by *fuses* or *time limit circuit breakers*. The ratings of these fuses or circuit breakers are governed by **Section 430-52** and also by **Tables 430-152** and **430-153.** This rating is for the largest motor connected to the branch circuit, to which is added amounts equal to the full-load currents of all other motors that are connected to the same branch circuit and the ratings of other loads connected to the same branch circuit, plus the ratings of other loads connected to the same branch circuit. *Where the calculations result in a rating less than the ampacity of the supply conductors, the rating of the fuses or circuit breakers may be increased to a value not exceeding the ampacity of the supply conductors.*

(5) Section 430-40 concerns **thermal cutouts and overload relays.** In calculating the branch-circuit fuses or time-limit circuit breakers, **Section 430-40** must be considered. The fuses or breakers shall not be larger than the thermal cutout or relay protecting the smallest motor of the group.

(6) *The conductors of any tap supplying a single motor need not have individual branch circuit protection, provided they comply with either of the following:*

(1) All of the conductors to the motor shall have an ampacity of at least that of the branch-circuit conductors.

(2) Conductors to a motor shall:

(a) Not have an ampacity of less than 1/3 that of the branch-circuit conductors.

(b) Meet the requirements of **Section 430-22,** which requires an ampacity of at least 125% that of the full-load current of the motor.

(c) The conductors to the motor-running protection shall not exceed 25 feet in length and shall be protected from physical damage.

(d) *For the purpose of this Section, a room air conditioner shall be treated as a single motor unit in determining its branch circuit requirements when all of the following conditions are met:*

(1) *The unit is cord connected.* You will recall that air-conditioning units are to have cords with an equipment grounding conductor.

(2) *Its rating is not more than 40 amperes full-load current and 250 volts, single-phase.* Referring back, it will be recalled that when one appliance is on a branch circuit, the full-load current shall not be more than 80% of the branch-circuit rating. Therefore, this allows an air conditioner with this rating to be installed on a 50-ampere branch circuit, provided that the circuit breaker is of the time-delay type.

(3) *Total full-load current is shown on the unit nameplate rather than that of the individual motor currents.* An air conditioner will have two or more motors, and the nameplate rating is to take care of the total current, not merely that of the compressor unit.

327

(4) The rating of the branch-circuit devices shall not exceed the ampacity of the branch-circuit conductors. The receptacle into which the air conditioner is plugged shall be of the proper rating and must comply with **Section 430-40.**

430-54. Multi-Motor and Combination Load Equipment—Multimotor and combination load equipment is covered in **Section 430-7(d).** The rating of the branch-circuit protective device for this purpose shall not exceed the rating on the equipment provided for this purpose.

430-55. Combined Overcurrent Protection—The overcurrent protection may be combined in one piece of equipment with the branch-circuit overcurrent protection and motor-running overcurrent protection when the setting or rating of the devices provides the 115% and 125% overcurrent running protection as specified in **Section 430-32.**

430-56. Overcurrent Devices—In Which Conductor—Overcurrent devices shall open all ungrounded conductors of the circuit as required by **Section 240-11.** They may also open the grounded conductor if it is opened simultaneously with the ungrounded conductors.

430-57. Size of Fuseholder—Where fuses are used in branch circuits for motor protection, the fuseholders shall not be smaller than required to accommodate fuses as specified by **Section 430-152.** An exception to this would be when time-delay fuses are used that have appropriate characteristics for motors, in which case the fuseholders may be smaller, but check to make certain that the switch and fuseholders are rated in a HP rating to accommodate the motor. Fuseholder adapters may be used to reduce the size of the fuseholder to adapt to the time-delay motor fuses, but this is not always the best policy as they may be easily removed and a larger size inserted. Check the horsepower rating of fusible switches. See NEC for Exception.

430-58. Rating of Circuit Breaker—*A circuit breaker for motor-branch-circuit protection shall have a current rating in accordance with* **Sections 430-52** *and* **430-110.**

430-59. Feeder Taps in Inacessible Location—If the location of the tap connection to feeder conductors is not accessible (this does not mean that taps can be made in concealed boxes or gutters), the motor-branch-circuit overcurrent device may be placed where it will be accessible, if:

(1) The conductors between the tap and the overcurrent device have the same ampacity as the feeder conductors.
(2) If they have an ampacity of not less than 1/3 that of the feeder conductors and do not exceed 25 feet in length.
(3) If they are not subject to physical damage.

430-60. Selection or Setting of Protective Devices—See NEC.

E. Motor-Feeder Short-Circuit and Ground Fault Protection

430-61. General—*The provisions of* **Part E** *specify overcurrent devices intended to protect feeder conductors supplying motors against overcurrents due to short circuits or grounds.*

430-62. Rating or Setting—Motor Load—

(a) A feeder that supplies a fixed motor load must be calculated as far as the conductor ampacity from **Section 430-24,** which allows a carrying capacity of 125% of the rating of the full-load current of the largest motor plus 100% of the full-load current rating of the other motors. This conductor shall further be protected by overcurrent protection which shall not be greater than allowed for the protection of the largest motor (as figured from **Tables 430-152)** plus the sums of the full-load currents of the other motors.

If two motors of the same rating are used, only one is considered as the larger. This motor is then used to calculate the excess rating and the other motor the 100% rating.

Where two or more motors are started simultaneously, the feeder sizes and overcurrent protection must be figured accordingly and will require higher ratings. See **Example No. 8** in **Chapter 9.**

(b) See NEC.

430-63. Rating or Setting—Power and Light Loads—Where a feeder carries a motor load in addition to lighting and/or appliance loads, the ampacity of the lighting and/or the appliance loads must be figured as in **Articles 210** and **220.** To this is added the capacity for the motor as figured in **Section 430-52** or **Section 430-62.** These totals are combined to determine the ampacity of the feeder conductors and the overcurrent protection for the feeders.

F. Motor Control Circuits

430-71. General—**Part F** *contains modifications of the general requirements and applies to the particular conditions of motor control circuits.*

Control Circuit (Definition): The control circuit of a control apparatus or system is the circuit which carries the electrical signals directing the performance of the controller, but does not carry the main power circuit. This definition should be kept in mind in order to prevent confusing power conductors with control conductors.

430-72. Overcurrent Protection—*Conductors of control circuits shall be protected against overcurrent in accordance with* **Section 240-5(a), Exception No. 4.** This exception is repeated here to assist in clarifying control circuits. *Exception No. 5. Remote Control. Except as provided in*

329

Article 725, *the conductors of the control circuits of remote-control switches shall be considered as protected from overcurrent by overcurrent devices that are not of the so-called time-lag type and are rated or set at not more than 500 per cent of the ampacity of the remote-control conductors, as specified in* **Tables 310-12** *through* **310-15**.

Thus a 500% rating will be considered as protecting control conductors, but only if they are not of the so-called time-lag type. This rules out dual-element fuses and most circuit breakers, as they are of the time-lag type. This is not to infer that they cannot be used for protection, but not for the 500% use which is referred to.

Exception. Such conductors shall be considered as being properly protected by the branch-circuit overcurrent devices under any one of the following conditions:

(1) *Where the rating or setting of the branch-circuit overcurrent device is not more than 500% of the ampacity of the control-circuit conductors.*

There is confusion between this **(1)** and **Exception No. 5** of **Section 240-5.** Part **(1)** overrides **Section 240-5, Exception No. 5** in regard to the time delay not being acceptable. The reason for this is that when delay or dual-element motor fuses are used, they are generally much smaller than the conventional fuse, and it is therefore felt that this part will not apply.

As an example, take the case of a motor protected by 150-ampere branch-circuit overcurrent protection. Unless No. 10 or larger conductors are used for the control circuit, overcurrent protection would have to be provided for the control wires. No. 10 conductors will carry 30 amperes, and 500% of 30 amperes is 150 amperes. Thus the fuses are acceptable as protection for the control wires.

(2) *Where the opening of the control circuit could create a hazard; as for example, the control circuit of fire-pump motors, and the like.*

Here overcurrent protection on the control circuit itself would offer another possible source of failure to prevent the fire pump from working.

For instance, the controls of a compressor, if all on the compressor, will be considered as protected even though the branch-circuit overcurrent protection is more than 500%, or where the control buttons of a magnetic starter are a part thereof.

430-73. Mechanical Protection of Conductor—*Where damage to a control circuit would constitute a hazard, all conductors of such remote-control circuit shall be installed in a raceway or be otherwise suitably protected from physical damage outside the control device itself.* Damage to control wiring might cause an important operation to stop, or might cause a machine to unintentionaly start, causing a hazard.

When one side of the control circuit is grounded, the control circuit shall be so arranged that an accidental ground in the remote control devices will not start the motor. Most circuits have a grounded conductor along with the ungrounded conductor. Extreme care should be exercised to connect the stop and start buttons of a magnetic starter so that it will not energize the magnetic coil and start the motor should one of the conductors become grounded. The same could very easily happen on an ungrounded 480-volt, three-phase circuit which uses a 115-volt grounded system to energize the controls. Grounding one side could cause the motor to start. This item is very important, but so often little attention is paid to the matter.

430-74. Disconnection—

(a) *Control circuits shall be so arranged that they will be disconnected from all sources of supply when the disconnecting means is in an open position. The disconnecting means may consist of two separate devices, one which disconnects the motor and the controller from the source of power supply for the motor, and the other, the control circuit from its power supply. Where the two separate devices are used, they shall be located immediately adjacent one to the other.*

(Author's Note) It is the author's recommendation that the two disconnecting means be marked indicating that both supply sources are disconnected when either of the disconnecting devices are opened.

(b) A transformer or other device is often used to obtain a reduced voltage for the control circuit and is located in the controller. Such a transformer or other device shall be connected to the load side of the disconnecting means for the control circuit, so that when the motor disconnecting means is opened, the control circuit is also de-energized.

G.   Motor Controllers

430-81.   General—*The provisions of* **Part G** *are intended to require suitable controllers for all motors.*

(a) Definition. *For definition of "Controller", see* **Article 100.** *For the purpose of this Article, the term "Controller" includes any switch or device normally used to stop and start the motor.*

(b) Stationary Motor of 1/8 Horsepower or Less. *For a stationary motor rated at 1/8 horsepower or less, that is normally left running and is so constructed that it cannot be damaged by overload or failure to start, such as clock motors and the like, the branch-circuit overcurrent device may serve as the controller.*

331

(c) **Portable Motor of 1/3 Horsepower or Less.** Motors of 1/3 HP or less may use a plug and receptacle and cord connection for a disconnecting means.

430-82. Controller Design—

(a) Every motor controller shall be capable of both starting and stopping the motor which it controls. Controllers for alternating-current motors shall be capable of interrupting the stalled-rotor current. Stalled-rotor current was covered in the first part of this Article. Recall that this current is much higher than the running current and, unless the controller is capable of interrupting this larger current, damage may result to the controller. Controller listings in catalogs show the horsepower rating and the voltage.

(b) **Autotransformer.** Autotransformer controllers are alternating-current devices which incorporate an autotransformer to reduce the voltage and increase the current at start. This will reduce the current drawn from the branch circuit at start.

Autotransformer controllers shall have an OFF, RUN, and at least one START position. More than one start position may be incorporated to accelerate the motor in steps. The design shall be such that the controller cannot remain in the start position, which would render the overcurrent protection inoperative.

(c) **Rheostats.** *Rheostats shall conform to the following:*

(1) **Internal Connections.** Motor-starting rheostats shall be so designed that they will not remain in any of the starting positions or segments when the starting handle is released, but will return to the off position. In addition the design will be such that the first contact will not engage any part of the rheostat.

(2) **Under-Voltage Release, Direct-Current Motors.** Rheostats used as motor-starters on direct current which operate from a constant voltage supply are to be equipped with a device which, should the voltage drop, will release the starter before the motor speed has dropped to less than one-third of its normal speed.

430-83. Rating. *The controller shall have a horsepower rating, which shall not be lower than the horsepower rating of the motor, except as follows:*

Exception No. 1. Stationary Motor of 2 Horsepower or Less. A general use switch may be used as a controller for motors rated at 2 HP or less and 300 volts or less, provided that it has a current rating of at least twice the full-load current rating of the motor with which it is to be used.

On AC circuits it is permissible to use an AC general-use snap switch, but not a general-use AC-DC snap switch, as the controller for motors of 2 HP or less and 300 volts or less, providing that the full-load current rating of the motor does not exceed 80% of the current rating of the snap switch.

Exception No. 2. Circuit Breaker as Controller. A branch circuit circuit breaker, rated in amperes only, may be used as a controller. Where this circuit breaker is also used for overcurrent protection, it shall conform to the appropriate provisions of this Article governing overcurrent protection.

Exception No. 3. Torque Motors. The motor controller shall have a continuous duty full-load current rating not less than the nameplate current of the motor. In case the motor controller is rated in horsepower, but is without the foregoing current rating, the equivalent current rating shall be determined from the horsepower rating by using **Tables 430-147, 430-148, 430-149** *or* **430-150.** These tables give the ampere ratings of different sizes and types of motors. See NEC.

430-84. **Need Not Open All Conductors—Section 430-11** covers controllers that serve as both the controller and the disconnecting means, and these shall open all ungrounded conductors. Where the controller does not serve as both the controller and the disconnect, it need not open all of the conductors, but only those necessary to start and stop the motor.

430-85. **In Grounded Conductors—**There is nothing that prohibits the opening of the grounded conductor if one is used to supply a motor. However, if the grounded conductor is opened, all ungrounded conductors shall be simultaneously opened.

430-86. **Motor Not in Sight from Controller—**A motor not in sight of the controller also includes motors that are at a distance of 50 feet or more, even though they can be seen from the control position. This Section causes many questions in the field. There was a time when a switch that opened a control wire would be accepted as a disconnecting means, but this is no longer true.

Where a motor and the driven machinery are not in sight from the controller location, the installation shall comply with one of the following conditions:

(a) *The controller disconnecting means is capable of being locked in the open position.*

This is a broad ruling and there are many interpretations in the field. A branch-circuit panel with a number of branch circuit breakers, even though the panel has a cover capable of being locked, will usually be ruled by most inspection authorities as not being passable. A switch that opens all ungrounded conductors and may be locked in an open position of course will comply.

333

A great many inspectors will probably require, and rightly so, that the disconnecting means be marked as to what motor-driven machinery it disconnects. They might also require a sign at the motor or machinery stating that the disconnecting means is to be locked in an open position. This is only common sense in that the main purpose of this ruling is safety to anyone who might perform mechanical or electrical work on the motor or the driven machinery.

(b) *A manually operable switch which will disconnect the motor from its source of supply is placed within sight from the motor location.*

This type of installation will give the electrician or mechanic the advantage of being able to see anyone approaching the disconnecting means who might energize the circuit to the motor. If there is a chance that anyone working on the machinery will not be in a position to see the disconnection means, then it should be locked in the open position.

430-87. Number of Motors Served by Each Controller—*Each motor shall be provided with an individual controller.*

Exception: For motors of 600 volts or less a single controller rated at not less than the sum of the horsepower ratings of all of the motors of the group may serve the group of motors under any one of the following conditions:

(a) A single machine or a piece of apparatus, such as metal or woodworking equipment, cranes, hoists, etc., might require several motors in its operation, in which case a single disconnecting means may serve all the motors. Other conditions of this Article, such as overcurrent protection, must also be met.

(b) In **Section 430-53(a)**, more than one motor was permitted to be protected by one overcurrent device if certain requirements as to current and voltage were met.

(c) If a group of motors is located in a single room, and all are within sight of the disconnecting means, then a single disconnecting means may be used.

430-88. Adjustable-Speed Motors—Some motors, especially shunt and compound-wound DC motors, have speed adjustment controlled by the regulation of the field current. Where such is the case, the controller shall be so designed that the motor can not be started with a weakened field unless the motor is specifically designed for such starting. Starting a motor with a weakened field is dangerous and may cause a current high enough to burn out the armature.

430-89. Speed Limitation—See NEC.

430-90. Combination Fuseholder and Switch as Controller—*The rating of a combination fuseholder and switch used as a motor-controller shall be such that the fuseholder will accommodate the size of fuses specified in Part C of* **Article 430,** *for motor-running overcurrent protection.* A fuseholder of larger capacity is permissible if fused down to proper value.

Exception. Where fuses having time delay appropriate for the starting characteristics of the motor are used, fuseholders of smaller size than specified in Part C of **Article 430** *may be used.* Time delay fuses have the advantage of giving additional protection to a motor.

It might be mentioned that, to the author's knowledge, there is presently no combination circuit breaker and magnetic starter that is approved by the Underwriter's Laboratories. A check with the inspector should be made to see if he will approve this type of unit if it is desired to use one.

H. Disconnection Means

430-101. General—*The provisions of* **Part H** *are intended to require disconnecting means capable of disconnecting motors and controllers from the circuit.* Referral is made to **Diagram 430-1(a).**

430-102. In Sight from Controller Location—*A disconnecting means shall be located in sight from the controller location.*

430-103. To Disconnect Both Motor and Controller—*The disconnecting means shall disconnect the motor and the controller from all ungrounded supply conductors and shall be so designed that no pole can be operated independently. The disconnecting means may be in the same enclosure with the controller.* See **Section 430-113.** This section covers those installations where energy is received from more than one source.

430-104. To Be Indicating—Any means of disconnection shall readily indicate whether it is OFF or ON.

430-105. Grounded Conductors—One pole of the disconnecting means may open the grounded conductors if one is used in the circuit. However, if it opens the grounded conductor, it shall also simultaneously open all conductors of the circuit.

430-106. Service Switch as Disconnecting Means—If the installation consists of only one motor, the service switch may be used as a disconnecting means if it meets all of the requirements of this Article.

430-107. Readily Accessible—There shall be no obstructions in the way or ladders needed in the operation of the disconnecting means.

430-108. Every Switch—See NEC.

430-109. **Type**—*The disconnecting means shall be a motor-circuit switch, rated in horsepower, or a circuit breaker, except as follows:*

Exception No. 1. One-Eighth Horsepower or Less. For stationary motors of ⅛ horsepower or less, the branch-circuit overcurrent device may serve as the disconnecting means.

Exception No. 2. Two Horsepower or Less. For stationary motors rated at 2 horsepower or less and 300 volts or less, the disconnecting means may be a general-use switch having an ampere rating not less than twice the full-load current rating of the motor.

Exception No. 3. Over Two Horsepower to and including 100 Horsepower. The separate disconnecting means required for a motor with an autotransformer type of controller may be a general-use switch where all of the following provisions are complied with: **(a) (b) (c)**

(a) *The motor drives a generator which is provided with over-current protection.*

(b) *The controller (1) is capable of interrupting the stalled-rotor current of the motor, (2) is provided with a no-voltage release, and (3) is provided with running-overcurrent protection not exceeding 125 per cent of the motor full-load current rating.* (125% is not allowed in all cases.)

(c) *Separate fuses or a circuit breaker, rated or set at not more than 150 per cent of the motor full-load current, are provided in the motor branch circuit.* Refer to **Tables 430-147** through **430-150** to determine if 150% is sufficient branch-circuit protection. Bear in mind the lower rating permitted with time-delay fuses of the proper and approved type.

Exception No. 4. Exceeding 100 Horsepower. For stationary motors rated at more than 100 horsepower, the disconnecting means may be a motor-circuit switch also rated in amperes, a general-use switch, or an isolating switch.

Isolation switches for motors exceeding 100 horsepower, not capable of interrupting stalled-rotor currents, shall be plainly marked "Do not open under load."

Exception No. 5. Portable Motors. Portable motors may be disconnected by means of a plug and receptacle.

Exception No. 6. Room Air-Conditioners. For room air-conditioners, see **Section 422-43.**

430-110. Ampacity and Interrupting Capacity—

(a) The disconnecting means is required to have an interrupting capacity of at least 115 percent of the full-load current rating of the motor.

(b) *The disconnecting means for a torque motor shall be selected on the basis of the nameplate current as follows:*

(1) *The ampacity shall be at least 115 per cent of the nameplate full-load current.*

(2) To select the type of disconnecting means, as required in **Section 430-109,** use **Tables 430-148** and **430-149.** Use **Table 430-150** for the full-load current rating, and the horsepower rating from **Table 430-151** to select the locked-rotor current.

In the event that the compressor current ratings do not match the current ratings in **Tables 430-148** through **430-150,** use the next higher rating in these tables. In the event that the horsepower ratings obtained by using **Tables 430-148** through **430-150,** and the horsepower obtained from locked-rotor current using **Table 430-151** do not match, use the larger of the two horsepower ratings.

(c) *Where one or more motors are used together or are used in combination with other loads, such as resistance heaters, and where the combined load may be simultaneous on a single disconnecting means, the rating and ampacity of the combined loads are to be determined as follows:*

(1) *The rating of the disconnecting means shall be determined from the summation of all currents, including resistance loads, at the full-load condition and also at the locked-rotor condition. The combined full-load current and the combined locked-rotor current so obtained shall be considered as a single motor for the purpose of this requirement as follows:*

The full-load current equivalent to horsepower rating of each motor shall be selected from **Tables 430-148, 430-149** *and* **430-150.** *These full-load currents shall be added to the rating in amperes of other loads to obtain an equivalent full-load current for the combined load.*

The locked-rotor current equivalent to the horsepower rating of each motor shall be selected from **Table 430-151.** *The locked-rotor currents shall be added to the rating in amperes of other loads to obtain an equivalent locked-rotor current for the combined load. Where two or more motors and/or other loads cannot start simultaneously, appropriate combinations of locked-rotor and full-load current may be employed to determine the equivalent locked-rotor current for the simultaneous combined loads.*

(2) *The ampacity of the disconnecting means shall be at least 115 percent of the summation of all currents at the full-load condition determined in accordance with* **Section 430-110(c)(1).**

(3) *For small motors not covered by* **Tables 430-147, 430-148,**

337

430-149 *or* **430-150,** *the locked-rotor current shall be as-sumed to be 6 times the full-load current.*

(4) *Where part of the concurrent load is resistance load and the disconnecting means is a switch rated in horsepower and amperes, the horsepower rating of the switch shall not be less than the combined load of the motor at the locked-rotor condition and the ampere rating shall not be less than the locked-rotor load plus the resistance load.*

430-111.   Switch or Circuit Breaker as Both Controller and Disconnecting Means—See NEC.

430-112.   Motors Served by a Single Disconnecting Means—See NEC.

430-113.   Energy From More Than One Source—If equipment receives its energy from more than one source, such as the control circuit from an isolation transformer of a different voltage than that of the motor or from a DC source and the motor from an AC source, the disconnecting means for each source (and there must be a disconnecting means for each) shall be located adjacent to each other. *Each source may have a separate disconnecting means.*

J.   Requirements for Over 600 Volts

430-121.   General—This **Part J** covers motors and controllers operating at more than 600 volts. There are special hazards that are encountered at these voltages that must be taken into consideration. Other requirements for circuits and equipment that operate at over 600 volts will be covered in **Article 710.**

430-122.   More Than 7500 Volts—See NEC.

430-123.   Motor Running Overcurrent (Overload) Protection—The overcurrent motor-running protection at voltages over 600 are calculated the same as covered elsewhere in this Article. The overcurrent protection units shall be either circuit breakers or overcurrent units that are an integral part of the controller and shall open all ungrounded conductors simultaneously.

430-124.   Short Circuit and Ground Fault Protection—*Each motor branch circuit and feeder of more than 600 volts shall be protected against overcurrent by one of the following means:*

(a) *A circuit breaker of suitable rating so arranged that it can be serviced without hazard.* An example of this arrangement could be a disconnecting switch or switches that are ahead of the circuit breaker, and that may be opened during work on the equipment. It could also be a form of interlocking equipment to assure the opening of the disconnect, etc. It is also recommended that,

338

after opening, a method of grounding be provided to assure safety while working on the equipment.

(b) Fuses may be oil-filled or another suitable type for use with high voltage. There shall be a suitable disconnecting means in conjunction with the fuses so that they will not have to be replaced while they are energized.

(c) *Differential protection may be employed to protect an alternating-current motor, the motor control apparatus, and the branch-circuit conductors against overcurrent due to short circuits or grounds. When all of these elements are included within the protected zone of a differential protective system, the ratings or settings specified in* **Section 430-52** *do not apply.*

DIFFERENTIAL PROTECTIVE SYSTEM (Definition): A differential protective system is a combination of two or more sets of current transformers and a relay or relays energized from their interconnected secondaries.

430-126. Disconnecting Means—See NEC.

K. Protection of Live Parts—All Voltages

430-131. General—*The provisions of* **Part K** *specify that live parts shall be protected in a manner judged adequate to the hazard involved.*

430-132. Where Required—*Exposed live parts of motors and controllers operating at 50 volts or more between terminals, shall be guarded against accidental contact by enclosure, or by location as follows:*

(a) They may be enclosed in a room or enclosure that is accessible only to qualified persons. The definition of "Qualified Person" in **Article 100:** *One familiar with the construction and operation of the apparatus and the hazard involved.*

(b) They may be installed on a suitable balcony, gallery, or platform that is so elevated and arranged as to keep all unqualified persons away. An open stairway that is not barred or that does not have a gate would not comply.

(c) They shall be elevated 8 feet or more above the floor. This 8-foot requirement appears often in the Code.

(d) They shall be protected by a guard rail when the operating voltage of the motor is 600 volts or less.

Exception: Stationary motors having commutators, collectors and brush rigging located inside of motor end brackets and not conductively connected to supply circuits operating at more than 150 volts to ground. An example might be a wound-rotor motor.

339

430-133. Guards for Attendants—See NEC.

L. Grounding

430-141. General—This **Part L** covers the grounding of motors and controller frames to prevent potentials above ground potential in the event of accidental contact of the live parts and the frames. There are permissible conditions where insulation, isolation, or guarding will suffice instead of grounding the frames.

430-142. Stationary Motors—*The frames of stationary motors shall be grounded where any of the following conditions exist:*

(a) Where the motors are supplied by means of wires in any type of metal raceway.

(b) Where motors are in wet locations and not properly guarded or isolated.

(c) Where a motor operates with any terminal at more than 150 volts to ground.

430-143. Portable Motors—Frames of motors (portable) that operate at more than 150 volts to ground are required to be either guarded or grounded. In **Section 250-45(d),** portable motors in other than residential occupancies were to be grounded where the location was of a damp or wet nature, or where persons might come into contact with grounded objects. An exception to this was that motors that operate at not more than 50 volts or are supplied by an isolation transformer did not need to be grounded. There was also a recommendation that motors that operate at more than 50 volts should be grounded.

430-144. Controllers—Controller cases shall be grounded, regardless of voltage, except as follows:

(1) Controllers attached to ungrounded portable equipment.
(2) Lined covers of snap switches; that is, where the cover is properly insulated.

430-145. Method of Grounding—Grounding of motors and controllers shall conform to **Article 250.**

(a) Grounding Through Terminal Housings. In **Article 250,** Type AC metal-clad cable or metal raceways was, in most cases (except in some hazardous installations), acceptable as a ground if properly installed. Where these types of wiring are used, a junction box shall be provided for the terminals of the motor, and the cable or raceway attached to this junction box as specified in **Article 250.**

(b) Separation of Junction Box from Motor. The junction box, as provided for in **(a)** above, may be separated from the motor a distance not to exceed 6 feet, provided that the leads to the motor are one of the following:

(1) Type AC metal-clad cable.

(2) Armored cable.

(3) Stranded leads enclosed in flexible or rigid conduit or in electrical metallic tubing no smaller than 3/8-inch trade size. Where stranded leads that are protected by one of the means above are used, they shall be no larger than No. 10, and all other requirements for conductors, as provided by the Code, shall be met.

(c) **Grounding of Controller Mounted Devices**—This is new with the 1965 Code. Instrument transformer secondaries and exposed noncurrent carrying metal or other conductive parts or cases of instrument transformers, meters, instruments, and relays shall be grounded as specified in **Sections 250-121** through **250-125.**

The values of current shown in Column 1 are to be taken from **Tables 430-147** through **430-150.** This is the full-load current. If the nameplate current and the current from the Table do not match, use the current given in the Table.

Columns 2 and 3 list the maximum running protection for the motor. This value must be modified if the nameplate full-load current values are different as provided in **Section 430-6.** The current values shown in Columns 2 and 3 must be reduced 8% for all motors other than open-types marked to have a temperature rise of not over 40°C as required by **Section 430-32.**

Columns 4, 5, 6, and 7 list the maximum rating or setting of branch-circuit protective devices, each column having a fuse rating and a circuit-breaker (nonadjustable overload trip) rating. To use this part find the type and Code letter of the motor involved.

There are certain exceptions for Columns 4, 5, 6, and 7, and reference is made to **Sections 430-52** and **430-59.**

See **Section 430-53** for values to be used for several motors on one branch circuit.

For running protection of motors, see **Section 430-32.** For setting motor branch-circuit protective devices, see the Tables in **Section 430-152** and **430-153.** For grouping small motors under the protection of a single set of fuses, see **Section 430-53.**

Read the material preceding the Table, but note in particular that for obtaining the full-load current ratings for motors operating on 208 and 200 volts, the full-load currents shown must be increased by 10 and 15 percent, respectively.

341

Note in the material preceding the Table that on a 2-phase, 3-wire system, the current rating in the conductors will be 1.41 times the values given. Also, at the end of the table, note that for 90 and 80 percent power factor the above figures should be multiplied by 1.1 and 1.25, respectively.

This Table is for use only with **Section 430-83, Exception No. 3,** and **Section 430-110(b).**

ARTICLE 440—AIR-CONDITIONING AND REFRIGERATION EQUIPMENT
A. General

Due to the great numbers of such units in use and the need for special information covering same, this New Article has been introduced.

440-1. Scope—

The provisions of this Article apply to electric motor-driven air-conditioning and refrigeration equipment, and to branch circuits and controllers for such equipment. It provides for the special considerations necessary for circuits supplying sealed (hermetic-type) motor-compressors and for any air-conditioning and/or refrigerating equipment which is supplied from an individual branch circuit which supplies a sealed (hermetic-type) motor-compressor.

440-2. Other Articles—

(a) Provisions in this Article are in addition to or amendatory to **Article 430** and other Articles in the NEC which will apply unless modified by this Article.

(b) Air-conditioning and refrigeration equipment which employ conventional motors, instead of hermetic-type motors, will come under **Articles 422, 424** or **430.** This will include the following units when driven by conventional motors:

(1) Refrigeration compressors.
(2) Furnaces with air-conditioning equipment.
(3) Fan-coil units.
(4) Remote forced-air-cooled condensers.
(5) Remote commercial refrigerators, etc.

(c) The following items are considered as appliances and come under **Article 422:**

1. Room air-conditioners.
2. Household refrigerators.

3. Household freezers.
4. Drinking-water coolers.
5. Beverage dispensers.

(d) *Hermetic motor-compressors, circuits, controllers, and equipment shall also comply with the applicable provisions of the following:*

Capacitors ....**Section 460-9**
Garages, Aircraft Hangars, Gasoline Dispensing and Service
  Stations, Bulk Storage Plants, Finishing Processes and Flamable Anesthetics ....**Articles 511, 513, 514, 516,** and **517E**
Hazardous Locations ....**Articles 500** thru **503**
Motion-Picture Studios ....**Article 530**
Resistors and Reactors ....**Article 470**

440-3. Marking on Sealed (Hermetic-Type) Motor-Compressors and Equipment—

(a) *A sealed (hermetic-type) motor-compressor shall be provided with a nameplate which shall give—*

1. Manufacturer's name, trademark or symbol.
2. Identifying designation.
3. The phase.
4. Voltage.
5. Frequency.

The rated-load current in amperes of the motor-compressor shall be marked on either or both the motor-compressor nameplate and the nameplate of the equipment in which the motor-compressor is used. The locked-rotor current of each single-phase motor-compressor having a rated-load current of more than 9 amperes at 115 volts or more than 4.5 amperes at 230 volts and each polyphase motor-compressor shall be marked on the motor-compressor nameplate. Where a thermal protector complying with **Sections 440-52(a)(2)** *and* **(b)(2)** *is used, the motor-compressor nameplate or the equipment nameplate shall be marked with the words "Thermally Protected". Where a protective system, complying with* **Sections 440-52(a)(4)** *and* **440-52(b)(4),** *is used and is furnished with the equipment, the equipment nameplate shall be appropriately marked. Where a protective system complying with* **Sections 440-52(a)(4)** *and* **440-52(b)(4)** *is specified, the equipment nameplate shall be appropriately marked.*

Note: The rated-load current for a sealed (hermetic-type) motor-compressor is the current resulting when the motor-compressor is operated at the rated-load, rated voltage and rated frequency of the equipment it serves.

(b) *Multimotor and combination-load equipment shall be provided with a visible nameplate marked with—*

343

1. Maker's name.
2. Rating in volts.
3. Frequency.
4. Number of phases.
5. Minimum circuit ampacity.
6. Maximum rating of the branch-circuit short-circuit and ground-fault protective device rating.

The ampacity calculations will be covered in Part **D,** a little later. Part **C** will cover ground-fault protection calculation. See NEC for further details.

(c) *Sealed (hermetic-type), motor-compressors or equipment containing such compressor(s) in which the protective system, approved for use with the motor-compressor which it protects, permits continuous current in excess of the specified percentage of nameplate rated-load current given in* **Section 440-52(b) (2)** *or* **(b) (4)** *shall also be marked with a branch-circuit selection current that complies with* **Section 440-52(b) (2)** *or* **(b) (4).** *This marking shall be on the nameplate(s) where the rated-load current(s) appears.*

Note. Branch-circuit selection current is the value in amperes to be used instead of the rated-load current in determining the ratings of motor branch-circuit conductors, disconnecting means, controllers and branch-circuit short-circuit and ground-fault protective devices, wherever the running overload protective device permits a sustained current greater than the specified percentage of the rated-load current.

440-4. Marking on Controllers—Controllers shall be marked with:

1. Maker's name, trademark or symbol.
2. Identifying designation.
3. Voltage.
4. Phase.
5. Full-load current.
6. Locked-rotor current or horsepower rating.
7. Any other pertinent information.

440-5. Ampacity and Rating—*Ampacity of conductors and rating of equipment shall be determined as follows:*

(a) *For a sealed (hermetic-type) motor-compressor, the rated-load current marked on the nameplate of the equipment in which the motor-compressor is employed shall be used in determining the rating or ampacity of:*

1. The disconnecting means.
2. The branch-circuit conductors.

3. The controller.
4. The ground-fault protection.
5. The separate motor overload protection.

If there is no rated-load current on the equipment nameplate, you shall use the rated-load on the compressor nameplate.

For disconnecting means and controllers, see **Sections 440-12** *and* **440-41.**

Exception No. 1, permits us to use *the branch-circuit selection current* when shown, instead of the rated-load current for determining:

1. Rating or ampacity of disconnecting means
2. Branch-circuit conductors
3. Controller size
4. Branch-circuit protection
5. Short-circuit protection
6. Ground-fault protection

Exception No. 2. See **Section 440-22(b)** *for branch-circuit, short-circuit and ground-fault protection of cord- and plug-connected equipment.*

(b) *For multimotor equipment employing a shaded-pole or permanent split-capacitor-type fan or blower motor, the full-load current for such motor marked on the nameplate of the equipment in which the fan or blower motor is employed shall be used instead of the horsepower rating to determine the ampacity or rating of the disconnecting means, the branch-circuit conductors, the controller, the branch-circuit short-circuit and ground-fault protection, and the separate overload protection. This marking on the equipment nameplate shall not be less than the current marked on the fan or blower nameplate.*

440-6. Highest Rated (Largest) Motor—In compliance with this, Article and with **Sections 430-24, 430-53(b), 430-53(c)** and **430-62(a),** the motor with the highest load-rated current is the largest motor. If there should be two or more motors of the same load-rating, only one is used. Any motors other than (hermetic-type) compressor motors, as were covered in **Section 440-5(b),** shall have their full-load current determined by using **Tables 430-148, 430-149,** or **430-150,** using horsepower to determine full-load current, not the nameplate current-rating.

Exception: When so marked, the branch-circuit selection current shall be used instead of the rated-load current in determining the highest rated (largest) motor-compressor.

440-7. Single Machine—*An air-conditioning or refrigerating system shall be considered to be a single machine under the provisions of*

345

Section 430-87 *Exception and* **Section 430-112** *Exception. The motors may be located remotely from each other.*

B. Disconnecting Means

440-11.   General—*The provisions of Part* **B** *are intended to require disconnecting means capable of disconnecting air-conditioning and refrigerating equipment, including motor-compressors, and controllers from the circuit feeder. See Diagram* **430-1(a),** *of the NEC.*

440-12.   Rating and Interrupting Capacity—

(a) *A disconnecting means serving a sealed (hermetic-type) motor-compressor shall be selected on the basis of the nameplate rated-load current or branch-circuit selection current, whichever is greater, and the locked-rotor current, respectively, of the motor-compressor as follows:*

1. Nameplate rated-load current, or
2. Branch-circuit selection current, whichever is greater, and
3. Locked-rotor current, respectively.

This gives the key for understanding the following:

We know that the three items mentioned will no doubt come up with different answers. To clarify the above, review **Section 430-109** which covers general types of motors.

(1) *The ampacity shall be at least 115 percent of the nameplate rated-load current or the branch-circuit selection current, whichever is greater.* This gives us a minimum, but on large units the 115% will not be of sufficient ampacity for opening under load.

(2) *To determine the equivalent horsepower in complying with the requirements of* **Section 430-109,** *select the horsepower rating from* **Tables 430-148, 430-149,** *or* **430-150** *corresponding to the rated-load current or branch-circuit selection current, whichever is greater, and also the horsepower rating from* **Table 430-151** *corresponding to the locked-rotor current.* See the NEC for the balance of this part.

The first three Tables mentioned, **Tables 430-148, 430-149,** and **430-150,** cover **HORSEPOWER TO FULL-LOAD CURRENT.** These may also convert, **FULL-LOAD CURRENT TO HORSEPOWER.** Table 430-151 gives us the locked-rotor conversion **Table.**

Sealed (hermetic-type) motor-compressors usually do not have a horse-

346

power rating on the nameplate, so we use the ampere rating and if the amperes and horsepower rating do not correspond when we convert to horsepower, we use the next larger horsepower in the **Tables.**

(b) *Where one or more sealed (hermetic-type) motor-compressors are used together or are used in combination with other motors and/or loads such as resistance heaters and where the combined load may be simultaneous on a single disconnecting means, the rating for the combined load is to be determined as follows:*

(1) The disconnecting means shall be determined by the summation of the currents, such as:

(a) Current of resistive load at rated load-current, plus

(b) Locked-rotor currents of the motor(s).

(c) The combined rated-load current and the combined locked-rotor current by summation of **(a)** and **(b)** to convert the ampacity needed as if the combination were just one motor.

a. The full-load current equivalent to the horsepower rating of each motor, other than a sealed (hermetic-type) motor-compressor, and fan or blower motors as covered in **Section 440-5(b)** *shall be selected from* **Tables 430-148, 430-149, or 430-150.** *These full-load currents shall be added to the motor-compressor rated-load current(s) or branch-circuit selection current(s), whichever is greater, and to the rating in amperes of other loads to obtain an equivalent full-load current for the combined load.*

b. The locked-rotor current equivalent to the horsepower rating of each motor, other than a sealed (hermetic-type) motor-compressor, shall be selected from **Table 430-151,** *and for fan and blower motors of the shaded-pole or permanent split-capacitor type marked with the locked-rotor current, the marked value shall be used. The locked-rotor currents shall be added to the motor-compressor locked-rotor current(s) and to the rating in amperes of other loads to obtain an equivalent locked-rotor current for the combined load. Where two or more motors or other loads cannot be started simultaneously appropriate combinations of locked-rotor and rated-load current or branch-circuit selection current, whichever is greater, may be employed to determine the equivalent locked-rotor current for the simultaneous combined load.*

347

Exception: Where part of the concurrent load is resistance load and the disconnecting means is a switch rated in horsepower and amperes, the horsepower rating of the switch shall be not less than the combined load of the motor-compressor(s) and other motor(s) at the locked-rotor condition and the ampere rating shall be not less than this locked-rotor load plus the resistance load.

(2) *The ampacity of the disconnecting means shall be at least 115 percent of the summation of all currents at the rated-load condition determined in accordance with* **Section 440-12(b) (1).**

(c) *For small motor-compressors not having the locked-rotor current marked on the nameplate, or for small motors not covered by* **Tables 430-147, 430-148, 430-149,** *or* **430-150,** *the locked-rotor current shall be assumed to be 6 times the rated-load current. See* **Section 440-3(a).**

(d) *Where the rated-load or locked-rotor current determined above would indicate a disconnecting means rated in excess of 100 HP, the provisions of* **Section 430-109,** *Exception No. 4, shall apply.*

440-13. Cord-Connected Equipment—*For cord-connected equipment such as room air-conditioners, household refrigerators and freezers, drinking water coolers and beverage dispensers, a separable connector or attachment plug and receptacle may serve as the disconnecting means. See also* **Section 422-23.**

C. Branch-Circuit Short-Circuit and Ground-Fault Protection

440-21. General—*The provisions of Part C specify overcurrent devices intended to protect the branch-circuit conductors, control apparatus, and motors in circuits supplying sealed (hermetic-type) motor-compressors against overcurrent due to short circuits and grounds. They are in addition to or amendatory of the provisions of* **Article 240.**

440-22. Application and Selection—

(a) Rating or Setting for Individual Motor-Compressor. The branch-circuit, short-circuit and ground-fault protective device of the motor-compressor, shall be capable of handling the motor starting current, but shall not be over 175% of the motor's rated-load current or branch-circuit selection current, whichever is the greater; 15 amperes is the minimum size.

Should the above 175% be too small to take care of the starting current, this 175% may be increased to a maximum of 225% with the same stipulations.

348

(b) Rating or Setting for Equipment. *The equipment branch-circuit short-circuit and ground-fault protective device shall be capable of carrying the starting current of the equipment. Where the sealed (hermetic-type) motor-compressor is the only load on the circuit, the protection shall conform with* **Section 440-20(a).** *Where the equipment incorporates more than one sealed (hermetic-type) motor-compressor or a sealed (hermetic-type) motor-compressor and other motors or other loads, the equipment protection shall conform with* **Section 430-53** *and the following:* (**Article 430** and **Article 440** are closely tied together. Refer back to **Section 430-53** which will give you the information required.)

    (1) If the sealed (hermetic-type) motor-compressor is the larger load, the rating or setting of the protective device shall conform to **Section 440-22(a)** plus the rated-load current or branch-circuit selection current, whichever is the greater of the other smaller motor-compressor(s) and/or the rating of any other loads covered by this protective device.

    (2) *Where a sealed (hermetic-type) motor-compressor is not the largest load connected to the circuit, the rating or setting of the protective device shall not exceed a value equal to the sum of the rated-load current or branch-circuit selection current, whichever is greater, rating(s) for the motor-compressor(s) plus the value specified in* **Section 430-53(c) (4)** *where only nonmotor loads are supplied in addition to the motor-compressor(s).*

Exception No. 1: A room air-conditioner shall be treated as a single motor unit in determining its branch-circuit requirements when all the following conditions are met:

    (a) The unit is cord-and-plug connected.

    (b) Its rating is not more than 40 amperes and 250 volts, single phase.

    (c) Total rated-load current is shown on the unit nameplate rather than individual motor currents.

    (d) The rating of the branch-circuit short-circuit and ground-fault protective device does not exceed the ampacity of the branch-circuit conductors or the rating of the receptacle, whichever is less. See **Section 422-40.**

Note: For the purpose of this paragraph, a room air-conditioner is an alternating-current sealed (hermetic-type) air-cooled window, console, or in-wall room air-conditioner which is installed in the conditioned room. It also applies to room air-conditioners having provisions for heating.

349

Exception No. 2: Equipment which will start and operate on a 15- or 20- ampere, 120-volt or 15-ampere, 208- or 240-volt, single-phase branch-circuit shall be considered as protected by the 15- or 20-ampere overcurrent device protecting the branch-circuit except that where the maximum circuit protective device rating marked on the equipment is less than these values, the circuit protective device shall not exceed the value marked on the equipment nameplate.

Usually such equipment will have protective devices built into the unit itself.

Exception No. 3: The nameplate marking of cord-and-plug-connected equipment rated not greater than 250 volts, single-phase, such as household refrigerators and freezers, drinking-water coolers, and beverage dispensers shall be used in determining the branch-circuit requirements, and each unit shall be considered as a single motor unless the nameplate is marked otherwise.

(c) *Where maximum protective device ratings shown on a manfacturer's heater table for use with a motor controller are less than the rating or setting selected in accordance with* **Section 440-22(a)** *and* **(b)**, *the protective device rating shall not exceed the manufacturer's values marked on the equipment.*

D. Branch-Circuit Conductors

440-31. General—Conductor sizes are specified in Part **D** and in **Articles 300** and **310.** Conductors shall be of large enough ampacity to carry the motor current, without heating. An Exception modifying this is in **Section 440-5(a),** *Exception No. 1,* which is copied here:

440-5. *Exception No. 1: When so marked, the branch-circuit selection current shall be used instead of the rated-load current to determine the rating or ampacity of the disconnecting means, the branch-circuit conductors, the controller, and the branch-circuit short-circuit and ground-fault protection.*

The provisions of **Articles 300** and **310,** do not cover the following:

1. Integral conductors of motor, motor controllers and the like,
2. Conductors which form an integral part of approved equipment. See **Sections 300-1(b)** and **310-1(c).**

440-32. Single Motor-Compressors—This is the same as for a single motor as covered in **Article 430,** that is, not less than 125% of either the motor-compressor rated-load current or the branch-circuit selection-current, whichever is greater.

440-33. Several Motor-Compressors—Where there are two or more motor-compressors on the same conductors, the conductors are figured on the basis of the sum of their rated-load currents, plus 25% of the rated-load current of the largest motor-compressor.

Exception: When the circuitry is so interlocked as to prevent the starting and running of a second motor-compressor or group of motor-compressors, the conductor size shall be determined from the largest motor-compressor or group of motor-compressors that is to be operated at a given time.

440-34. Combination Load—*Conductors supplying a motor-compressor load in addition to a lighting or appliance load as computed from* **Article 220** *and other applicable Articles, shall have an ampacity sufficient for the lighting or appliance load plus the required ampacity for the motor-compressor load determined in accordance with* **Section 440-33,** *or, for a single motor-compressor, in accordance with* **Section 440-32.**

Exception: When the circuitry is so interlocked as to prevent simultaneous operation of the motor-compressor(s) and all other loads connected, the conductor size shall be determined from the largest size required for the motor-compressor(s) and other loads to be operated at a given time.

440-35. Multimotor and Combination-Load Equipment—For such equipment we use the minimum circuit ampacity marked on the equipment in accordance with **Section 440-3(b),** which need not be repeated here as it has just been covered.

E. Controllers for Motor-Compressors

440-41. Rating—

(a) *A motor-compressor controller shall have both a continuous-duty full-load current rating, and a locked-rotor current rating, not less than the nameplate rate-load current or branch-circuit selection current, whichever is greater, and locked-rotor current, respectively (see* **Sections 440-5** *and* **440-6***) of the compressor. In case the motor controller is rated in horsepower, but is without one or both of the foregoing current ratings, equivalent currents shall be determined from the ratings as follows: Use* **Tables 430-148, 430-149** *or* **430-150** *to determine the equivalent full-load current rating. Use* **Table 430-151** *to determine the equivalent locked-rotor current rating.*

This is basically no different than for the conventional type of motor and the ampacity of the controller is determined in the same manner and with the use of the same Tables.

(b) Where there are other loads in addition to the motor-compressor, the controller rating shall be determined by the summation of all loads and the use of **Section 440-12(b).**

F. Motor-Compressor and Branch-Circuit Overload Protection

440-51. General—*The provisions of Part* **F** *specify devices intended to protect the motor-compressor, the motor-control apparatus, and the branch-circuit conductors against overheating due to motor overload and failure to start. See* **Section 240-5(a),** *Exception No. 3, which refers to* **Article 430.**

Note: Overload in electrically driven apparatus is an operating overcurrent which, when it persists for a sufficient length of time, would cause damage or dangerous overheating. It does not include short ciruits or ground faults.

440-52. Application and Selection—

(a) Protection of Motor-Compressor. *Each motor-compressor shall be protected against overload and failure to start by one of the following means:*

(1) This tells us the separate overload relay shall be responsive to not over 140% of the motor-compressor rated-load current.

(2) A thermal protector built into the compressor-motor is acceptable, if it prevents damage from overheating due to overload or failure to start.

The current-interrupting device may be external and operated by a thermal device in the motor, provided that it is so arranged that the control circuit from the thermal device will cause interruption of current to the motor-compressor.

(3) Fuses or time-limit circuit breakers that respond to the motor current, are approved, if they are not rated at more than 125% of the motor-compressor rated-load current. Time-delay shall be sufficient to take care of the starting current.

Either the motor-compressor or the equipment shall be marked with the maximum size of branch-circuit fuse or time-limit circuit-breaker rating.

Exception: If standard sizes of fuses or time-limit circuit breakers are not capable of handling the circuit at 125%

rating, the size may be increased provided 140% rating is not exceeded.

(4) *A protective system, furnished or specified and approved for use with the motor-compressor which it protects on the basis that it will prevent dangerous overheating of the motor-compressor due to overload or failure to start. If the current interrupting device is separate from the motor-compressor and its control circuit is operated by a protective device which is not integral with the current-interrupting device, it shall be so arranged that the opening of the control circuit will result in interruption of current to the motor-compressor.*

(b) Protection of Motor-Compressor Control Apparatus and Branch-Circuit Conductors. This portion explains that the motor-compressor controller(s), the disconnecting means and branch circuit conductors are to be protected from overcurrent due to motor overload or failure to start. It also gives us the means that we may use to accomplish this and tells us that these means may be the same device or system that protects the motor-compressor as called for in **Section 440-52(a).**

1. An overload relay that meets the requirements of **(a) (1)** of this Section.

2. *A thermal protector applied in accordance with* **Section 440-52(a) (2)** *and which will not permit a continuous current in excess of 156 percent of the marked rated-load current or branch-circuit selection current.*

3. A fuse or time-limit circuit breaker which meets the requirements of **(a) (3)** of this **Section.**

4. *A protective system in accordance with* **Section 440-52(a) (4)** *and which will not permit a continuous current in excess of 156 percent of the marked rated-load current or branch-circuit selection current.*

440-53. Overload Relays—*Overload relays and other devices for motor overload protection which are not capable of opening short circuits, shall be protected by fuses or time-limiting circuit breakers with ratings or settings in accordance with Part C unless approved for group installation or for part-winding motors and marked to indicate the maximum size of fuse or time-limit circuit breaker by which they must be protected.*

Exception: The fuse or time-limit circuit-breaker-size marking may be located on the nameplate of approved equipment in which the overload relay or other overload device is used.

353

440-54. Motor-Compressors and Equipment on General Purpose Branch Circuits—When motor-compressors and equipment are used on general purpose branch circuits as covered in **Article 210** (*Branch Circuits*), overload protection shall be provided, see **(a)**, **(b)**, and **(c)** below.

(a) *Motor-compressors and equipment may be connected to general-purpose branch circuits only if the motor-compressor is provided with overload protection selected as specified in* **Section 440-52(a).** *Both the controller and the motor-overload protective device shall be approved for installation with a short-circuit and ground-fault protective device of the branch circuit to which the equipment is connected.* The short-circuit and ground-fault devices used shall be approved for use with the overcurrent protection on the branch circuit.

(b) When connecting a motor-compressor or equipment to a general-purpose branch circuit by means of a cap and receptacle, these shall not exceed 20 amperes on 125 volts and 15 amperes on 250 volts.

(c) The branch circuit short-circuit or ground-fault protective device (usually fuse or circuit breaker), shall have a sufficient time-delay to take care of the starting current.

ARTICLE 445—GENERATORS

See NEC.

ARTICLE 450—TRANSFORMERS AND TRANSFORMER VAULTS
(Including Secondary Ties)

450-1. Application—This Article applies to the installation of all transformers with the following exceptions:

(1) Current transformers.
(2) Dry-type transformers which are a component part of apparatus and which conform to the requirements of this apparatus.
(3) Transformers for use with X-ray and high-frequency.
(4) Transformers used with Class 1 low-voltage power circuits or Class 2 remote-control low-energy power and signal circuits which shall conform to **Article 725.**
(5) Transformers for sign and outline lighting conforming to **Article 600.**
(6) Transformers for discharge lighting as covered in **Article 410.**

There are provisions supplemental to this Article, covering hazardous locations, in **Article 500.** In **Article 710,** which covers circuits of over 600

354

volts, there is additional information concerning terminations, installation, and other pertinent facts pertaining to conductors which by necessity are a part of the transformer installations. Part L of **Section 230** covers services of over 600 volts which also apply to the total installation of transformers.

A. General Provisions

450-2. Location—*Transformers and transformer vaults shall be readily accessible to qualified personnel for inspection and maintenance.*

Exception No. 1: Dry-type transformers 600 volts or less, located in the open on walls, columns or structures, need not be readily accessible.

Note the *need not be readily accessible.* This indicates that the height is not a problem. In this line the supporting comment with Proposal No. 27 on page 179 of the 1971 Preprint might be in order:

This requirement (readily) throughout the country has never been enforced simply because transformers in general where readily accessible have been damaged in many cases. It would be far bettr to elevate same where dry-type transformers are installed. This further would not cause any problems where vaults are considered or required.

Exception No. 2: See NEC. This clarifies the installation of dry-type transformers above drop-ceilings, where the hollow space is fire-resistant. The main requirement is the ventilation must be sufficient to keep temperatures not in excess of those prescribed in ANSI C57.12.00-1968. A limitation of 50 kva and 600 volts is put on transformers thus installed.

It is impossible to cover everything pertaining to transformer locations in this section, so oil-insulated transformers are found in **Sections 450-24, 450-25,** and **450-41.** Dry-type transformers are covered in **Section 450-21,** and askarel-insulated transformers in **Section 450-23.**

450-3. Overcurrent Protection—A definition for the word "Transformer," as used in this Section, is *a transformer or polyphase bank of transformers of two or three single phase transformers operating as a unit.* The overcurrent protection shall conform to the following:

(a) Askarel- and Oil-Insulated Transformers.

(1) **Primary Side.** The term "primary" is often inferred in the field as being the high side and the term "secondary" as being the low side of a transformer. This is not the case, however. The primary is always the input side of a transformer and the secondary is always the output side. Thus, voltage has nothing to do with the terms.

Each transformer is to be protected by an overcurrent device rated or set at not more than 250% of the rated primary current

355

of the transformer. The question often arises that perhaps 250% is too high, but this has been a practice for many years and has been found to be highly satisfactory.

This overcurrent protection may be mounted in the vault, or at the transformer if approved for the purpose. It may also be mounted to protect the circuit supplying the transformer. Thus, in the case of a vault, it could be mounted out-of-doors on a pole, but a disconnecting means will have to be provided in the vault. See Fig. 450-1.

(2) **Primary and Secondary Side.** If the askarel- or oil-insulated transformer is protected on the secondary side by an overcurrent device rated or set at not more than 250% of the rated secondary current, there need be no overcurrent protection on the primary side. Also, if there is a thermal overload protection provided by the mnaufacturer in the transformer, there need be no primary protection as provided in (a) if the primary feeder circuit is protected at no more than 600% by an overcurrent device. This value is to be based on the primary current for transformers that do not have more than 6% impedance. For transformers having more than 6% impedance, but not more than 10%, the primary feeder shall not be protected by more than four times the primary current of the transformers.

Recall that **Section 110-10** was changed considerably to take into consideration fault currents. The impedance of the transformer plays a very important part in the values that will be reached by fault currents.

(b) **Dry-Type Transformers.**

(1) **Primary Side.** Every dry-type transformer is required to be protected by its individual overcurrent device on the primary side with a setting not to exceed 125% of the full-load primary current-rating. An exception to the requirement is that individual overcurrent devices in the primary side are not required, when the primary circuit overcurrent device gives protection as herein provided if the provisions of **Section 450-3(b) (2)** are met.

(2) A dry-type transformer that has an overcurrent device in the secondary side that has a rating which does not exceed 125% of the full-load secondary current-rating, will not be required to have individual OC device in the primary circuit, provided that the primary feeder OC device is rated or set to open and not to exceed 250% of the rated primary full-load current of the transformer.

Dry-type transformers which have built-in thermal overload protection by the manufacturer, are not required to have individual OC devices in the primary circuit if the primary feeder circuit is protected at not more than 600% by OC devices for transformers having not more than 6% impedance and not more than 400% rated-current of the transformer or transformers having more than 6% impedance but not more than 10% impedance. **Section 240-15, Exception No. 7,** and **Section 384-16,** will cover the overcurrent protection required in the secondary side.

(c) Potential (Voltage) Transformers. *Potential transformers installed indoors or enclosed shall be protected with primary fuses.* To the author, it is just good practice to install protection for all potential transformers.

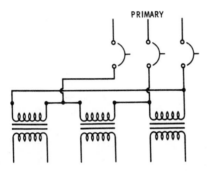

PRIMARY

Fig. 450-1. Overcurrent protection may be at the transformer or in the circuit supplying the transformer, but shall not exceed 250% of the current rating of the primary.

450-5. Secondary Ties—The definition of transformer, as it pertains to this Section, was given in **Section 450-3.** *A secondary tie is a circuit operating at 600 volts or less between phases which connects two power sources or power supply points, such as the secondaries of two transformers. The tie may consist of one or more conductors per phase.*

(a) Tie Circuits. Article 240 covers overcurrent protection in general, and tie circuits shall be provided with overcurrent protection at each end as provided in **Article 240.**

Exceptions are under the conditions described in **Section 450-5 (a-1 and a-2),** and in these cases the overcurrent protection may be in accordance with **Section 450-5 (a-3).**

(1) Loads at Transformer Supply Points Only. Where transformers are tied together (parallel) and connected by tie conductors that do not have overcurrent protection as per **Article 240,** the ampacity of the ties (connecting conductors) shall not be

357

less than 67% of the rated secondary current of the largest transformer in the tie circuit. This applies where the loads are at the transformer supply points.

The paralleling of transformers is rather common, but great care should be taken to assure that the transformers are similar in all characteristics. If they are not, one transformer will attempt to take all the load. If the transformers are of equal capacity and similar characteristics, they would theoretically each take 50% of the load. The 67% allows for any difference in transformer sizes. See Fig. 450-2.

(2) Loads Connected Between Transformer Supply Points. *Where load is connected to the tie at any point between transformer supply points and overcurrent protection is not provided in accordance with* **Article 240**, *the rated ampacity of the tie shall be not less than 100 per cent of the rated secondary current of the largest transformer connected to the secondary tie system except as otherwise provided in* **Section 450-5(a-4).** See Fig. 450-3.

(3) Tie Circuit Protection. In **Sections 450-5(a-1** and **a-2)**, both ends of each tie connection shall be equipped with a protective device which will open at a predetermined temperature of the tie conductor. This is to prevent damage to the tie conductor and its insulation, and may consist of (1) A limiter, which is a fusible link cable connector (not a common fuse) which is designed for the insulation, conductor material, etc., on the tie conductors. This is ordinarily a copper link enclosed in a protective covering. (2) A circuit breaker actuated by devices having comparable characteristics to the above. See Figs. 450-2 and 450-3.

(4) Interconnection of Phase Conductors Between Transformer Supply Points. *Where the tie consists of more than one conductor per phase, the conductors of each phase shall be interconnected in order to establish a load supply point, and the protection specified in* **Section 450-5(a-3)** *shall be provided in each tie conductor at this point, except as follows.*

Exception: Loads may be connected to the individual conductors of a multiple-conductor tie without interconnecting the conductors of each phase and without the protection specified in **Section 450-5(a-3)** *at load connection points provided; the tie conductors of each phase have a combined capacity not less than 133 per cent of the rated secondary current of the largest transformer connected to the secondary tie system; the total load of such taps does not exceed the rated secondary current of the largest transformer; the loads*

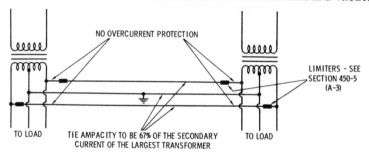

NO OVERCURRENT PROTECTION

LIMITERS - SEE SECTION 450-5 (A-3)

TO LOAD

TIE AMPACITY TO BE 67% OF THE SECONDARY CURRENT OF THE LARGEST TRANSFORMER

TO LOAD

Fig. 450-2. Secondary ties.

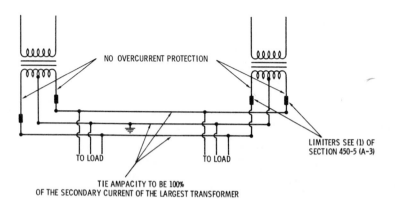

NO OVERCURRENT PROTECTION

LIMITERS SEE (1) OF SECTION 450-5 (A-3)

TO LOAD

TO LOAD

TIE AMPACITY TO BE 100% OF THE SECONDARY CURRENT OF THE LARGEST TRANSFORMER

Fig. 450-3. Loads connected between transformer supply points.

are equally divided on each phase and on the individual conductors of each phase as far as practicable.

The use of multiple conductors on each phase and the requirement that loads do not have to tap both of the multiple conductors of the same phase could possibly set up unbalanced currents in the multiple conductors on the same phase. This is taken care of in the requirement that the combined capacity of the multiple conductors on the same phase be rated at 133% of the secondary current of the largest transformer. Limiters are necessary at the tap or connections to the transformers that are tied together.

(5) Tie Circuit Control. If the operating voltage of secondary ties exceeds 150 volts to ground, there shall be a switch ahead of the limiters and tie conductors which will de-energize the tie conductors and the limiters. This switch shall meet the following conditions:

(1) The current rating of the switch shall not be less than the current rating of the conductors connected to the switch.

(2) The switch shall be capable of opening its rated current.

(3) The switch shall not open under the magnetic forces resulting from short-circuit current.

(b) Overcurrent Protection for Secondary Connections. When secondary ties from transformers are used, there shall be an overcurrent device in the secondary of each transformer that is rated or set at not more than 250% of the rated secondary current of the transformer. In addition, there shall be a circuit breaker actuated by a reverse-current relay, the breaker to be set at not more than the rated secondary current of the transformer. The overcurrent protection takes care of overloads and shorts, while the reverse-current relay and circuit breaker takes care of any reversal of current flow into the transformer.

450-6. **Parallel Operation—Section 450-5** covered ties for transformer connections which, in essence, is a form of paralleling. However, this Section covers the actual paralleling of transformers. Paralleled transformers may be switched as a unit provided that the overcurrent protection meets the requirements of **Section 450-3.**

Anyone working with paralleled transformers or transformer tie circuits should be extremely cautious that there are no feedbacks or other conditions which would affect safety. In order to secure a balance of current between paralleled transformers, all transformers should have characteristics that are very much alike, such as voltage, impedance, etc. These pertinent facts may be obtained from the manufacturer of the transformers.

450-7. **Guarding—***Transformers shall be guarded as follows:*

(a) Mechanical Protection. When exposed to physical damage, transformers shall be protected to minimize damage from external causes.

(b) Case or Enclosure. *Dry-type transformers shall be provided with a noncombustible moisture-resistant case or enclosure which will provide reasonable protection against the accidental insertion of foreign objects.*

(c) Exposed Live Parts. Section 110-16 will apply to live parts of transformers operating at 600 volts or less. **Article 710** covers transformers operating at voltages higher than 600 volts.

(d) Voltage Warning. Signs indicating the voltage of live exposed parts of transformers, or other suitable markings, shall be used in areas where transformers are located.

450-8. **Ventilation**—*The ventilation shall be adequate to prevent a transformer temperature in excess of the values prescribed in ANSI C57.12.00-1968.*

450-9. **Grounding**—See NEC.

450-10. **Marking**—Nameplates with the following information shall be provided for transformers:

(1) Name of manufacturer.

(2) Rated kilovolt-amperes.

(3) Frequency.

(4) Primary voltage.

(5) Secondary voltage.

(6) Amount and kind of insulating liquid (where used) and where the transformer capacity exceeds 25 KVA.

(7) Where Class B insulation is used in dry-type transformers rated at 100 KVA or more, the temperature rise for the type insulation used shall be marked.

B. Specific Provisions Applicable to Different Types of Transformers

450-21. **Dry-Type Transformers Installed Indoors**—Transformers of 112-1/2 KVA or less shall be:

(1) Separated a minimum of 12 inches from combustibles, or

(2) Separated therefrom by a fire-resistant heat-insulating barrier, or

(3) If rated at not more than 600 volts and completely enclosed (except for ventilating areas), they do not have to meet the other requirements.

Transformers of more than 112-1/2 KVA shall be:

(1) Installed in a fire-resistant room, unless

(a) They are constructed with 80° C rise (Class B) insulation, or

(b) 150° C rise (Class H) insulation and are separated from combustible material by a minimum of 6 feet horizontally and 12 feet vertically or are separated by a fire-resistant heat-insulating material.

NEMA has specifications for transformers, and the NFPA has Codes pertaining to buildings and fire-resistant materials, which may be referred to.

Transformers rated at more than 35,000 volts shall be installed in a vault. Vaults are covered in **Part C** of this Article.

450-22. Dry-Type Transformers Installed Outdoors—*Dry-type transformers installed outdoors shall have an approved weatherproof enclosure.*

450-23. Askarel-Insulated Transformers Installed Indoors—The term askarel is defined in **Article 100** as *A synthetic nonflammable insulating liquid which, when decomposed by an electrical arc, evolves only nonflammable gaseous mixtures.*

Askarel-insulated transformers in excess of 25 KVA rating must be furnished with a pressure-relief valve. They are to be installed in well ventilated areas or, if installed in a poorly ventilated area, they must be furnished with a means of absorbing any gases generated by electrical arcing, or the pressure-relief vent that is installed on the transformer shall be connected to a chimney or flue to carry the gases to the outside of the building. If rated at more than 35,000 volts, this type of transformer must be installed in a vault.

450-24. Oil-Insulated Transformers Installed Indoors—All oil-insulated transformers installed indoors are to be in vaults, with the following exceptions:

(a) **Not over 112-1/2 KVA Total Capacity**. The specifications for vaults in **Part C** of this Article may be modified so that the vault may be constructed of reinforced concrete not less than 4 inches thick.

(b) **Not over 600 volts.** A vault is not necessary when the transformer rating is 600 volts or less, if the following conditions are met: Proper means are provided to prevent a transformer-oil fire from igniting other materials, and if the total transformer capacity in this location does not exceed 10 KVA if the section of the building in which they are installed is classified as combustible, or if the total transformer capacity is from 10 to 75 KVA and the surrounding structure is classified as fire-resistant.

(c) **Furnace Transformers.** Electric-furnace transformers that do not exceed 75 KVA need not be installed in a vault if the building or room is of fire-resistant construction and if a suitable drain or other means is provided for preventing an oil fire from spreading to combustible materials.

(d) **Detached Buildings.** A building detached from other buildings—that is an entirely separate building or one which may be defined as such by proper walls, etc.—may be used for transformers provided that it complies with the following:

(1) That neither the building or its contents is a fire hazard to other buildings or property.

(2) That it is used only in supplying electrical service.

362

(3) That the interior is accessible only to qualified persons.

450-25. Oil-Insulated Transformers Installed Outdoors—Oil-insulated transformers that are installed outdoors shall be installed so that no hazard to combustible materials, combustible buildings and parts of buildings, fire escapes, and door and window openings will exist in case of fire. These transformers may also be attached to or adjacent to buildings or combustible materials if precautions are taken to prevent fire hazards to the buildings or combustible materials.

The following safeguards are recognized:

(1) Space separation.
(2) Fire-resistant barriers.
(3) Automatic water-spray systems.
(4) Enclosures which confine the oil of a ruptured transformer. The degree of hazard will depend on the quantity of oil involved, and the precautions taken to keep the oil from a ruptured transformer case from becoming a hazard. To take care of this oil, enclosures shall be provided and they may consist of the following:

   (a) Fire-resistant dikes.
   (b) Curbed areas or basins.
   (c) Trenches filled with coarse crushed rock (dry wells).
   (d) Trapped drains in cases where the exposure and the quantity of oil involved are such that removal of oil is important.

Whether or not the requirements are met according to these standards will be up to the inspection authority to decide.

C. Provisions for Transformer Vaults

450-41. Location—Where practical, transformer vaults shall be located so that they will be ventilated to the outside air without the use of flues or ducts.

450-42. Walls, Roof, and Floor—Reference is made in this Section to standards covering building materials, construction, etc. These become a part of the Code by reference.

The walls and roofs of vaults shall be constructed of reinforced concrete, brick, load bearing tile, concrete block, or other fire resistive constructions which have adequate structural strength for the conditions, and a minimum fire resistance of 2-1/2 hours according to American Standard A2.1—Methods of Fire Tests of Building Construction and Materials

363

(ASTM Standard E119-58; NFPA No. 251). When the floors of vaults are in contact with the earth, the floors shall be of concrete with a minimum thickness of 4 inches. When the floor of a vault is constructed with a vacant space below, or other stories below, the floor shall have adequate structural strength for the load imposed thereon and have a minimum fire resistance of 2-1/2 hours. The strength factor is an engineering problem while the fire resistance may be found in the Standards referred to.

450-43. Doorways—*Vault doorways shall be protected as follows:*

(a) Type of Door. Doors for vaults are covered in the NFPA Standard for the Installation of Fire Doors and Windows, No. 80, and this becomes a part of this Code. They shall be Class A installations, tight fitting, and the inspection authority may require a door on each side of the wall.

(b) Sills. The door shall not extend completely to the floor, but a sill shall be provided which is high enough to take care of the oil from the largest transformer in the vault. In no case shall this door sill be less than 4 inches high.

(c) Locks. All doors shall be provided with locks which shall be kept locked so that access will be to qualified persons only. Latches and locks shall be such that they are readily opened from the inside of the vault. Many authorities require crash bars.

450-44. Ventilation—*Transformer temperatures are covered in USAS C57. 1200-1965, and ventilation shall be provided to meet these specifications.*

450-45. Ventilation Openings—When required by **Section 450-44,** openings for ventilation shall be provided in accordance with the following:

(a) Location. *Ventilation openings shall be located as far away as possible from doors, windows, fire escapes, and combustible material.*

(b) Arrangement. Where vaults are ventilated by a natural circulation of air, the total area of the openings for ventilation may be divided, with half of the area at the floor level and the remainder in one or more openings in the roof or near the ceiling. All of the area required for ventilation may be supplied by one or more openings near or in the roof.

(c) Size. When vaults are ventilated directly to the outdoor area, and ducts or flues are not used, the net area of the ventilation openings (after deducting the area that the screen, gratings, or louvres occupy) shall not be less than 3 square inches per KVA of transformer capacity in the vault. For any vault with a transformer capacity of less than 50 KVA, the area of the ventilation opening shall not be less than 1 square foot.

(d) Covering. The covering for ventilation openings in vaults is left up to the inspection authority for the final decision, but they shall be covered with durable gratings, screens, or louvres. The final decision will be made on the basis of avoiding unsafe conditions.

(e) Dampers. If automatic dampers are installed in vaults where oil-filled transformers are used, they shall be actuated by the temperature that will prevail from the operation of the transformers. These dampers shall be so constructed that accidental closing is not possible.

(f) Ducts. *Ventilating ducts shall be constructed of fire-resistant material* and shall be adequate to take care of the demand that might be imposed upon them.

When foreign systems cannot be avoided, access to them shall be other than the entry into the vault. Any leaks or other malfunction of the foreign systems shall not cause damage to the transformers and their equipment.

450-48. Storage in Vaults—*Materials shall not be stored in transformer vaults.* This means that transformer vaults are only transformer vaults and not warehouses or storage areas. The vault is to be kept clear at all times—there is high voltage involved and safety is a very important factor.

ARTICLE 460—CAPACITORS

460-1. Application—*This Article applies to installation of capacitors on electric circuits in or on buildings.*

Exception No. 1. Capacitors that are components of an apparatus shall conform to the requirements for the particular apparatus involved.

Exception No. 2. **Articles 500** through **517** cover the installation of capacitors in hazardous area.

460-2. Location—See NEC.

460-3. Mechanical Protection—See NEC.

460-4. Cases and Supports—See NEC.

460-5. Transformers Used with Capacitors—**Article 450** will apply to transformers that are a component part of a capacitor installation, in which case the KVA rating of the transformers shall be 135% of the KVAR rating of the capacitor.

365

460-6. Drainage of Stored Charge—Capacitors store up a charge of electricity and the larger sizes may be lethal. Therefore, it is necessary to provide some means of draining off this charge.

(a) **Time of Discharge.** *The residual voltage of a capacitor shall be reduced to 50 volts or less within one minute after the capacitor is disconnected from the source of supply in the case of capacitors rated 600 volts or less and in five minutes in the case of capacitors rated more than 600 volts.*

(b) **Means of Discharge.** The means of discharging a capacitor (such as a resistor) may be permanently connected to the terminals of the capacitor, or the disconnecting means to the capacitor may be so arranged that, upon opening, the capacitor is automatically connected to some discharging means. A manual discharging means is prohibited. The windings of transformers, motors, or other equipment that are directly connected to capacitors without a switch will act as the discharging means for the capacitor.

460-7. Power-Factor Correction—Motor Circuit—Capacitors are used for lagging power-factor correction with motors. When these capacitors are connected on the load side of the motor controller, the KVAR capacity of the capacitors shall not exceed that value which is just necessary to bring the power-factor up to unity.

460-8. Conductor Rating—

(a) The two statements in this part are not to be confused.

(1) The ampacity of conductors to capacitors shall not be less than 135% of the rated current of the capacitor. Power factor enters into this rating as the capacitors have a leading power factor.

(2) This part concerns a capacitor connected to the terminals of a motor for power-factor correction. The ampacity of the conductors connecting the capacitor must meet two requirements; (a) they shall be not less than 1/3 the ampacity of the motor conductors; (b) they shall not be less than 135% of the rated current capacity of the capacitor, whichever is the larger size.

(b) **Overcurrent Protection.**

(1) *An overcurrent device shall be provided in each ungrounded conductor for each capacitor bank.*

Exception: A separate overcurrent device is not required on the load-side of a motor running overcurrent device.

(2) *The rating or setting of the overcurrent device shall be as low as practicable.*

(c) **Disconnecting Means.**

(1) *A disconnecting device shall be provided in each ungrounded conductor for each capacitor bank.*

> *Exception: A separate disconnecting means is not required for a capacitor connected on the load side of a motor-running overcurrent device.*

(2) *The disconnecting device need not open all ungrounded conductors simultaneously.*

(3) *The disconnecting device may be used for disconnecting the capacitor from the line as a regular operating procedure.*

(4) *The continuous ampacity of the disconnecting device shall be not less than 135 per cent of the rated current of the capacitor.*

460-9. Rating or Setting of the Motor-Running Overcurrent Device— Due to the fact that a capacitor connected to a motor through the motor overcurrent devices (running protection devices), and also due to the fact that a capacitor in a motor circuit corrects the lagging power factor of the motor, the current to the motor will be less than that of the same motor if it did not have capacitors for power-factor correction.

Use **Section 430-32** for calculating the rating or setting of the motor overcurrent devices, but the actual value of current drawn by the motor must be used instead of the nameplate current, which will be less in value.

Section 430-22 applies to the rating of the conductors. This is not derated because of the capacitor but is used as if the capacitor were not in the circuit.

460-10. Grounding—See NEC.

460-11. Guarding—See NEC.

460-12. Marking—See NEC.

ARTICLE 470—RESISTORS AND REACTORS

See NEC.

ARTICLE 480—STORAGE BATTERIES

See NEC.

Chapter 5. Special Occupancies

Articles 500 through **517** refer to hazardous areas and should be well understood by anyone concerned with the wiring in such locations. Such areas are dangerous from many standpoints and each has its own problems which require special methods for taking care of the electrical systems installed in these places.

ARTICLE 500—HAZARDOUS LOCATIONS

500-1.   Scope—It is the responsibility of the Code-enforcing authority to judge whether or not areas come under **Articles 500** through **503** as indicated by the classifications indicated in these Articles. The intent is that each room, section, or area (including motor and generator rooms and rooms for enclosure of control equipment) shall be individually considered in determining the classification suitable for the conditions.

In judging of these areas and what equipment is allowable therein, the inspection authority refers to the Underwriters' Laboratories listings for approval of the equipment that is installed in each area. All other wiring methods of the Code are applicable except as modified by these Articles covering hazardous areas.

The following are definitions of some of the terms which will appear often:

Approved: Acceptable to the authority enforcing this Code.

Dustproof: So constructed or protected that dust will not interfere with its successful operation.

Dust-Ignition Proof: Enclosed in a manner which will exclude ignitible amounts of dusts or amounts which might affect performance or rating and which, when installation and protection are in conformance with this Code, will not permit arcs, sparks or heat otherwise generated or liberated inside of the enclosure to cause ignition of exterior accumulations or atmospheric suspensions of a specific dust on or in the vicinity of the enclosure.

Dust-Tight: So constructed that dust will not enter the enclosing case.

Explosion-Proof Apparatus: Apparatus enclosed in a case which is capable of withstanding an explosion of a specified gas or vapor which may occur within it and of preventing the ignition of a specified gas or vapor surrounding the enclosure by sparks, flashes, or explosion of the gas or vapor within, and which operates at such an external temperature that a surrounding flammable atmosphere will not be ignited thereby.

The following paragraph is a direct quote from the Code:

Equipment and associated wiring approved as intrinsically safe may be installed in any hazardous location for which it is approved, and the provisions of **Article 500-517** *need not apply to such installation. Intrinsically safe equipment and wiring are incapable of releasing sufficient electrical energy under normal and abnormal conditions to cause ignition of a specific hazardous atmospheric mixture. Abnormal conditions will include accidental damage to any part of the equipment or wiring, insulation or other failure of electrical components, application of overvoltage, adjustment and maintenance operations, and other similar conditions.*

For further information see NFPA No. 493, 1969 Standard for Intrinsically Safe Process Control Equipment for use in Class I Hazardous Locations.

In designing the wiring and selecting the equipment to use in a hazardous location, less expensive materials and equipment can often be used by relocation or by adequate ventilation, forced or otherwise.

Anyone doing installations in hazardous areas, but more especially inspectors, should become familiar with other Codes published by the National Fire Protection Association, such as:

Flammable and Combustible Liquids Code, NFPA No. 30.
Standard for Dry Cleaning Plants, NFPA No. 32.
Organic Coatings Manufacture, NFPA No. 35M.
Standard for Solvent Extraction Plants, NFPA No. 36.
Storage and Handling of Liquified Petroleum Gases—NFPA 58
Storage and Handling of Liquid Petroleum Gases at Utility Gas Plants. NFPA 59-1968.

In reading the National Electrical Code, references are sometimes made to other NFPA Codes. Wherever such references are found, they become a part of the National Electrical Code.

Designers and inspectors will find many items pertaining to the subjects covered in this chapter in many other of the NFPA Codes. These Codes are available individually or in a 10-volume set, and will often assist in arriving at many decisions which must be made, especially by the inspector.

For electrical installations in hazardous areas where it is necessary to use rigid metal conduit, the Code requires that the joints be made up wrench tight—this applies to threaded joints and connections. Please note that the Code states *wrench tight* and not *plier tight*. In addition, standard conduit dies which provide a taper of 3/4 inch taper per foot shall be used. All of this amounts to the fact that, even though the proper equipment is used and the wiring methods are as required, a loose threaded connection, when subject to fault current, may spark and cause an explosion. Where it is impossible to make a proper threaded connection, the joint shall be bonded.

500-2. Special Precaution—The intent of **Articles 500-503** is that more than ordinary precaution must be exercised in the construction of equipment and the installation and maintenance of the entire wiring system for safe operation. This becomes the responsibility of all concerned in the matter.

The atmospheric mixtures of various gases, vapors, and dusts, and the hazard involved, depends upon the concentrations, temperatures, and many other things. It is impossible to cover all these variables here, but they may be found in the various NFPA Codes.

The explosive characteristics of air mixtures of hazardous gases, vapors, or dusts vary with the specific material involved. Classification of a hazardous mixture into a Class I hazardous location, Group A, B, C, or D, involves determinations of maximum explosion pressure, maximum safe clearance between parts of a clamped joint in an enclosure, and the minimum ignition temperature of the atmospheric mixture. For Class II location, Groups E, F and G, the classification involves the tightness of the joints of assembly and shaft openings to prevent entrance of dust in the dust-ignition-proof enclosure, the blanketing effect of layers of dust on the equipment that may cause overheating, electrical conductivity of the dust, and the ignition temperature of the dust. It is necessary, therefore, that equipment be approved not only for the class of location but also for the specific group of gas, vapor or dust that will be present.

For purposes of testing and approval, various air mixtures (not oxygen enriched) have been grouped on the basis of their hazardous characteristics, and facilities have been made available for testing and approval of equipment for use in the following groups.

For Groups A, B, C and D see **Table 500-2(c).**

Group E, Atmospheres containing metal dust, including aluminum, magnesium, and their commercial alloys, and other metals of similarly hazardous charactersitics.

Group F, Atmospheres containing carbon black, coal or coke dust.

Group G, Atmospheres containing flour, starch or grain dust.

Certain chemical atmospheres may have characteristics which would require safeguards beyond those required for any of the above groups. Carbon disulfide is one of these chemicals because of its low ignition temperature (100°C) and the small joint clearance required to arrest its flame. For a complete list noting properties of flammable liquids, gases and solids refer to NFPA No. 325M-1969.

There are atmospheric limits for explosive mixtures of the various explosive items. A few are given to illustrate:

Group A. Acetylene—0 to 2.5% not dangerous, 2.5 to 80% dangerous, and 80 to 100% not dangerous. (The 80 to 100% reduces in hazard because of the lack of oxygen).

Group B. Hydrogen—0 to 4.1% not dangerous, 4.1 to 74.2% dangerous, and 74.8 to 100% not dangerous.

Group C. Ethyl Ether—0 to 1.85% not dangerous, 1.85 to 36.5% dangerous, and 36.5 to 100% not dangerous.

Group D. Gasoline—0 to 1.3% not dangerous, 1.3 to 6% dangerous, and 6 to 100% not dangerous.

In addition to the first portion of this Section, which was copied from the NEC, there has also been added parts **(a)**, **(b)** and **(c)** to this Section. I sincerely recommend that you spend some time studying the material for **Section 500-2** as it appears in the NEC. The 1971 NEC has added a great deal of very valuable information, plus **Table 500-2(b)** and **500-2(c)**. All of this was much needed information and a great deal of effort has gone into assembling this material.

Temperature range, if provided shall be indicated by identification numbers, as shown in **Table 500-2(b).**

Identification numbers marked on equipment nameplates shall be in accordance with **Table 500-2(b).**

Table 500-2(c) has chemicals by Groups with important notes that follow. This information has always been rather hard to find and a topic for lengthy discussions. One item which comes to mind is ammonia (Anhydrous Ammonia) used for farm fertilizer.

The main point that I gain from *Section 500-2* is that equipment will carry identification numbers and we should use NFPA No. 325M, to come up with a safe installation. Use your *Red* UL book on **Hazardous Classifications.**

500-3. Specific Occupancies—*See* **Articles 510** *to* **517** *inclusive for rules applying to garages, aircraft hangers, gasoline dispensing and service stations, bulk storage plants, finishing processes, and flammable anesthetics.*

500-4. Class I Locations—*Class I locations are those in which flammable gases or vapors are or may be present in the air in quantities suf-*

371

ficient to produce explosive or ignitible mixtures. Class I locations shall include the following:

(a) Class I, Division 1. *Locations:*

(1) In which hazardous concentrations of flammable gases or vapors may exist continuously, intermitently, or periodically under normal operating conditions.

(2) In which hazardous concentrations of such gases or vapors may exist frequently because of repair or maintenance operations or because of leakage.

(3) In which breakdown or faulty operation of equipment or processes which might release hazardous concentrations of flammable gases or vapors, might also cause simultaneous failure of electrical equipment.

A volatile flammable liquid is defined in **Article 100** as: *A flammable liquid having a flash point below 100°F. or whose temperature is above its flash point.*

Class I, Division 1 areas also include:

(1) Locations where volatile flammable liquids or liquified flammable gases are transferred from one container to another.

(2) Interiors of spray booths.

(3) Areas in the vicinity of spraying and painting operations where volatile flammable solvents are used.

(4) Areas with open tanks or vats of volatile flammable liquids.

(5) Drying rooms or compartments for the evaporation of flammable solvents.

(6) Areas containing fat and oil extraction apparatus using volatile flammable solvents.

(7) Portions of cleaning and dyeing plants where hazardous liquids are used.

(8) Gas generator rooms and other portions of gas manufacturing plants where flammable gas may escape.

(9) Inadequately ventilated pump rooms for flammable gas or for volatile flammable liquids.

(10) Interiors of refrigerators or freezers in which volatile, flammable materials are stored in open, lightly stoppered, or easily ruptured containers.

(11) Any other locations where flammable vapors or gases are likely to occur in the course of normal operations.

(b) Class 1, Division 2. *Locations:*

(1) In which volatile flammable liquids or flammable gases are handled, processed or used, but in which the hazardous liquids, vapors or gases will normally be confined within closed containers or closed systems from which they can escape only in case of accidental rupture or breakdown of such containers

or systems, or in case of abnormal operation of equipment.

(2) In which hazardous concentrations of gases or vapors are normally prevented by positive mechanical ventilation, but which might become hazardous through failure or abnormal operation of the ventilating equipment.

(3) Which are adjacent to Class I, Division 1 locations, and to which hazardous concentrations of gases or vapors may occasionally be communicated unless such communication is prevented by adequate positive-pressure ventilation from a source of clean air, and effective safeguards against ventilation failure are provided.

The locations under this classification usually include those where volatile flammable liquids or flammable gases or vapors are used, but in the judgment of the Code-enforcing authority would become hazardous only in case of accident or unusual operations. In deciding whether or not this would be a Class I, Division 2 location, the Code-enforcing authority must take into account the quantity of hazardous materials that might escape in case of an accident, the records of similar locations with respect to fires and explosions, and any other condition which might affect the amount of hazard present or which could be present.

Piping that is without valves, checks, meters, and similar devices would not ordinarily be considered as being capable of introducing a hazard, neither would storage areas for hazardous liquids or of liquified or compressed gases in sealed containers which would normally not be hazardous.

There are special instances where storage of material such as anesthetics is considered as Class I, Division 1 locations.

Electrical conduits and their associated enclosures separated from process fluids by a single seal or barrier shall be classed as Division 2 locations if the outside of conduit and enclosures is a nonhazardous area.

500-5. Class II Locations—The presence of combustible dust creates Class II locations and includes the following:

(a) Class II, Division 1. *Locations:*

(1) In which combustible dust is or may be in suspension in the air continuously, intermittently, or periodically under normal operating conditions, in quantities sufficient to produce explosive or ignitible mixtures.

(2) Where mechanical failure or abnormal operation of machinery or equipment might cause such mixtures to be produced, and might also provide a source of ignition through simultaneous

failure of electrical equipment, operation of protection devices, or from other causes.

(3) In which dusts of an electrically conducting nature may be present.

Also included in this classification are:

(1) Grain handling and storage plants.
(2) Rooms containing grinders or pulverizers, cleaners, graders, scalpers, open conveyors or spouts, open bins or hoppers, mixers or blenders, automatic or hopper scales, packing machinery, elevator heads and boots, stock distributors, dust and stock collectors (except all-metal collectors vented to the outside), and all similar dust producing machinery and equipment in grain processing plants, starch plants, sugar pulverizing plants, malting plants, hay grinding plants, and any other occupany of a similar nature.
(3) Coal pulverizing plants, unless the pulverizing equipment is essentially tight.
(4) All working areas where metal dusts and powders are produced, processed, handled, packed, or stored (except in tight containers).
(5) All other similar locations where combustible dust may, under normal operating conditions, be present in the air in sufficient quantities to produce explosive or ignitible mixtures.

Combustible dusts which are electrically non-conducting include grain dusts, pulverized sugar and cocoa, dried egg and milk powders, pulverized spices, starch and pastes, potato and woodflour, oil meal from beans and seed, dried hay, and other organic materials which will produce combustible dusts when handled or processed. Electrically conducting nonmetallic dusts include dusts from pulverized coal, coke and charcoal. Dusts containing aluminum or magnesium are especially dangerous.

(b) Class II, Division 2. This classification covers locations in which, during the normal operation of apparatus and equipment, dust is not likely to be in suspension in the air in quantities sufficient to produce explosive or ignitible mixtures, but:

(1) Where deposits or accumulations of such dust may be of sufficient quantity to interfere with the safe dissipation of heat from electrical equipment and apparatus.

(2) Where such deposits or accumulations of dust on or in electrical equipment or apparatus may be ignited by sparks, arcs, or burning material from same.

The decision whether an area is a Class II, Division 1, or a Class

II, Division 2 location is determined by the inspection authority. Such locations might include:

(1) Rooms containing closed spouts and conveyors.
(2) Closed bins or hoppers.
(3) Machines and equipment from which appreciable quantities of dust might escape under abnormal operating conditions.
(4) Rooms adjacent to Class II locations.
(5) Rooms in which control over suspension of dust in explosive or ignitible quantities is exercised.
(6) Warehouses and shipping rooms where dust-producing materials are stored.
(7) Any similar location.

500-6. Class III Locations—Class III locations include those where ignitible fibers or flyings are not likely to be in suspension in quantities likely to produce explosive or ignitible conditions, but in which they are present. The following are included in Class III locations:

(a) Class III, Division 1. *Locations in which easily ignitible fibers or materials producing combustible flyings are handled, manufactured or used.* Such locations may include:

(1) Some parts of rayon and cotton or other textile mills.
(2) Combustible fiber manufacturing and processing plants.
(3) Cotton gins and cotton-seed mills.
(4) Flax processing plants.
(5) Clothing manufacturing plants.
(6) Other establishments and industries involving similar hazards.

Included in easily ignitible fibers and flyings are:

(1) Rayon.
(2) Cotton.
(3) Cotton linters and cotton waste.
(4) Sisal or henequen.
(5) Istle.
(6) Hemp and jute.
(7) Tow.
(8) Cocoa fiber.
(9) Oakum.
(10) Baled waste kapok.
(11) Spanish moss.
(12) Excelsior.
(13) Other similar materials.

(b) Class III, Division 2. *Locations in which easily ignitible fibers are stored or handled (except in process of manufacture).*

ARTICLE 501—CLASS I INSTALLATIONS—
HAZARDOUS LOCATIONS

501-1. General—The general requirements of the Code covering wiring and the installation thereof and the provisions of **Article 500** as classified under **Section 500-4** will apply with the modifications covered in this Article.

501-2. Transformers and Capacitors—It was stated in **Articles 450** and **460** that transformers and capacitors in hazardous locations would also be affected by the Articles covering hazardous locations. The installation of transformers and capacitors shall conform to the following:

(a) **Class I, Division 1.** *In Class I, Division 1 locations, transformers and capacitors shall conform to the following:*

    (1) **Containing a Liquid that Will Burn.** Transformers and capacitors containing a flammable liquid shall be installed only in vaults conforming to the provisions in **Part C** of **Article 450, Section 450-41** to **540-48** inclusive, but the following will also apply:

        (a) There shall be no door or other communicating opening between the vault and the hazardous area.

        (b) Sufficient ventilation shall be provided to remove hazardous vapors or gases.

        (c) All vent ducts and openings shall lead to a safe location outside of the building.

        (d) Vent ducts and openings shall be of sufficient size to relieve any explosive pressures that might occur in the vault.

        (e) Portions of vent ducts within the building shall be of reinforced concrete.

    (2) **Not Containing a Liquid that Will Burn.** Transformers and capacitors that do not contain a flammable liquid shall:

        (a) Be installed in vaults conforming to the requirements in **Section 501-2 (a-1).**

        (b) Be approved for explosion-proof Class I locations.

(b) **Class I, Division 2.** *In Class I, Division 2 locations, transformers and capacitors shall conform to* **Sections 450-21** *to* **450-25** *inclusive.*

501-3. Meters, Instruments and Relays—*The installation of meters, instruments, and relays shall conform to the following:*

(a) **Class I, Division 1.** Enclosures that are approved for Class I locations shall be used in Class I, Division 1 locations for meters, instruments and relays, including kilowatt-hour meters, instrument transformers and resistors, rectifiers and thermionic tubes. It should be determined that the Group Letter is applicable for the location.

(b) Class I, Division 2. The installation of meters, instruments, and relays in Class I, Division 2 locations shall conform to the following:

(1) Contacts. *Switches and circuit breakers, and make and break contacts of push buttons, relays, and alarm bells or horns, shall have enclosures approved for Class I locations, unless general purpose enclosures are provided, and current interrupting contacts are:*

(a) Immersed in oil.
(b) Enclosed in a chamber hermetically sealed against the entrance of gases or vapors.
(c) In circuits that, under normal conditions, do not release enough energy to ignite the specific hazardous atmospheric mixture.

(2) Resistors and Similar Equipment. *Resistors, resistance devices, thermionic tubes, and rectifiers, which are used in or in connection with meters, instruments and relays, shall conform to Section 501-3(a), except that enclosures may be of general purpose type when such equipment is without make and break or sliding contacts (other than as provided in Section 501-3(b) (1) above) and when the maximum operating temperature of any exposed surface will not exceed eighty per cent (80%) of the ignition temperature in degrees Celsius of the gas or vapor involved as determined by A.S.T.M. test procedure (Designation D2155-66).*

(3) Without Make or Break Contacts. When the following do not have sliding or make-and-break contacts; the enclosure may be of a general-purpose type:

(a) Transformer windings.
(b) Impedance coils.
(c) Solenoids.
(d) Other windings.

(4) General Purpose Assemblies. *Where an assembly is made up of components for which general purpose enclosures are acceptable under Sections 501-3(b-1, 2, 3), a single general purpose enclosure is acceptable for the assembly. Where such an assembly includes any of the equipment described in Section 501-3 (b-2) the maximum obtainable surface tem-*

perature of any component of the assembly shall be clearly and permanently indicated on the outside of the enclosure.

(5) Fuses. *Where general purpose enclosures are permitted under* **Paragraphs 501-3(b), (1), (2), (3), (4),** *fuses for overcurrent protection of the instrument circuits may be mounted in general purpose enclosures provided such fuses do not exceed 3 ampere rating at 120 volts and provided each such fuse is preceded by a switch conforming to* **Paragraph 501-3(b) (1).**

(6) Connections. *To facilitate replacements, process control instruments may be connected through flexible cord, attachment plug and receptacle provided:*

(1) *a switch conforming to* **Section 501-3(b)(1)** *is provided so that the plug is not depended on to interrupt current, and*

(2) *current does not exceed 3 amperes at 120 volts, and*

(3) *power supply cord does not exceed 3 feet, is of a type approved for extra hard usage or for hard usage if protected by location and is supplied through a plug and receptacle of the locking and grounding type, and*

(4) *only necessary receptacles are provided, and*

(5) *the receptacle carries a label warning against unplugging under load.*

501-4. Wiring Methods—*Wiring methods shall conform to the following:*

(a) Class I, Division 1.

(1) Rigid metal conduit.

(2) MI cable with fittings approved for the location.

(3) Boxes, fittings, and joints shall be threaded for connection to conduit or approved cable terminations.

(4) The devices in (3) above shall be approved as explosion-proof.

(5) Threaded joints shall be made up at least five full threads. This is to cool any escaping gases and to prevent loose joints which may spark or arc in case of a fault.

(6) Type MI cable shall be supported so that there will be no strain at termination fittings.

(7) Flexible connections shall be explosion-proof and approved for Class I locations. Liquid-tight flexible metal conduit is NOT approved for this purpose.

(b) Class I, Division 2.

(1) MI, MC, ALS, or SMN cable with approved termination fittings.

(2) MI cable with fittings approved for the purpose.

(3) Approved type MC cable approved for Class I and approved fittings for this location.

(4) Type ALS cable with fittings approved for Class I locations.

(5) Types MI, MC, and ALS cables shall be supported so there will be no strain on the fittings that are used.

(6) Boxes, fittings, and joints need not be explosion-proof, except as provided in **Section 501-(b) (1)** and **(2).**

Where provisions must be made for a flexible connection, as at motors, the following may be used, but additional grounding must be provided around these flexible connections:

(1) Flexible metal fittings.

(2) Flexible metal conduit with approved fittings.

(3) Extra hard usage flexible cord with approved bushed fittings and an extra grounding conductor.

(4) Liquidtight flexible metal conduit with approved fittings.

501-5. Sealing and Drainage—Seals are to be provided in conduit and cable systems to prevent the passage of gases or vapors from one portion of the system to another portion. Type MI cable is inherently sealed, but sealed fittings must be used at terminations to keep moisture and other liquids from entering the insulation of the MI cable. Seals in conduit and cable systems shall conform to the following:

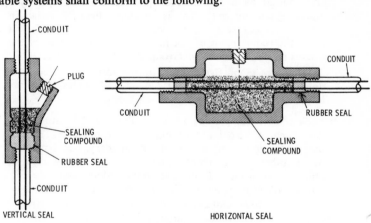

Fig. 501-1. Horizontal and vertical seals.

(a) **Class I, Division 1.** *In Class I, Division 1 locations, seals shall be located as follows:*

(1) In each conduit run entering an enclosure for switches, circuit breakers, fuses, relays, resistors or other apparatus which may

produce arcs, sparks, or high temperature. These seals are to be located as close as practical to the enclosure but in no case shall be more than 18 inches away from the enclosure. The purpose of the seals is to keep from transmitting an explosion or to keep ignition from traveling between sections of the system. Seals are made for vertical and horizontal installation and are to be used only for the purpose for which they are designed. Thus, a vertical seal is not to be placed horizontally. See Fig. 501-1.

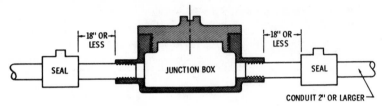

Fig. 501-2. Junction boxes with splices or taps shall have seals.

(2) When a conduit run of 2-inch conduit or larger enters an enclosure or fitting housing terminals, splices, or taps, there shall be a seal within 18 inches of such enclosure or fitting. See Fig. 501-2. When two or more enclosures for which seals are required, as in **Sections 501-5(a-1, 2)**, are connected by a nipple or conduit run which is no longer than 36 inches in length, only one seal will be required (Fig. 501-3). This will fulfill the requirement of not more than 18 inches from the enclosure. *See notes under* **Group B** *in* **Section 500-2.**

When L, T, or Cross-type fittings, normally called **condulets**, are used, they do not require seals unless they are larger than the conduit which enters them.

(3) Each conduit run leaving a Class I, Division 1 location shall have a seal at the point of leaving the hazardous area. This seal may be located on either side of the boundary, but there shall be no other fitting, union, coupling, box, or any type of fitting between the seal and the nonhazardous area. See Fig. 501-4. This also applies to Class I, Division 2 locations.

Exception: Rigid unbroken conduit which passes completely through a Class I, Division 1 area with no fittings 12 inches beyond each boundary, providing that the termination points of the unbroken conduit are in nonhazardous areas, need not be sealed.

(b) **Class I, Division 2.** *In Class I, Division 2 locations, seals shall be located as follows:*

(1) The wiring methods as outlined in **Section 501-4(a)** will apply.

Also, seals shall be provided as in **Section 501-5(a-1, 2).**

(2) The provisions that were covered in **Section 501-5(a-3)** apply to Class I, Division 2 areas where conduit leaves that area and passes into a nonhazardous area.

Exception: Rigid unbroken conduit which passes completely through a Class I, Division 2 area with no fittings 12 inches beyond each boundary, providing that the termination points of the unbroken conduit are in non-hazardous areas, need not be sealed.

(c) Class I, Divisions 1 and 2. Seals used in Class I, Division 1 and 2 locations shall conform to the following:

(1) Fittings. Enclosures for connections or equipment in all Class I locations shall be provided with approved seals. These may be an integral part of the enclosure or fitting or they may be a sealing fitting. For instance, most explosion-proof lighting fixtures have the seal inherently built in, and curb

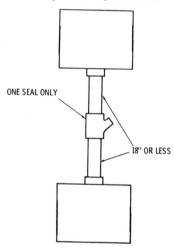

Fig. 501-3. One seal only on runs of 36 inches or less.

ONE SEAL ONLY

18" OR LESS

junction boxes for use with gasoline dispensing islands may be purchased with a built-in provision to make a seal off from it.

(2) Compound. The compound used in seals shall not be affected by temperature or liquids that it might come into contact with. It shall be a compound that is approved for this purpose and shall have a melting point of not less than 90° C (200°F).

(3) Thickness of Compound. The sealing compound, when put into the seal, shall not be less than 5/8 inch thick and in no case shall it be less than the trade size of the conduit it is designed for. Thus, for a 1-inch conduit seal, the thickness of the compound shall not be less than 1 inch. If the conduit is

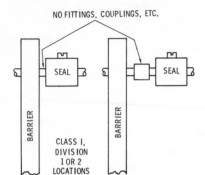

NO FITTINGS, COUPLINGS, ETC.

SEAL

SEAL

BARRIER

BARRIER

CLASS I,
DIVISION
1 OR 2
LOCATIONS

Fig. 501-4. Location of seals when leaving
Class I locations.

1/2 inch trade size, the thickness of the compound shall not be less than 5/8 inch.

(4) Splices and Taps. Splices and taps shall not be made within fittings that are made for sealing only, and neither shall boxes that are made only for taps and splices be used as a seal. There are, however, combinations available.

(5) Assemblies. *In an assembly where equipment which may produce arcs, sparks or high temperatures is located in a compartment separate from the compartment containing splices and taps, and an integral seal is provided where conductors pass from one compartment to the other, the entire assembly shall be approved for Class I locations. Seals in conduit connections to the compartment containing splices or taps shall be provided in Class I, Division 1 locations where required by* **Section 501-5(a-2).**

(d) Drainage.

(1) Control Equipment. In control equipment where there is a possibility of liquid accumulating or vapor condensing and becoming trapped in the enclosure, provision shall be made for periodically draining off this liquid, and the draining means shall be of an approved type.

(2) Motors and Generators. The authority enforcing the Code has the responsibility of deciding where there is a probability of liquid or condensed vapor accumulating in motors and generators. If judged that there is this accumulation, the conduit system shall be arranged so as to minimize this possibility and, if a means of permitting periodic draining is judged necessary by the inspector, such means shall be provided at the time of manufacture and shall be an integral part of the machine.

(3) Canned Pumps, Process Connections for Flow, Pressure or

Analysis Measurement, Etc., *frequently depend upon a single seal diaphragm or tube to prevent process fluids from entering the electrical conduit system. An additional approved seal or barrier shall be provided with an adequate drain between the seals in such a manner that leaks would be obvious.* This is a new ruling in the 1965 edition of the NEC and is also covered by footnote in **Section 500-4(b),** which states: *Electrical conduit and their associated enclosures separated from process fluids by a single seal or barrier shall be classed as Division 2 locations if the outside of conduit and enclosures is a non-hazardous areas.*

501-6. Switches, Circuit Breakers, Motor Controllers and Fuses— *Switches, circuit breakers, motor controllers and fuses shall conform to the following:*

(a) **Class I, Division 1.** Class I, Division 1 locations shall have the switches, circuit breakers, motor controllers and fuses, including push buttons, relays, and similar devices in approved enclosures together with the apparatus enclosed therein approved for Class I locations. It shall also have the Group letter for the group that the location is classed in.

(b) **Class I, Division 2.** Switches, circuit breakers, motor controllers, and fuses in Class I, Division 2 locations shall conform to the following:

(1) **Type Required.** Switches, circuit breakers, and motor controllers that are intended to interrupt current in the normal performance of the function for which they are installed shall shall be approved, along with the enclosures for same, for Class I locations. Exceptions to this are:

(a) Where the interruption of the current occurs within a chamber hermetically sealed against the entrance of gases and vapors.

(b) Where the current-interrupting contacts are oil-immersed and the device is approved for locations of this class and division. Included in these items are:

(1) Branch-circuit switches.
(2) Branch-circuit breakers.
(3) Motor controllers and their push buttons.
(4) Pilot switches.
(5) Relays.
(6) Motor overcurrent protective devices.
(7) Switches and circuit breakers for the control of lighting and appliances.

General-purpose oil-immersed circuit breakers and controllers may not completely confine the arcs that might be produced under heavy overloads, so they shall be specifically approved for locations in Class I, Division 2 Locations.

(2) **Isolating Switches.** Isolating switches need not have fuses included as they are not intended to be opened under load or to interrupt current, their purpose is to isolate the equipment after the electricity is shut off by other means approved for that purpose, so they may be of the general-purpose type. Most inspectors prefer that they be marked, "Do Not Open Under Load."

(3) **Fuses.** Except as provided in **Section 501-6(b-4),** the following may be used for the protection of motors, appliances, and lamps:

(a) If installed in enclosures approved for the purpose and the location, cartridge fuses and plug fuses may be used if of the proper voltage for the job.

(b) Some fuses have the operating element immersed in oil or other liquid, such as carbon tetrachloride. These may be used or they may be enclosed in hermetically sealed chambers sealed against the entrance of gases or vapors. These types are adjudged approved for the purpose and location.

(4) **Fuses or Circuit Breakers for Overcurrent Protection.** *When not more than 10 sets of approved enclosed fuses, or not more than 10 circuit breakers which are not intended to be used as switches for the interruption of current, are installed for branch or feeder circuit protection in any one room, area or section of this class and division, the enclosures for such fuses or circuit breakers may be of the general purpose type, provided the fuses or circuit breakers are for the protection of circuits or feeders supplying lamps in fixed positions only.* Please note that this does not cover portable lamps. For the purpose of this part, three fuses on a three-phase system to protect the three ungrounded conductors is considered as a set. Also a single fuse to protect the ungrounded conductor of a single-phase circuit is considered as one set. Fuses which conform to **Section 501-6(b-3)** need not be counted in the 10 sets covered in this part.

501-7. Control Transformers and Resistors—*Transformers, impedance coils and resistors used as or in conjunction with control equipment for motors, generators and appliances shall conform to the following:*

(a) **Class I, Division 1.** Transformers, impedance coils, and resistors, together with their switching equipment. shall be provided with approved (explosion-proof) enclosures for Class I, Division 1 locations.

(b) Class I, Division 2. *In Class I, Division 2 locations, control transformers and resistors shall conform to the following:*

(1) Switching Mechanisms. *Switching mechanisms used in conjunction with transformers, impedance coils and resistors shall conform to* **Section 501-6(b).** In other words, shall be approved for Class I locations.

(2) Coils and Windings. If provided with adequate vents to take care of the prompt escape of gases or vapors that may enter the enclosure, transformers, solenoids, and impedance coils may be of the general-purpose type.

(3) Resistors. *Resistors shall be provided with enclosures and the assembly shall be approved for Class I locations, unless resistance is nonvariable and maximum operating temperature, in degrees Celsius, will not exceed eighty percent (80%) of the ignition temperature of the gas or vapor involved as determined by ASTM test procedure (Designation D2155-66).*

501-8. Motors and Generators—*Motors and generators shall conform to the following:*

(a) Class I, Division 1. Motors and generators used in Class I, Division 1 locations shall be:

(1) Explosion-proof and approved for Class I locations.
(2) Totally enclosed types with positive-pressure ventilation from a source of clean air and the air discharged into a safe area. A totally-enclosed motor is not necessarily an explosion-proof motor. The motor and ventilating fan must be interlocked electrically so that the motor cannot be started until the fan has purged the motor with air in a quantity of at least ten (10) times that volume of air in the motor. The interlock must also be arranged to stop the motor if the air source fails.
(3) The motor may be a totally-enclosed type, pressurized by a suitable and reliable source of inert gas with interlocking to stop the motor in the event that the gas pressure drops.

In (2) and (3), the operating temperature of any external surface of the motor shall not exceed 80% of the ignition temperature of the gases or vapors involved in the hazardous location. These temperatures are to be determined by ASTM test procedure (Designation D2155-66). Any device used to detect the rise in temperature shall be of an approved type. All auxiliary equipment used for ventilating or pressurizing must also be approved for the location.

385

(b) Class I, Division 2. Motors, generators, and other rotating electrical machinery used in Class I, Division 2 locations shall be approved for Class I locations (explosion-proof) if they have:

(1) Sliding contacts.

(2) Centrifugal or other switching devices or mechanisms including motor overcurrent devices.

(3) Integral resistance devices, either while starting or running, unless the sliding contacts or switching devices and resistance devices are provided for in enclosures approved for the location.

The above rules do not prohibit the use of open-squirrel-cage, nonexplosion-proof motors that do not use brushes or switching mechanisms.

501-9. Lighting Fixtures—*Lamps shall be installed in fixtures which shall conform to the following:*

(a) Class I, Division 1. In Class I, Division 1 locations, fixtures for lighting shall conform to the following:

(1) Approved Fixtures. All fixtures shall be approved for Class I, Division 1 locations and shall be approved as a complete unit with the maximum wattage of lamps that may be used plainly marked on them. Portable fixtures shall also be approved as a complete unit.

Many times in the field, explosion-proof and dust-tight lighting fixtures are confused. They definitely are not the same. An explosion-proof fixture has to contend primarily with explosions from within, so the glass enclosure must be thick and strong. While the temperature of operation is also a factor, it is not the same as with dust-tight fixtures. In dust-tight units, the operating temperature of the fixture is the important factor, so the glass will be thinner, but the enclosure will be larger so the heat will have more surface to dissipate from. Look for the Group Letter on the fixture and check with the atmospheric groups that are listed in the first part of **Article 500.**

(2) Physical Damage. The fixtures shall be protected from physical damage, either by guards or by location. The breaking of a lamp bulb might cause the hot filament to start an explosion or fire.

(3) Pendant Fixtures. Rigid metal conduit shall be used to suspend pendant fixtures. The conduit shall have threaded joints and a set screw shall be provided to prevent loosening. Fixtures having stems longer than 12 inches may be installed in one of two ways:

(a) The stems shall be securely supported at a height not to

386

exceed 12 inches above the fixture. These supports shall secure the fixture laterally and shall be of a permanent nature.

(b) An approved, explosion proof, flexible connector may be used if it is not more than 12 inches below the box or fitting which supports the fixture.

(4) Supports. Support boxes and fittings used to support fixtures shall be approved for the purpose and also be approved for Class I locations.

(b) Class I, Division 2. *In Class I, Division 2 locations, lighting fixtures shall conform to the following:*

(1) Portable Lamps. *Portable lamps shall conform to* **Section 501-9(a-1).** In other words, they shall be approved as a complete unit for Class I locations.

(2) Fixed Lighting. Fixed lighting fixtures shall be protected from physical damage by guards or by location. If there should be a danger of hot particles falling from lamps or fixtures, they shall be suitably guarded to prevent these hot particles falling into areas of concentrations of flammable gases or vapors. Where the lamps are of a size or type which might reach an operating temperature of more than 80% of the ignition temperature of the gases or vapors involved, as determined by ASTM test procedure (Designation D286-30), the fixtures shall conform to **Section 501-9(a-1).**

(3) Pendant Fixtures. This is a repetition of **Section 501-9(a-3).** Please refer to that Section.

(4) Supports. *Boxes, box assemblies, or fittings used for the support of lighting fixtures shall be approved for the purpose.*

(5) Switches. Section 501-6(b-1) covers switches that are a part of an assembled fixture or of an individual lampholder.

(6) Starting Equipment. *Starting and control equipment for electric-discharge lamps shall conform to the requirements of* **Section 501-7(b).** This Section requires that they be in an approved enclosure, or that they are not capable of emitting sparks or arcs that will ignite or explode the gases or vapors in that area.

501-10. Utilization Equipment, Fixed and Portable—*Utilization equipment, fixed or portable, shall conform to the following:*

(a) Class I, Division 1. All utilization equipment, including electrically-heated and motor-driven equipment, that is used in Class I, Division 1 locations, shall be approved for the location.

(b) Class I, Division 2. *In Class I, Division 2 locations, utilization*

387

equipment, fixed and portable, shall conform to the following:

(1) Heaters. *Electrically-heated utilization equipment shall be approved for Class I locations.*

(2) Motors. Motors in this location will be treated the same as other motors, as explained in **Section 501-8(b).**

(3) Switches, Circuit-breakers, and Fuses. These were covered in **Section 501-6(b).**

501-11. Flexible Cords, Class I, Divisions 1 and 2—*A flexible cord may be used only for connection between a portable lamp or other portable utilization equipment and the fixed portion of its supply circuit and where used shall:*

(1) Be of a type approved for extra hard usage.

(2) Contain, in addition to the conductors of the circuit, a grounding conductor conforming to **Section 400-14**—that is, of green color and used for no other purpose than for grounding.

(3) Be connected to terminals or to supply conductors in an approved manner.

(4) Be supported by clamps or other suitable means in such a manner that there will be no tension on the terminal connections.

(5) Have suitable seals provided where the flexible cord enters boxes, fittings, or enclosures of the explosion-proof type.

501-12. Receptacles and Attachment Plugs, Class I, Divisions 1 and 2 —Receptacles and plugs shall be of a type approved for Class I locations (explosion-proof), and shall be equipped with a connection for a grounding conductor. The grounding conductor shall make connection first and the other terminals shall be so arranged that, upon insertion or removal, no sparks will result in ignition or explosion. *Except as provided in* **Section 501-3(b)(6).**

501-13. Conductor Insulation Class I, Divisions 1 and 2—Where condensed vapors or liquids may come in contact with the insulation on conductors or cords, the insulation shall be of an approved type for use in this location or the conductors shall be protected by a lead sheath or other approved means.

TW insulation, as such, is not approved for use where it will be exposed to gasoline. However, there is a TW wire with a nylon cover that is approved, as well as THWN and many others that go by the trade names of the manufacturer. The best method of finding out whether the insulation is approved for contact with any liquid is to refer to the Underwriter's Laboratories listing and check. If approved, it will be there.

501-14. Signal, Alarm, Remote-control and Communication Systems— *Signal, alarm, remote-control and communication systems shall conform to the following:*

(a) Class I, Division 1. All apparatus, equipment, etc., used in Class I, Division 1 locations for signalling systems, alarms, remote-control, and communications shall be approved for Class I locations, irrespective of the voltages that are involved. The wiring methods and sealing, as prescribed in **Sections 501-4(a)** and **501-5 (a** and **c),** shall apply to the installation of same. There are no exceptions.

(b) Class I, Division 2. *In Class I, Division 2 locations, signal, alarm, remote-control and communication systems shall conform to the following:*

  (1) Contacts. The enclosures for switches, circuit breakers, the make and break contacts of push buttons, relays, and alarm bells and horns shall be approved for Class I locations, with the following exceptions:

  (a) Where immersed in oil.
  (b) Where enclosed in a chamber hermetically sealed against the entrance of gases or vapors.
  (c) In circuits which, under normal conditions, do not release sufficient energy to ignite a specific hazardous atmospheric mixture.

  (2) Resistors and Similar Equipment. *Resistors, resistance devices, thermionic tubes and rectifiers,* shall meet the same requirements as covered in **Section 501-3(b-2).**
  (3) Protectors. The enclosures for lightning protective devices and for fuses may be of the general-purpose type.
  (4) All wiring must conform to the requirements for Class I locations covered in **Section 501-4(b)** and the sealing shall conform to the requirements of **Section 501-5(b).**

501-15. **Live Parts, Class I, Divisions 1 and 2**—*There shall be no exposed live parts.*

501-16. **Grounding, Class I, Divisions 1 and 2**—*Wiring and equipment shall be grounded in conformity with the following:*

(a) Exposed Parts. *The exposed noncurrent-carrying metal part of equipment such as the frames or metal exteriors of motors, fixed or portable lamps or other utilization equipment, lighting fixtures, cabinets, cases, and conduit, shall be grounded as specified in* **Article 250** *of the Code.*

(b) Bonding. This part is very important and should be thoroughly understood. The locknut-bushing and double-locknut types of contacts, such as used in ordinary wiring methods, shall not be depended upon in Class I locations. It is required that, where locknuts are used, bonding by use of approved fittings supplement the locknut connections. Bonding also shall apply to all of the following:

(1) All intervening raceways.
(2) Fittings, boxes, and enclosures.
(3) Between hazardous areas and the point of grounding of the service.
(4) In **Section 501-4(b),** flexible conduit was permitted for some uses. This must be bonded and approved fittings shall be used. A copper strap is not permitted for bonding. Approved malleable clamps, of a metal suitable to prevent electrolysis action, shall be used.

In summary, the wiring system must be completely bonded by means of threaded connections to hubs, etc., or by means of bonding jumpers properly installed.

(c) **Lightning Protection.** Class I locations in areas where lightning disturbances are prevalent, when served from an overhead supply, are required to have a lightning arrester installed in each ungrounded conductor. These lightning protective devices shall be of an approved type installed ahead of the service disconnecting means, and shall be bonded to the raceway system at the service entrance.

Reference is made to **Section 502-3.** This Section also requires that surge-protection capacitors be installed ahead of the disconnecting means for the service and protected by 30-ampere fuses or a circuit breaker of a suitable type. It is suggested that, in the use of surge-protection capacitors, the fuses have a tattle light of some sort that will indicate when a fuse is blown.

(d) **Grounded Service Conductor Bonded to Raceway.** *Wiring in a Class I location, when supplied from a grounded alternating current supply system in which a grounded conductor is a part of the service, shall have the grounded service conductor bonded to the raceway system and to the grounding conductor for the raceway system. The bonding connection to the service conductor shall be made on the supply side of the service disconnecting means.*

(e) **Transformer Ground Bonded to Raceway.** *Wiring in a Class I location, when supplied from a grounded alternating current supply system in which no ground-conductor is a part of the service, shall be provided with a metallic connection between the supply system ground and the raceway system at the service entrance. The metallic connection shall have an ampacity not less than 1/5 that of the service conductors, and shall in no case be smaller than No. 10 when of soft copper, or No. 12 when of medium or hard-drawn copper.*

This is a little hypothetical since, beginning January 1, 1964, any secondary system that was grounded at any point was required to have the grounded conductor run in each individual service. The utility companies, in most all cases, bond the secondary ground and the transformer ground together.

(g) Multiple Grounds. *Where, in the application of* **Section 250-21,** *it is necessary to abandon one or more grounding connections to avoid objectionable passage of current over the grounding conductors, the connection required in* **Section 501-16(d** *and* **e)** *shall not be abandoned while any other grounding connection remains connected to the supply system.*

ARTICLE 502—CLASS II INSTALLATIONS— HAZARDOUS LOCATIONS

502-1.   General—In **Section 500-5,** Class II locations were covered and thoroughly outlined as to the coverage included in this classification. The general rules of the Code will apply to all Class II locations, with the exception that they are modified by this **Article 502.**

It will be recalled that Class II locations were those areas where dusts were in suspension or otherwise present to the extent that they might be ignitable or explosive. This Article covers the supplemental requirements in wiring installations which are necessary to take care of this hazardous condition. In dealing with this Article, it should be remembered that most dusts in the proper suspension might become explosive. All of the dusts are not covered in the Code and it becomes the responsibility of the inspection authority to judge whether or not these dusts may be a problem and to what extent.

A few definitions that are applicable to these locations are as follows:

Dust-ignition-proof—as used in this Article, shall mean enclosed in a manner which will exclude ignitible amounts of dusts or amounts which might affect performance or rating and which, when installation and protection are in conformance with this Code, will not permit arcs, sparks or heat otherwise generated or liberated inside of the enclosure, to cause ignition of exterior accumulations or atmospheric suspensions of a specified dust on or in the vicinity of the enclosure.

Dustproof—So constructed or protected that dust will not interfere with its successful operation.

Dust-tight—So constructed that dust will not enter the enclosing case.

One major problem of Class II locations is temperature. *Equipment installed in Class II locations shall be able to function at full rating without developing surface temperatures high enough to cause excessive dehydration or gradual carbonization of any organic dust deposits that may*

391

occur. Dust which is carbonized or is excessively dry is highly susceptible to spontaneous ignition. In general, maximum surface temperatures under actual operating conditions shall not exceed 165°C (329°F) for equipment which is not subject to overloading, and 120°C (248 F) for equipment such as motors, power transformers, etc., which may be overloaded.

In the above, the answer is in the fact that not only will arcs and sparks cause explosions when dust is in suspension in the proper amounts in the atmosphere, but also the fact that the temperatures of ignition are very low, and when organic dusts are exposed to a high temperature over a prolonged period, the composition of the dust will change and, in most cases, the flash point will even be lowered.

Equipment and wiring of the type defined in **Article 100** *as explosion-proof is not required in Class II locations, and may not be acceptable unless approved for such locations.* The point here is that the explosion possibility may be taken care of, but the temperature also has to be considered, since many dusts have a lower flash point than gases or vapors in Class I locations. The NFPA Code mentioned in other parts concerning hazardous locations will give the flash points and other pertinent facts that will be encountered with dusts. Inspectors and anyone concerned with design and installation of wiring in these areas should be familiar with (or at least know where to find) the facts applicable to the conditions that might prevail.

502-2. **Transformers and Capacitors**—The installation of transformers and capacitors shall conform to the following:

(a) **Class II, Division 1.** *In Class II, division 1 locations, transformers and capacitors shall conform to the following:*

(1) **Containing a Liquid that Will Burn. Sections 450-41** to **450-48** inclusive covered transformer vaults. These requirements will apply to transformers in Class II locations that contain a liquid that will burn. In addition:

(a) *Door or other openings communicating with the hazardous areas shall have self-closing fire doors on both sides of the wall, and the doors shall be carefully fitted and provided with suitable seals (such as weather stripping) to minimize the entrance of dust into the vault.*

(b) Vent openings and ducts from the vault shall communicate only with the outside air and shall not enter into the hazardous area.

(c) *Suitable pressure-relief openings communicating with the outside air shall be provided.* This is to relieve any pressures that might occur from an explosion in the vault and communicate this pressure to the outside air away from the hazardous locations.

(2) Not Containing a Liquid that Will Burn. Transformers and capacitors which contain a liquid that will not burn shall be installed in a transformer vault that conforms to the requirements of **Sections 450-41** to **450-48** inclusive, or they shall be approved as a complete assembly, including terminal connections, for Class II locations.

(3) Metal Dusts. Transformers and capacitors shall not be installed in locations in which dust from magnesium, aluminum, aluminum bronze powders, or other metals of similar hazardous characteristics may be present. Recall that, in **Section 500-5(a)**, electrically conducting dusts from materials such as coal, charcoal, or coke were mentioned. Even though these are not considered as metallic dusts, it will be found that most inspection authorities will, in practically all cases, treat them as metal dusts.

(b) Class II, division 2. Class II, Division 2 locations are treated as having a lesser hazard than Class II, Division 1 locations, and transformers and capacitors shall conform to the following:

(1) Containing a Liquid that Will Burn. Transformers and capacitors containing a liquid that will burn, in Class II, Division 2 locations, shall conform to the requirement for transformer vaults as covered in **Sections 450-41** to **450-48** inclusive.

(2) Containing Askarel. *Transformers containing askarel and rated in excess of 25 KVA shall:*

  (a) *Be provided with pressure-relief vents.* These, of course, should vent into the air away from hazardous areas.

  (b) *Be provided with means for absorbing any gases generated by arcing inside the case, or* else *the pressure-relief vents shall be connected to a chimney or flue which will carry such gases outside the building.*

  (c) Have an air space of not less than 6 inches between the transformer cases and any combustible materials.

(3) Dry-Type Transformers. *Dry-type transformers shall be installed in vaults or shall:*

  (a) *Have their windings and terminal connections enclosed in tight metal housings without ventilating or other openings.* This means that they should be hermetically sealed.

  (b) Operate at a voltage not to exceed 600 volts. This includes both the primary and secondary voltages.

502-3. **Surge Protection, Class II, Division 1 and 2**—In areas where

393

lightning disturbances are prevalent, the wiring systems for Class II locations shall be provided with protection if they are supplied from overhead lines. This protection shall be suitable to protect against high-voltage surges and shall include lightning protective devices, interconnection of grounds, and surge-protective capacitors.

An explanation is offered here as there seems to be considerable misinterpretation in the field. First, take the interconnection of grounds. This includes:

(1) Grounds for primary and secondary lightning protection.
(2) Secondary system grounds, if any.
(3) Grounds of conduit and equipment in the interior wiring system.

For ungrounded secondary systems, secondary lightning protective devices may be provided both at the service and at the point where the secondary system receives its supply, and the intervening secondary conductors may be accepted as the metallic connection between the secondary protective devices, provided grounds for the primary and secondary devices are metallically interconnected at the supply end of the secondary system and the secondary devices are grounded to the raceway system at the load end of the secondary system.

Surge protective capacitors act as a sort of sponge to absorb electrical surges and thus assist in protection of equipment. These surge protective capacitors are specially designed for the purpose and are to be connected to each ungrounded conductor (service conductor) and shall be grounded to the interior conduit system. The capacitors shall be connected to a 30-ampere fuse switch, with 30-ampere fuses of a suitable type and voltage rating for the system, or automatic circuit breakers may be used if of the right size and voltage rating. The surge capacitors are to be connected ahead of the service disconnecting means. Fig. 502-1 illustrates a primary and secondary system with the necessary lightning protective devices and surge protection capacitors and their points of connection.

502-4. Wiring Methods—*Wiring methods shall conform to the following:*

(a) **Class II, Division 1.** The only two wiring methods approved for Class II, Division 1 locations are threaded rigid conduit or MI cable with fittings approved for the location and properly supported so that there will be no strain on the fittings.

    (1) **Fittings and Boxes.** Fittings and boxes in which taps, joints, or terminal connections are made shall be designed to minimize the entrance of dust and they shall:

        (a) Be equipped with telescoping or close-fitting covers.
        (b) Have other effective means to prevent the escape of sparks or burning materials.

(c) Have no openings (such as screw holes for attachment) through which, after installation, sparks or burning material might escape, or through which adjacent combustible materials might be ignited.

The above, in summary, states that all fittings and boxes shall be dust-tight and approved for Class II locations. See Fig. 502-2.

(2) Flexible Connections. Flexible connections are often a necessity. When they are, the following types may be used, except where the dusts are *of an electrical conducting nature, flexible metal conduit shall not be used and flexible cords shall be provided with dust-tight seals at both ends:*

(a) Dust-tight flexible connectors.

(b) Flexible metal conduit with approved fittings.

(c) Liquid tight flexible metal conduit with approved fittings.

(d) Flexible cord approved for extra-hard usage and provided with bushed fittings.

When using the above methods, some precautions shall be required, such as a grounding conductor in flexible cords and when the flexible connections are subject to oil or other corrosive conditions, *the insulation of the conductors shall be of a type approved for the condition or shall be protected by means of a suitable sheath.*

(b) Class II, Division 2. Rigid metal conduit, EMT, or Types MI, MC or ALS cable with approved termination fittings are permitted in Class II, Division 2 locations, as well are dust-tight wireways.

(1) Wireways, and Fittings and Boxes. Wireways, fittings and boxes in which taps, joints, or termination connections are made shall be designed to minimize the entrance of dust, and they shall:

(1) Meet the requirements of **(a)** of **502-4 (a) (1),**

(2) Flexible Connections. *Where flexible connections are necessary the provisions of* **Section 501-4(a-2)** *shall apply.*

502-5. Sealing, Class II, Divisions 1 and 2—In the installation of a dust-ignition-proof enclosure and one that is not, there may be communication of dust between the two enclosures. The entrance of dust into the dust-ignition-proof enclosure must be prevented. This may be done by one of the following means:

(1) By use of an effective and permanent seal, such as used in Class I locations.

(2) By connection to a horizontal raceway that is not less than 10 feet in length.

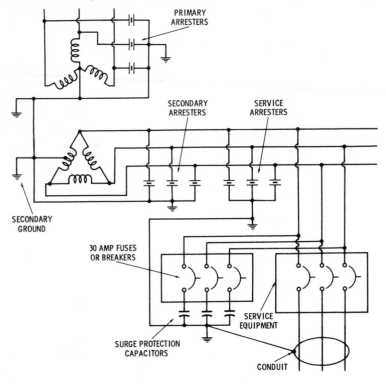

Fig. 502-1. Lightning and surge protection.

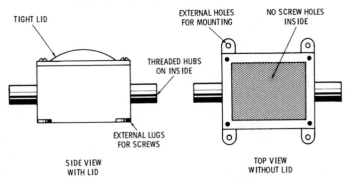

Fig. 502-2. Type of boxes for Class II locations.

(3) By means of a vertical raceway not less than 5 feet in length, which extends downward from the dust-ignition-proof enclosure. Note this carefully—if the raceway extends downward from the conventional enclosure, it will not meet the requirements.

Where seals are used they are to be accessible. See Fig. 502-3.

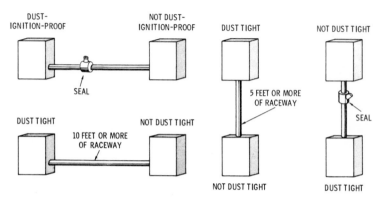

Fig. 502-3. Sealing in Class II locations.

502-6. Switches, Circuit Breakers, Motor Controllers, and Fuses— *Switches, circuit breakers, motor controllers and fuses shall conform to the following:*

(a) Class II, Division 1. *In Class II, Division 1 locations, switches, circuit breakers, motor controllers and fuses shall conform to the following:*

(1) Type Required. The emphasis of this part is on any device that is intended to interrupt a current, such as switches, circuit breakers, motor controllers, and fuses. This also includes push buttons, relays, and similar devices installed in Class II, Division 1 locations. Mention is also made of dusts having an electrical conductive nature.

Such devices shall be installed in dust-ignition-proof enclosures and shall be approved for Class II locations. In this discussion it should be mentioned that there is an enclosure available for industrial use which is termed a dust-tight enclosure. However, to secure approval, the enclosure shall be listed for a hazardous location and classified by a Group number, as covered in **Article 500**. In this classification are included the following:

(a) Service and branch-circuit fuses.

397

    (b) Switches and circuit breakers.

    (c) Motor controllers, including:

        (1) Push buttons.

        (2) Pilot switches.

        (3) Relays.

        (4) Motor overload protective devices.

        (5) Switches, fuses, and circuit breakers for the control and protection of lighting and appliance circuits.

(2) Isolating Switches. Isolating switches do not need to contain fuses and are not intended to interrupt current. Their purpose is to isolate the conductors for working on motors and the equipment driven by the motors. When isolating switches are installed in locations that do not have dusts of an electrical-conducting nature, they shall be so designed as to minimize the entrance of dusts, and shall:

    (a) Be equipped with telescoping or close-fitting covers, or with other means of preventing the escape of sparks or burning material.

    (b) Have no holes or openings (such as holes for attachment screws) through which, after installation, sparks or burning material might escape, or through which exterior accumulations of dust or adjacent combustible material might be ignited.

    It might be stated that, while not required by the Code, some insurance companies and some inspectors suggest that these and other sheet-metal enclosures be mounted on fireproof material such as 1/4-inch asbestos board. This is a relatively small expense which might pay large dividends.

(3) Metal Dusts. *In locations where dust from magnesium, aluminum, aluminum bronze powders, or other metals of similarly hazardous characteristics may be present, fuses, switches, motor controllers and circuit breakers shall have enclosures specifically approved for such locations.*

(b) Class II, Division 2. Enclosures for switches, circuit breakers, motor controllers, including push buttons, relays, and similar devices for Class II, Division 1 locations, shall be the same as required in **Section 502-6(a-2).**

502-7.　Control Transformers and Resistors—*Transformers, solenoids, impedance coils and resistors used as or in conjunction with control equipment for motors, generators and appliances shall conform to the following:*

(a) **Class II, Division 1.** Dust-ignition-proof enclosures approved for Class II, Division 1 locations shall be required for transformers, solenoids, impedance coils, and resistors. There shall be no transformer, impedance coil, or resistor installed in locations where dusts from magnesium, aluminum, aluminum bronze powders or other similar metal dusts are present unless the enclosures in which they are installed have been specifically approved for such a location.

(b) **Class II, Division 2.** *In Class II, Division 2 locations, transformers and resistors shall conform to the following:*

(1) **Switching Mechanisms: Section 502-6(a-2)** also applies here for switching mechanisms (including overcurrent devices) associated with control transformers, solenoids, impedance coils, and resistors. That Section basically called for enclosures that were designed to minimize the entrance of dusts and to prevent sparks or burning material from escaping from the enclosure.

(2) **Coils and Windings.** When not located in the same enclosure with the switching mechanism, then control transformers, solenoids, and impedance coils are to be mounted in tight metal enclosures and shall have no ventilation openings.

(3) **Resistors.** Resistors become heated when current passes through them, so they are required to be mounted in dust-ignition-proof enclosures approved for Class II locations. The maximum operating temperature of the resistor shall not exceed 120°C (248°F) for nonadjustable resistors and resistors which are a part of an automatically-timed starting sequence. In the case where the temperature does not exceed that just specified, the resistors may have enclosures conforming to **Section 502-7(b-2)**—that is, tight metal cases without ventilation openings.

502-8. Motors and Generators—*Motors and generators shall conform to the following:*

(a) **Class II, Division 1.** Motors, generators, and other rotating electrical machinery installed in Class II, Division 1 locations shall be:

(1) Totally enclosed but not ventilated.
(2) Totally enclosed with pipe ventilation.
(3) Totally enclosed, fan-cooled, and approved as dust-ignition-proof for Class II locations.

Motors, generators, or rotating electrical machinery located in areas where metal dust such as magnesium, aluminum, aluminum bronze, or similar dusts are present, shall not be installed unless they are specifically approved for such locations and are totally enclosed or totally enclosed and fan-cooled.

(b) Class II, Division 2. *In Class II, Division 2 locations, motors, generators and other rotating electrical machinery shall be dust-ignition-proof or totally enclosed pipe-ventilated, for which maximum surface temperature shall not exceed 120°C. (248°F.).*

There are exceptions to this which may be granted if the authority having jurisdiction believes that the accumulations of nonconducting, nonabrasive dust will be moderate. They may also be granted if the machines may be easily reached for routine cleaning and maintenance. If these conditions are met and approval is given, the following may be installed:

Standard open-type machines without sliding contacts, centrifugal or other types of switching mechanism (including motor overcurrent devices) or integral resistance devices.

Standard open-type machines with such contacts, switching mechanisms or resistance devices enclosed within tight metal housings without ventilating or other openings.

Self-cleaning textile motors of the squirrel-cage type.

The NEC is a very fair instrument placed in our hands, with permission granted in many instances to deviate from the strict portions, provided that we are sure that such deviations will not cause unsafe conditions. We must always consider what might happen after the inspection is made and ask ourselves if the same conditions will be lived up to.

502-9. Ventilating Piping—Vent pipes for motors, generators, or other rotating electrical machinery, or for enclosures for electrical apparatus, where it is permissible to use vents for these types of enclosures, shall:

(1) Be of a metal not lighter than No. 24 USS gage.
(2) Be of other substantial noncombustible material.
(3) Lead directly out to clean air outside the building.
(4) Be screened to prevent the entrance of small animals or birds.
(5) Be protected from physical damage.
(6) Be protected against rust and other corrosion.

In addition to the above, they shall conform to the following:

(a) Class II, Division 1. *In Class II, Division 1 locations, vent pipes, including their connections to motors or to the dust-ignition-proof enclosures for other equipment or apparatus, shall be dust-tight throughout their length.* When metal pipes are used, they shall be:

(1) Riveted (or bolted) and soldered.
(2) Welded.

(3) Rendered dust-tight by some other equally effective means.

(b) Class II, Division 2. *In Class II, Division 2 locations, vent pipes and their connections shall be sufficiently tight to prevent the entrance of appreciable quantities of dust into the ventilated equipment or enclosure, and to prevent the escape of sparks, flame or burning material which might ignite dust accumulations or combustible material in the vicinity.* For metal pipes, the following may be used:

(1) Lock seams.
(2) Riveted joints.
(3) Welded joints.
(4) Tight-fitting slip joints where some flexibility is necessary, as at motor connections.

502-10. Utilization Equipment, Fixed and Portable — *Utilization equipment, fixed and portable, shall conform to the following:*

(a) Class II, Division 1. Utilization equipment, fixed and portable, located in Class II, Division 1 locations, also includes electrically-heated and motor-driven equipment. They shall be dust-ignition-proof and approved for Class II, Division 1 locations. Where dusts from metals such as magnesium, aluminum, aluminum bronze powders, or other similar dust are present, the equipment shall be approved for these locations. This will be Group E equipment.

(b) Class II, Division 2. *In Class II, Division 2 locations, utilization equipment, fixed and portable, shall conform to the following:*

(1) Heaters. *Electrically heated utilization equipment shall be dust-ignition-proof approved for Class II locations.*

(2) Motors. *Motors of motor-driven utilization equipment shall conform to* **Section 502-8(b).** This Section allowed some latitude and left up to the inspection authority to decide what was involved and the equipment permitted.

(3) Switches, Circuit Breakers and Fuses. *Enclosures for switches, circuit breakers, and fuses shall conform to* **Section 502-6(a-2).** Isolating switches in Class II, Division 1 locations were covered in that Section. Switches, circuit breakers, etc., other than dust-ignition-proof, were allowed provided that they had telescoping or close-fitting doors.

(4) Transformers, Impedance Coils and Resistors. These shall conform to **Section 502-7(b).** There were three parts to this Section and it is suggested it be read again.

502-11. Lighting Fixtures—Recall that in Class II locations the ignition of dusts can be caused by either sparks, arcs, or heat. Bear this in mind while reading the following:

(a) Class II, Division 1. *In Class II, Division 1 locations, lighting fixtures for fixed and portable lighting shall conform to the following:*

(1) Approved Fixtures. For Class II, Division 1 locations where ordinary dusts are present, the fixtures shall be approved and plainly marked. In locations where dusts from magnesium, aluminum, aluminum bronze, or similar metal dusts with hazardous characteristics are present, the fixtures shall be approved and so marked.

(2) Physical Damage. *Each fixture shall be protected against physical damage by a suitable guard or by location.* The *"by location"* means that they are to be mounted high enough so that they are not likely to be bumped or hit.

(3) Pendant Fixtures. Pendant fixtures shall be suspended by:

    (a) Rigid conduit stems.
    (b) Chains with approved fittings.
    (c) Other approved means.

If the stems are longer than 12 inches they shall either be rigidly braced laterally at a point not more than 12 inches above the lower end of the stem, or there shall be an approved flexible fitting or flexible connection used and these shall not be mounted more than 12 inches from the attachment to the supporting box or fitting.

The wiring shall be by rigid conduit or, where necessary, a flexible rubber cord that is approved for hard usage may be used if it is sealed properly where attachments are made. The cord shall not support the fixture but shall be supported by other suitable means. Where stems are used, a set screw shall be provided to keep the stem from loosening.

(4) Supports. *Boxes, box assemblies or fittings used for the support of lighting fixtures shall be approved for the purpose and for Class II locations.* Class II boxes and fittings, of course, are to be dust tight.

(b) Class II, Division 2. *In Class II, Division 2 locations, lighting fixtures shall conform to the following:*

(1) Portable Lamps. Portable lamps shall be approved for Class II locations and shall be plainly marked as such. Also, the maximum size of lamp that may be used in them shall also be plainly marked.

(2) Fixed Lighting. Fixed lighting shall be approved for Class II locations except, if not approved, they shall be enclosed to prevent an accumulation of dust on the lamps and to prevent the escape of sparks, burning material, or hot metal. Each fixture shall be plainly marked to indicate the maximum size lamp that may be used in the fixture and, when in use, the maximum temperature of the exposed surface shall not exceed 165°C (329°F) under normal use.

(3) Physical Damage. *Lighting fixtures for fixed lighting shall be protected from physical damage by suitable guards or by location.*

(4) Pendant Fixtures. The requirements for pendant fixtures for Class II, Division 1 locations are practically the same as for pendant fixtures in Class II, Division 1. Please refer to **Section 502-11(a-3).**

(5) Supports. *Boxes, box assemblies and fittings used for the support of lighting fixtures shall be approved for that purpose.*

(6) Electric Discharge Lamps. *Starting and control equipment for electric-discharge lamps shall conform to the requirement of* **Section 502-7(b).**

502-12.   Flexible Cords, Class II, Divisions 1 and 2—*Flexible cords used in Class II locations shall conform to the following:*

(1) Be of a type approved for extra hard usage.

(2) Contain, in addition to the circuit conductors of the circuit, a grounding conductor conforming to **Section 400-14.**

(3) Be connected to terminals or to supply conductors in an approved manner.

(4) Be supported by clamps or by other suitable means in such a manner that there will be no tension on the terminal connections.

(5) Be provided with suitable seals to prevent the entrance of dust where the flexible cord enters boxes or fittings which are required to be dust-ignition-proof.

502-13.   Receptacles and Attachment Plugs—

(a) Class II, Division 1. Plugs and receptacles for use in Class II, Division 1 locations shall:

(1) Be provided with a grounding conductor connection for the flexible cord.

(2) Be dust-ignition-proof approved for Class II locations.

(b) Class II, Division 2. Plugs and receptacles for use in Class II, Division 2 locations shall:

(1) Be provided with a grounding conductor connection for the flexible cord.

(2) Be so designed that connection to the supply circuit cannot be made or broken while live parts are exposed.

403

502-14. Signal, Alarm, Remote-Control, and Local Loud-Speaker Intercommunication Systems—Referral is made to **Article 800** covering the rules governing the installation of communication circuits, and to the definition in **Article 100**.

The communication circuits will include telephone, telegraph, fire and burglar alarms, watchman, and sprinkler systems. Signal, alarm, remote-control, and local loudspeaker intercommunication systems shall conform to the following:

(a) **Class II, Division 1.** In this classification, they shall conform to the following:

    (1) **Wiring Methods.** In any location where accidental damage or breakdown of insulation might cause arcs, sparks, or heating, the wiring method to be used shall be by rigid conduit, electrical metallic tubing, or type MI cable with approved fittings. The number of conductors to be installed in conduit or EMT is not the same as for current-carrying conductors, but is only limited by the 40% fill requirement. This is to prevent damage to the insulation when pulling in the conductors. Flexible cord approved for extra hard usage may be used where flexibility is required and where it will not be subject to physical damage.

    (2) **Contacts.** Class II, Groups E, F, or G, as required, shall be the types of enclosures for switches, circuit breakers, relays, contactors, and fuses which may interrupt other than voice currents, and for current-breaking contacts for bells, horns, howlers, sirens, and other devices in which sparks or arcs may be produced. An exception to this is if the contacts are immersed in oil or when the interruption of current occurs within a sealed chamber; then the first part need not apply. The purpose of all this is to be certain that any sparks or arcs are isolated so that no ignition or explosion will occur.

    (3) **Resistors and Similar Equipment.** *Resistors, transformers and choke coils which may carry other than voice currents, and rectifiers, thermionic tubes, and other heat generating equipment or apparatus shall be provided with dust-ignition-proof enclosures approved for Class II locations.*

    (4) **Rotating Machinery.** *Motors, generators and other rotating electrical machinery shall conform to* **Section 502-8(a).**

    (5) **Electrical Conducting Dusts.** Where dusts are present that will conduct electricity, all wiring and equipment shall meet the Class II requirements.

    (6) **Metal Dusts.** *Where dust from magnesium, aluminum, aluminum bronze powders, or other metal of similarly hazardous characteristics may be present, all apparatus and equipment shall be specifically approved for such conditions.*

(b) Class II, Division 2. *In Class II, Division 2 locations, signal, alarm, remote-control and local loudspeaker intercommunication systems shall conform to the following:*

(1) Contacts. Enclosures for contacts in Class II, Division 2 locations shall either conform to the requirements for contacts in Class II, Division 1, as outlined in **Section 502-14(a-2),** or be enclosed in tight metal enclosures that are designed to minimize the entrance of dust, and shall have telescoping or tight-fitting covers with no openings through which, after installation, sparks or burning materials might escape.

(2) Transformers and Similar Equipment. *The windings and terminal connections of transformers and choke coils shall be provided with tight metal enclosures without ventilating openings.*

(3) Resistors and Similar Equipment. In the installation of resistors, resistance devices, thermionic tubes, and rectifiers in Class II, Division 2 locations, they shall either conform to the requirements in **Section 502-14(a-3),** or thermionic tubes, nonadjustable resistors, or rectifiers which have a maximum operating temperature that will not exceed 120°C (248°F) may be installed in general-purpose type enclosures.

(4) Rotating Machinery. The same requirements apply to rotating machinery of this type as apply to other rotating machinery in Class II, Division 2. See **Section 502-8(b).**

502-15. Live Parts, Class II, Divisions 1 and 2—*There shall be no exposed live parts.*

502-16. Grounding, Class II, Divisions 1 and 2—*Wiring and equipment shall be grounded in conformity with the following:*

(a) Exposed Parts. The exposed noncurrent-carrying parts of all equipment, such as the frames and metal exteriors of motors, fixed or portable lamps or other utilization equipment, lighting fixtures, cabinets, cases, and conduit, shall be grounded as specified in **Article 250.**

(b) Bonding. Locknut bushings or the double-locknut types of grounding contacts are not accepted for bonding continuity of grounding in either Class II, Divisions 1 or 2 locations. Where locknuts are used, bonding is required by approved fittings or other approved means. Recall that the sheet-metal type of bonding clamp is not approved.

Approved means of bonding are to be used not only in hazardous locations, but also in intervening raceways, fittings, boxes, enclosures, etc., between hazardous locations and the point of grounding for service equipment.

405

Where flexible conduit is used, it is not accepted for grounding. Therefore, flexible conduit shall have approved fittings and a bond around it.

(c) Lightning Protection. Each ungrounded conductor of the service in Class II locations that is supplied from an overhead supply system in an area where lightning disturbances are prevalent shall be protected by a lightning protective device of the proper type. These lightning protective devices shall be connected to the service conductors on the supply side of the service disconnecting means. It is also required that the ground from the lightning protective devices shall be bonded to the raceway system at the service entrance. Although not mentioned in this Section, surge protective capacitors, as covered in **Section 502-3,** also play a large part in lightning protection.

(d) Grounded Service Conductor Bonded to Raceway. As required in another part of the Code, where there is a service supplied from a grounded system, even though the grounded conductor is not required in the operation of the system which it supplies, this grounding conductor is required to be run into the service entrance equipment.

Wiring in a Class II location, when supplied from a grounded alternating-current supply system in which a grounded conductor is a part of the service, shall have the grounded service conductor bonded to the raceway of the system and to the grounding conductor for the raceway system. The bonding connection to the grounded service conductor shall be made on the supply side of the service disconnecting means.

(e) Transformer Ground Bonded to Raceway. This ruling ties in with **(d)** above and with **Section 250-23(b).** *Wiring in a Class II location, where supplied from a grounded alternating-current supply system in which no grounded conductor is a part of the service, shall be provided with a metallic connection between the supply system ground and the raceway system at the service entrance. The metallic connection shall have an ampacity not less than 1/5 that of the service conductors, and shall in no case be smaller than No. 10 when of soft copper, or No. 12 when of medium or hard-drawn copper.* With regard to the No. 10 and No. 12 sizes, it must be remembered that consideration shall be given to tensile strength of the conductor in relation to the length of the span and, as a good practice, the size should be increased to that which is capable of safety.

(f) Multiple Grounds. *Where, in the application of **Section 250-21,** it is necessary to abandon one or more grounding connections to avoid objectionable passage of current over the grounding* *conductors, the connection required in* **Section 502-16 (d** or **e)** *shall not be abandoned while any other grounding connection remains connected to the supply system.*

ARTICLE 503—CLASS III INSTALLATIONS— HAZARDOUS LOCATIONS

While Class III locations might be considered as having less hazards than Class I or II locations, the hazards are not to be minimized. Wherever there is a likelihood of fire or explosion, the hazard must be given the respect that is due it.

503-1. General—The general wiring and installation requirements of the Code apply to Class III locations as classified in **Section 500-6,** with the exceptions that are covered in this Article.

Class III locations are areas in which fibers and flyings are present. The major item to remember is that the wiring, equipment, and apparatus shall operate at full rating without causing excessive dehydration or gradual carbonization of fibers or flyings. Any organic substance that is carbonized or very dry is susceptible to spontaneous combustion (ignition). The maximum surface temperatures under operating conditions:

(1) Shall not exceed 165°C (329°F) for equipment not subject to overloading.
(2) Shall not exceed 120°C (248°F) for motors, power transformers, etc., which may be overloaded.

503-2. Transformers and Capacitors, Class III, Divisions 1 and 2— *Transformers and capacitors shall conform to* **Section 502-2(b).** Recall that **Section 502-2(b)** covered transformers and capacitors in Class II, Division 2 locations, and should be referred to for the requirements in Class III, Divisions 1 and 2 locations.

503-3. Wiring Methods—*Wiring methods shall conform to the following:*

(a) Class III, Division 1. *In Class III, Division 1 locations, rigid mental conduit, or approved Type MI, MC or ALS cables shall be the wiring method employed.*

(1) Boxes and Fittings. *Fittings and boxes in which taps, joints or terminal connections are made shall be provided with:*

(a) Telescoping lids.
(b) Close-fitting covers.
(c) Other effective means of preventing the escape of sparks or burning materials.
(d) Have no openings (attachment screw holes) through which, after installation, sparks or burning material might

407

escape or through which adjacent combustible material might be ignited.

(2) **Flexible Connections.** *Where flexible connections are necessary the provisions of* **Section 502-4(a-2)** *shall apply.* **Section 502-4(a-2)** approved dust-tight flexible connectors, flexible metal conduit with approved fittings, or flexible cord approved for extra-hard usage and with approved fittings and seals. Grounding conductors were also required for bonding.

(b) **Class III, Division 2.** Wiring methods shall be the same as for Class III, Division 2 locations covered in **Section 503-3(a),** with the exception that in sections, compartments, or areas used solely for storage and containing no machinery, open wiring on insulators conforming to the requirements of **Article 320** may be used, but only on the condition that protection as required by **Section 320-12** be provided where conductors are not run in roof spaces, and well out of reach of sources of physical damage. **Section 320-12** provides for the protection of open wiring from physical damage.

503-4.   Switches, Circuit Breakers, Motor Controllers and Fuses, Class III, Divisions 1 and 2—*Switches, circuit breakers, motor controllers and fuses, including push buttons, relays, and similar devices, shall be provided with tight metal enclosures designed to* prevent the escape of sparks or burning material and designed to minimize the entrance of fibers or flyings, and which shall:

(1) Be equipped with telescoping covers or with other effective means of preventing the escape of sparks or burning materials.
(2) Have no openings (attachment screw holes) through which, after installation, sparks or burning materials might escape or through which exterior accumulations of fibers of flyings or adjacent combustible materials might be ignited.

503-5.   Control Transformers and Resistors, Class III, Divisions 1 and 2—The same requirements apply here as in Class II, Division 2 locations covered in **Section 502-7(b).** An exception to this is that, in Class III, Division 1 locations, if these devices are in the same enclosure with the switching devices of control equipment, and are only used for starting or for short time duty, the enclosure may have telescoping covers or other effective means for preventing the escape of sparks or burning material as covered in **Section 503-4.**

503-6.   Motors and Generators—*Motors and generators shall conform to the following:*

(a) **Class III, Division 1.** Motors, generators, and other rotating electrical machinery, shall be:

(1) Totally enclosed, not ventilated.
(2) Totally enclosed, pipe ventilated.
(3) Totally enclosed, fan cooled.

An exception to the above is that the code-enforcing authority may accept the following if, in his judgment, there is only moderate accumulations of lint and flyings:

(1) Squirrel-cage textile motors.
(2) Standard open-type motors that do not have open arcing contacts.
(3) Standard open-type motors with enclosed arcing contacts that are used only where they are accessible for maintenance and routine cleaning.

(b) Class III, Division 2. Motors, generators, and rotating electrical machinery in Class III, Division 2 locations shall be:

(1) Totally enclosed, not ventilated.
(2) Totally enclosed, fan-cooled.
(3) Totally enclosed, pipe ventilated.

(c) Partially Enclosed Type, Class III, Divisions 1 and 3. *Motors, generators or other rotating electrical machinery of the partially enclosed or splash-proof type shall not be installed in Class III locations.*

503-7. Ventilating Piping, Class III, Divisions 1 and 2—Vent pipes for motors, generators or other rotating eelctrical machinery, or for enclosures for electrical apparatus or equipment, shall:

(1) Be of metal not less than No. 24 USS Gage.
(2) Be of other suitable noncombustible material.
(3) Be screened at the outer end to prevent the entrance of small animals or birds.
(4) Lead directly to the outside of the building into a source of clean air.
(5) Be protected against:
   (a) Rusting.
   (b) Physical damage.
   (c) Other corrosive influences.
(6) Have connections sufficiently tight to prevent:
   (a) The entrance of appreciable quantities of fibers or flyings into the ventilating equipment or enclosures.
   (b) The escape of sparks or burning materials which might ignite accumulations of fibers or flyings or combustible material in the vicinity.

503-8. Utilization Equipment, Fixed and Portable, Class III, Divisions 1 and 2—*Utilization equipment shall conform to the following:*

(a) **Heaters.** *Electrically heated utilization equipment shall be approved for Class III locations.*

(b) **Motors.** Motors of motor-driven utilization equipment that is used in Class III locations are subject to the same requirements as for motors covered in **Section 503-6(b).** When motor-driven utilization equipment is readily movable from one location to another, it shall be required to meet the standards required for the most hazardous location in which it is to be used.

(c) **Switches, Circuit Breakers, Motor Controllers and Fuses. Section 503-4** applies to switches, circuit breakers, motor controllers, and fuses, and also to the same items used with utilization equipment.

503-9. Lighting Fixtures, Class III, Divisions 1 and 2—*Lamps shall be installed in fixtures which shall conform to the following:*

(a) **Fixed Lighting.** There shall be enclosures for fixed lamps and lampholders that shall:

(1) Be designed to minimize the entrance of fibers and flyings.
(2) Prevent the escape of sparks, burning materials, or hot metal.
(3) Be plainly marked for the maximum wattage lamp that shall be used.
(4) Be capable of being used without exceeding a maximum exposed surface temperature of 165°C (329°F) under normal operating conditions.

(b) **Physical Damage.** Fixtures are to be either guarded or located so as not to be subject to physical damage.

(c) **Pendant Fixtures.** *Pendant fixtures shall be suspended by stems of:*

(1) Rigid metal conduit.
(2) Threaded metal tubing of equivalent thickness.

If the stem is longer than 12 inches, it shall:

(1) Be permanently and effectively supported laterally against displacement, and this bracing shall not be more than 12 inches above the lamp fixture.
(2) Have a flexible connector approved for the purpose provided at a distance of not more than 12 inches from the point of attachment to the supporting box or fitting.

(d) **Supports.** *Boxes, box assemblies or fittings used for the support of lighting fixtures shall be of a type approved for the purpose.*

410

(e) Portable Lamps. Portable lamps shall conform to all of the requirements of **(a)** of this Section and, in addition, shall:

(1) Be provided with a handle.
(2) Have a suitable guard for the lamp.
(3) Have a lampholder:

    (a) Of the unswitched type.
    (b) With no exposed metal parts.
    (c) With no means for receiving an attachment plug.

503-10. Flexible Cords, Class III, Divisions 1 and 2—*Flexible cords shall conform to* **Section 502-12.**

503-11. Receptacles and Attachment Plugs, Class III, Divisions 1 and 2—See NEC.

503-12. Signal, Alarm, Remote-Control and Local Loudspeaker Intercommunication Systems, Class III, Divisions 1 and 2—See NEC.

503-13. Electric Cranes and Hoists, and Similar Equipment, Class III, Divisions 1 and 2—Where traveling cranes and hoists for handling materials, and similar installed equipment operate over fibers or accumulations of flyings, they shall conform to the following:

(a) The power supply shall be isolated from all other systems (this may be done by isolation transformers) and shall be ungrounded. A recording ground detector shall be installed which will:

(1) Give an audible and visual alarm, maintaining the alarm as long as power is supplied to the system and the ground fault remains.
(2) Automatically de-energize the contact conductors in the case of a fault to ground.

(b) Contact conductors for cranes and hoists shall be:

(1) So located or guarded as to be inaccessible to other than authorized persons.
(2) Protect against accidental contact with foreign objects.

(c) Current collectors shall be so located or guarded so as to:

(1) Confine normal sparking.
(2) Prevent the escape of sparks or hot particles.

    In order to reduce sparking, there shall be:

(1) Two or more separate contact surfaces for each contact conductor.
(2) A reliable means for keeping the contact conductors and current collectors free of accumulations of dusts and of flyings and lint.

411

(d) Sections 503-4 and **503-5** covered various control equipment. The requirements of **Sections 503-4** and **5** apply to control equipment for electric cranes, hoists, and similar equipment in Class III, Divisions 1 and 2 locations.

503-14. Electric Trucks—National Fire Protection Association pamphlet No. 505 covers the use, maintenance and operation of industrial trucks. By reference this pamphlet becomes a part of the National Electrical Code and all electric trucks shall conform to this Standard.

503-15. Storage-Battery Charging Equipment, Class III, Divisions 1 and 2—*Storage-battery charging equipment shall be located in separate rooms built or lined with substantial non-combustible materials so constructed as to adequately exclude flyings or lint, and shall be well ventilated.* Not only are the lint and flyings a problem, but so are the fumes from the batteries. Proper ventilation will also assist in taking care of these fumes.

503-16. Live Parts, Class III, Division 1 and 2—There shall be no live parts exposed in Class III locations, with the exception provided for in **Section 503-13** pertaining to electric cranes and hoists.

503-17. Grounding, Class III, Divisions 1 and 2—All wiring and equipment shall be grounded in Class III locations in the same manner as required for Class II locations in **Section 502-16.**

ARTICLE 510—HAZARDOUS LOCATIONS—SPECIFIC

510-1. Scope—Articles **501, 502** and **503** give the general requirements for Class I, II, and III locations. The Provisions of **Articles 511** to **517** inclusive shall apply to occupancies or parts of occupancies which are hazardous because of:

(1) Atmospheric concentrations of hazardous gases or vapors.
(2) Deposits or accumulations of materials which may be readily ignited.

The intent of these Articles is to assist Code-enforcing authorities in the classification of areas or locations with respect to hazardous conditions. These hazardous conditions may or may not require construction and equipment conforming to **Articles 501, 502,** and **503.** They also set forth additional requirements that may be necessary in specific hazardous locations.

510-2. General—The general rules of the Code shall apply to the installation of electrical wiring and equipment for use in the occupancies covered within the scope of **Articles 511** to **527** inclusive, and the inspection authority is responsible for judging with respect to the application of specific rules. These include:

412

It is recommended by the Code that the authorities enforcing the Code become familiar with the National Fire Protection Association's Standards that apply to occupancies included within the scope of **Articles 511 to 517** inclusive. Not only should inspectors be familiar with these Codes and Standards, but anyone that designs or makes electrical installations should also be familiar with them. Some of the NFPA Standards involved are listed below, and most, if not all, of these are a part of the Code by reference.

NFPA No. 88—Construction and Protection of Garages.
NFPA No. 86A—Class A Ovens and Furnaces.
NFPA No. 33—Spray Finishing Using Flammable Liquids.
NFPA No. 30—Storage and Handling of Flammable Liquids.
NFPA No. 34—Dip Tanks Containing Flammable Combustible Liquids.
NFPA No. 56—Safe Practice for Hospital Operating Rooms.
NFPA No. 76—Hospital Electrical Service.
NFPA No. 77—Static Electricity.
NFPA No. 68—Explosion Venting, Guide.
NFPA No. 30E—Self Service Gasoline Stations.
NFPA No. 32—Dry Cleaning Plants.
NFPA No. 325—Properties of Flammable Liquids.
NFPA No. 36—Solvent Extraction.

There are others that will be of great assistance in evaluating the hazards that might be involved, and these may be purchased from the National Fire Protection Association, 60 Batterymarch St., Boston, Mass. in a 10-volume set that includes all standards. The individual Codes may also be purchased.

ARTICLE 511—COMMERCIAL GARAGES, REPAIR AND STORAGE

511-1. Scope—Commercial garages include the following:

(1) Locations used for service and repair of self-propelled vehicles (including passenger automobiles, buses, trucks, tractors, etc.).
(2) Locations in which three or more such vehicles are or may be stored at the same time.

413

The above shall be vehicles in which volatile flammable liquids or flammable gases are used as the fuel for operation. In the classification of garages, refer to NFPA Standard for Garages, NFPA. No. 88.

511-2. Hazardous Areas—The classification of these areas are also covered under **Article 500.** This is for further clarification of this particular usage.

(a) *For each floor at or above grade, the entire area up to a level 18 inches above the floor shall be considered to be Class I, Division 2 locations.* Fig. 511-1 will help to clarify the classification.

(b) The entire area of any floors below grade will be considered as Class I, Division 2 locations up to a point of 18 inches above the

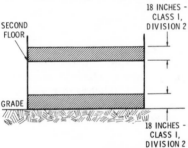

Fig. 511-1. Hazardous areas of commercial garages above grade level.

grade level. Also, if the outside doors are at or above grade level, this classification will be 18 inches above the bottom of the outside doors or other openings.

In cases where there is adequate and positive ventilation of the floors below grade level, it is up to the inspection authority to classify the areas. He may judge the floors to be Class I, Division 2 up to a height of 18 inches above the floors, even though they are below grade level. It is not mandatory that he judge them this way however. See Fig. 511-2.

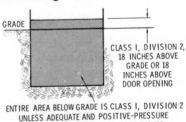

Fig. 511-2. Hazardous areas of commercial garages below grade level.

(c) Pits or depressions below floor level, but which extend up to the floor level, shall be considered as Class I, Division 2 locations, except that if the pit or depression is unventilated, the authority enforcing the Code may judge the area to be a Class I, Division 1 location. See Fig. 511-3.

(d) Areas adjacent to Class I, Division 2 locations in which there is no likelihood of hazardous vapors being released (such as stockrooms) are also Class I, Division 2 locations unless the floor of the adjacent area is elevated 18 inches above the floor of the

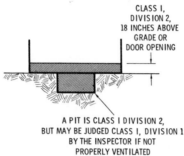

CLASS I,
DIVISION 2,
18 INCHES ABOVE
GRADE OR
DOOR OPENING

A PIT IS CLASS I DIVISION 2,
BUT MAY BE JUDGED CLASS I, DIVISION 1
BY THE INSPECTOR IF NOT
PROPERLY VENTILATED

Fig. 511-3. Hazardous areas and classification of pits or depressions in garage floors.

hazardous area, or unless a separation between the two areas is provided by an 18-inch tight curb or partition.

Gasoline vapors are heavier than air and settle to the floor area. The intent here is that, since these vapors settle to the floor, they may be transmitted into other rooms which might look to be nonhazardous areas since there are no vapors likely to be released in that room. Transmittal of the hazardous vapors may be stopped by an elevated floor, tight curb, or a partition, each at least 18 inches high, between the two rooms.

(e) *Adjacent areas, which by reason of ventilation, air pressure differentials or physical spacing are such that in the opinion of the authority enforcing this Code no hazards exists, shall be classified as non-hazardous.*

This gives the inspection authority some latitude in classification. There are very often border line cases where decisions of this nature are very practical, but the inspector must be very careful to weigh all aspects.

511-3. Wiring and Equipment in Hazardous Areas—In hazardous locations as defined in **Section 511-2,** all of the requirements of **Article 501** shall apply. The location will have to be judged either Class I, Division 1, or Class I, Division 2, and the wiring and equipment conform to the classification.

415

As an example take the case of a garage at grade level with the doors opening at grade level. The classification would be Class I, Division 2 to a height of 18 inches above the floor. If all of the wiring and equipment is kept above the 18-inch height from the floor, EMT and general-duty equipment and devices can be used. If the wiring goes below the 18-inch point (possibly conduit is run in the floor slab), this part would be Class I, Division 2 and the wiring would have to meet the requirements of this classification, and would have to have seals above the 18-inch height to pass from the hazardous area into the nonhazardous area. Any equipment that is below the 18 inch level will also have to be approved for a Class I, Division 2 location.

511-4. Sealing—See NEC.

511-5. Wiring in Spaces Above Hazardous Areas—

(a) The only types of wiring permitted above hazardous areas are metal raceways, Type MI cable, or Type ALS cable. This may be confirmed by checking the uses of the different wiring methods as covered in Chapter 3. Cellular metal floor raceways may be used only to supply ceiling outlets or extensions to the area below the floor. Outlets shall not be connected above the floor.

(b) *For pendants, flexible cord suitable for the type of service and approved for hard usage shall be used.*

(c) *For connection of portable lamps, motors or other utilization equipment, flexible cord suitable for the type of service and approved for extra hard usage shall be used.*

(d) *When a circuit which supplies portables or pendants includes an identified grounded conductor as provided in* **Article 200,** *receptacles, attachment plugs, connectors, and similar devices shall be of polarized type, and the identified conductor of the flexible cord shall be connected to the screw shell of any lampholder or to the identified terminal of any utilization equipment supplied.*

In explanation, the standard 110-volt receptacle has two different length slots, but the majority of attachment plugs have both prongs the same width. The wider slot of the receptacle connects

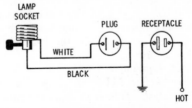

Fig. 511-4. Receptacles and attachment plugs.

416

to the identified or neutral conductor of the circuit (the white screw). In garages, plugs that have the two different width prongs are to be used. Thus, the attachment plug can only go into the receptacle one way. The neutral of the cord is attached to the wide prong and, if this is an extension cord with a portable lamp, the identified conductor is to be connected to the screw shell of the lampholder. Thus, the polarity of the circuit can be maintained. See Fig. 511-4. Care shall also be taken to connect the identified terminal of utilization equipment to the identified conductor of the cord or circuits.

(e) If a pendant is used to supply a portable cord or utilization equipment, the female portion of a polarized pin-plug goes into the pendant connection, and the male portion attached to the cord for the utilization equipment. These shall be designed to break connection easily; that is to pull apart from any position. The pendant shall be above the hazardous area, which in most cases would be the 18-inch height. Also, all fixed attachment plug receptacles shall be placed above the 18-inch hazardous area.

511-6. Equipment Above Hazardous Areas—

(a) Any equipment that may produce arcs, sparks, or particles of hot metal shall be located at least 12 feet above the floor, or shall be totally enclosed to prevent the escape of sparks or hot metal particles. Such items include cutouts, switches, receptacles, charging panels, generators, motors, or other equipment that has make-and-break or sliding contacts.

(b) *Lamps and lampholders for fixed lighting which are located over lanes through which vehicles are commonly driven or which may otherwise be exposed to physical damage, shall be located not less than 12 feet above the floor level unless of totally enclosed type or so constructed as to prevent escape of sparks or hot metal particles.* The 12-foot height will give the sparks or hot metal particles time to cool off before reaching the hazardous area.

(c) Portable lamps shall be equipped with handles, lampholder, hook and substantial guard attached to the lampholder or handle. Exterior surfaces that are likely to come into contact with battery terminals, wiring terminals, or other objects shall be of a nonconducting material or shall be effectively insulated. Lampholders shall be of the unswitched type and shall have no plug-in for attachment plugs. The outer shell shall be of moulded composition or other material approved for the purpose. Metalshell, lined lampholders, either of the switched or unswitched type, shall not be used.

Unless the lamp and cord are supported or arranged so that

417

they cannot be used in hazardous areas classified in **Section 511-2,** they shall be of an approved type for hazardous locations.

511-7.   Battery-Charging Equipment—See NEC.

511-8.   Electric Vehicle Charging—See NEC.

ARTICLE 512—RESIDENTIAL STORAGE GARAGES

512-1.   Definition—A residential garage is a room or building in which:

(1) Not more than three vehicles of the type described in **Section 511-1** will or can be stored.
(2) Vehicles will not normally be serviced or repaired. When over three vehicles are stored, or vehicles are regularly serviced or repaired, it then becomes a commercial garage by definition in **Section 511-1.**

512-2.   At or Above Grade—A residential garage will not be classified as a hazardous location where:

(1) The lowest floor is at or above grade level.
(2) There is at least one outside door at or above grade level.

512-3.   Below Grade—*Where the lowest floor is below adjacent ground or driveway level, the following shall apply:*

(a) This condition changes the classification to a Class II, Division 2 location for the entire area of the garage, or of any enclosed space which includes the garage, up to a height of 18 inches above the garage floor. This classification requires that all wiring and equipment located in the hazardous area conform to the provisions of **Article 501.**

(b) Wiring and equipment above any area of a residential garage that would be classified nonhazardous shall conform to the requirements of the Code for wiring in nonhazardous locations. This means that the same wiring methods are not required for residential garages as required for commercial garages.

(c) Adjacent areas shall be classed nonhazardous in which:

(1) Hazardous vapors or gases are not likely to be released.
(2) Floors are elevated at least 18 inches above the garage floor.
(3) They are separated from the garage floor by tight curbs or partitions at least 18 inches high.

ARTICLE 513—AIRCRAFT HANGARS

513-1.   Definition—This shall include occupancies that are used for storage or servicing of aircraft in which gasoline, jet fuels, or other volatile flammable fuels or flammable gases are used. Not included are:

(1) Locations used exclusively for aircraft which have never contained such volatile flammable gases or liquids.

(2) Aircraft which have been drained or properly purged.

513-2. Hazardous Areas—*Classification under* **Article 500.**

(a) Pits or depressions below the hanger floor level shall be considered as Class I, Division 1 locations, and this classification shall extend to the floor level. See Fig. 513-1.

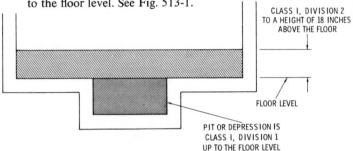

Fig. 513-1. Hazardous areas in aircraft hangers.

(b) The entire area of the hanger shall be considered as a Class I, Division 2 location to a height of 18 inches above the floor and shall also include adjacent areas into which the hazards may be communicated into unless suitably cut-off from the hangar as described in **(d)** below. See Fig. 513-1.

(c) The area immediately adjacent to the aircraft shall be a Class I, Division 2 location. Such an area is defined as being within 5 feet horizontally from aircraft power plants, aircraft fuel tanks, or aircraft structures containing fuel. These locations shall extend from the floor level vertically to a level of 5 feet above the wings and above the engine enclosures.

(d) See **(b)** above. Any adjacent area into which hazardous vapors are likely to be communicated or released, such as stockrooms and electrical control rooms, shall be a Class I, Division 2 location up to a height of 18 inches. These adjacent areas need not be classified as hazardous if they are effectively cut off from the hanger itself by walls or partitions and are adequately ventilated.

513-3. Wiring and Equipment in Hazardous Areas—All wiring, whether portable or fixed, and all equipment that is located in the hazardous area of an aircraft hangar (hazardous as defined in **Section 513-2**) shall conform to the provisions of **Article 501.** If above the floor, the area shall be a Class I, Division 2 location, and if in or under the floor, it shall be a Class I, Division 1 location. If any wiring is located in

ARTICLE 513—AIRCRAFT HANGARS

vaults, pits, or ducts, adequate drainage shall be provided, and the wiring shall not be placed in the same compartment with any other service, with the exception that wiring may be placed in a duct with compressed air. *Attachment plugs and receptacles in hazardous locations shall be explosion-proof or shall be so designed that they cannot be energized while the connections are being made or broken.*

513-4. Wiring Not Within Hazardous Areas—

(a) Fixed wiring located out of the hazardous area of a hangar shall be in metal raceways, or shall be Type MI or Type ALS cable. Wiring in adjacent cut-off areas, as defined in **Section 513-2(d),** may be any approved wiring method as covered in **Chapter 3.**

(b) *For pendants, flexible cord suitable for the type of service and approved for hard usage shall be used. Each such cord shall include a separate grounding conductor.*

(c) *For portable utilization equipment and lamps, flexible cord suitable for the type of service and approved for extra hard usage shall be used. Each such cord shall include a separate grounding conductor.*

(d) When circuits supplying portables and pendants include an identified grounded conductor (**Article 200**), they shall have the following devices of the polarized type and the identified conductor of the flexible cord shall be connected to the screw shell of any lampholder or to the identified terminal of all utilization equipment:

(1) Receptacles.
(2) Attachment plugs.
(3) Connectors.
(4) Similar devices.

Grounding continuity that is acceptable shall be provided between fixed raceways and the noncurrent-carrying parts (metallic) of:

(1) Pendant fixtures.
(2) Portable lamps.
(3) Portable utilization equipment.

This may be accomplished by bonding or attaching the grounding conductor to the fixed raceway system.

513-5. Equipment Not Within Hazardous Areas—

(a) In locations other than those described in **Section 513-2,** equipment which may produce arcs, sparks, or particles of hot metals, such as lamps and lampholders for fixed lighting, cutouts, switches, receptacles, charging panels, generators, motors, or other

420

equipment having make-and-break or sliding contacts, shall be of such a type that the escape of sparks or hot metal particles will be prevented by being of the totally-enclosed type, or so constructed as to prevent escape of sparks or hot metal particles. In areas described in **Section 513-2(d),** equipment may be of the general-purpose type.

(b) *Lampholders of metal shell, fiber-lined types shall not be used for fixed incandescent lighting.*

(c) *Portable lamps which are or may be used within a hangar shall be approved for Class I locations.*

(d) *Portable utilization equipment which is or may be used within a hangar shall be of a type suitable for use in Class I, Division 2 locations.*

513-6. Stanchions, Rostrums and Docks—

(a) *Electric wiring, outlets and equipment (including lamps) on or attached to stanchions, rostrums or docks which are located or likely to be located in a hazardous area as defined in* **Section 513-2(c)** *shall conform to the requirements for Class I, Division 2 locations.*

(b) Stanchions, rostrums, or docks which are not, or will not likely be, located in the hazardous areas defined in **Section 513-2(c),** shall have wiring and equipment that conform to areas which are not classified as hazardous. The wiring for these areas was covered in **Section 513-4,** and the equipment for these areas was covered in **Section 513-5.** Exceptions to these requirements are as follows:

(1) Wiring and equipment that will be within the 18-inch classification above the floor shall be approved for Class I, Division 2 locations as covered in **Section 513-6(a).**

(2) Receptacles and attachment plugs shall be of the locking type that will not be readily pulled apart.

(c) Mobile stanchions with electrical equipment which conforms to part **(b)** above shall carry at least one sign, permanently affixed to the stanchion, which shall read:

WARNING
KEEP 5 FEET CLEAR
OF AIRCRAFT ENGINES
AND FUEL TANK AREAS

513-7. Sealing—Sealing in Class I locations was covered in **Sections 501-5, 501-5(a-3)**, and **501-5(b-2).** The requirements of these sections shall apply to horizontal as well as to vertical boundaries of the hazardous areas. Raceways that are embedded in or under concrete will be in the same hazardous area that is above the floor when any connections lead

421

into or through such areas. This will require seal-offs when connecting to enclosures where there is a possibility of arcs or sparks, or when going from a hazardous to a nonhazardous area.

513-8. Aircraft Electrical Systems—See NEC.

513-9. Aircraft Battery—Charging and Equipment—

(a) *Aircraft batteries should not be charged when installed in an aircraft located inside or partially inside a hangar.*

(b) Battery chargers and their control equipment, tables, racks, trays, and wiring must conform to the provisions of **Article 480** and shall not be located in a hazardous area as defined in **Section 513-2,** but should be located in a separate building or in an area as defined in **Section 513-2(d),** that is an area suitably isolated from the hazardous area. Mobile chargers shall have at least one permanently affixed sign reading:

WARNING
KEEP 5 FEET CLEAR
OF AIRCRAFT ENGINES
AND FUEL TANK AREAS

513-10. External Power Sources for Energizing Aircraft—

(a) Aircraft energizers shall be so designed and mounted that all of the electrical equipment and fixed wiring will be at least 18 inches above the floor and will not be operated in a hazardous area as defined in **Section 513-2(c).**

(b) Mobile energizers shall have at least one permanently affixed sign reading:

WARNING
KEEP 5 FEET CLEAR
OF AIRCRAFT ENGINES
AND FUEL TANK AREAS

(c) Aircraft energizers should be equipped with polarized external power plugs and should have automatic control equipment to electrically isolate the ground power unit from the aircraft in case excessive voltage is generated by the grounding power unit.

(d) *Flexible cords for aircraft energizers and ground support equipment shall be approved for the type of service and extra hard usage and shall include a ground conductor.*

513-11. Mobile Servicing Equipment with Electrical Connections—

(a) Mobile servicing equipment that is not suitable for Class I, Division 2 locations shall be so designed and mounted that all fixed wiring and equipment will be at least 18 inches above the floor. This equipment includes vacuum cleaners, air compressors, air movers, and similar equipment. None of this equipment shall be operated in the hazardous areas which were defined in **Section 513-2(c).** All such equipment shall have at least one permanently affixed sign reading:

WARNING
KEEP 5 FEET CLEAR
OF AIRCRAFT ENGINES
AND FUEL TANK AREAS

(b) Flexible cords for mobile equipment shall be suitable for the type of service and be approved for extra hard usage. They shall also include a grounding conductor. Receptacles and attachment plugs shall be suitable for the type of service and approved for the location in which they are installed. There shall also be a means of connecting the grounding conductor to the raceway system. This grounding may be accomplished in any approved manner.

(c) *Equipment not of a type suitable for Class I, Division 2 locations should not be operated in areas where maintenance operations likely to release hazardous vapors are in progress.*

513-12. Grounding—*All metallic raceways, and all non-current-carrying metallic portions of fixed or portable equipment, regardless of voltage, shall be grounded as provided in* **Article 250.** Recall that **Article 250** covers grounding.

ARTICLE 514—GASOLINE DISPENSING AND SERVICE STATIONS

514-1 Definition—This classification shall include locations where fuel is transferred to the fuel tanks of self-propelled vehicles, or to auxiliary tanks. The fuels referred to are gasoline or other volatile flammable liquids or liquified flammable gases.

Volatile Flammable Liquid is defined in **Article 100** as *a flammable liquid having a flash point below 100°F or whose temperature is above its flash point.*

A responsibility is placed on the inspection authority by the following part: *Where the authority enforcing the Code can satisfactorily determine that flammable liquids having a flash point below 100°F. such as gasoline will not be handled, he may classify such an area as nonhazardous.*

Reference is also made to the NFPA Flammable and Combustible Liquids Code (No. 30).

In practically every gasoline-dispensing location there are also lubritoriums, service rooms, repair rooms, offices, salesrooms, compressor rooms, storage rooms, rest rooms, and possibly a furnace room, as well as other areas that might be associated with a filling station. The wiring in these locations shall conform to **Articles 510** and **511.**

514-2. Hazardous Areas—

(a) The space below, within, and around the dispenser in which wiring or electrical equipment may be present will be Class I, Division 1 locations, as follows:

The area within the dispenser and extending to a distance of 18 inches horizontally in all directions from the dispenser and up to a height of 4 feet. See Fig. 514-1.

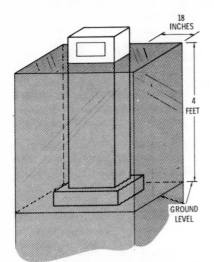

Fig. 514-1. Hazardous areas around a gasoline dispenser.

(b) Any area in an outside location, including any buildings that are not suitably isolated, and excluding the Class I, Division 1 area immediately at the gasoline dispensers, shall be a Class I, Division 2 location for a distance of 20 feet horizontally from the dispenser in all directions, and to a height of 18 inches above the driveway or ground. See Fig. 514-2. As shown in Fig. 514-2, if there is a suitable curb or wall at least 18 inches high cutting off the hazardous area, then the building will not be a Class I, Division 2 location, except that the lubritorium portion comes under **Article 511** and the classification there will have to conform.

(c) Fill pipes for tanks located outside but that are not in a Class I, Division 1 location, will have a Class I, Division 2 location extending horizontally for a distance of 10 feet in all directions from the fill pipe, and to a minimum height of 18 inches. Any building or portion of a building that is located in this 10-foot

424

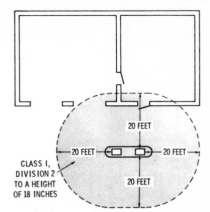

Fig. 514-2. Hazardous areas around gasoline service stations.

area and that is not cut off by a suitable wall or curb will also be included in the Class I, Division 2 location.

(d) In Class I, Division 1 and 2 locations, any wiring or equipment that is below the ground level in the areas covered in **Sections 514-2(a), (b),** and **(c)** will be in Class I, Division 1 locations, at least to the point of emergence from the grade level. Thus, if the area above ground is a Division 2 location, the area below becomes a Division 1 area. All wiring and equipment shall conform to the requirement for this area.

(e) *Where the dispensing unit, including the hose and hose nozzle valve, is suspended from a canopy, ceiling or structure support, the Class I, Division 1 location shall include the volume within the enclosure and shall also extend 18 inches in all directions from the enclosure where not suitably cut off by a ceiling or wall. The Class I, Division 2 location shall extend 2 feet horizonally in all directions beyond the Division 1 classified area and extend to grade below this classified area. In addition, the horizontal area 18 inches above grade for a distance of 20 feet, measured from a point vertically below the edge of any dispenser enclosure, shall be classified Division 2. All electrical equipment integral with the dispensing hose or nozzle shall be suitable for use in a Division 1 location.*

(f) *In addition to the requirements of* **Section 514-1** *the area within any pit or space below grade in a lubrication room shall be considered a Class I, Division 1 location. The area within the entire lubrication room up to 18 inches above the floor or grade, and the area within 3 feet measured in any direction from the dispensing point of a hand-operated unit dispensing Class I liquids shall be considered a Class I, Division 2 location.*

This was inserted in the Code because of the practice of dispensing such liquids as "white gasoline" from 55-gallon drums, etc., for special purposes. Please note that this is a hazard.

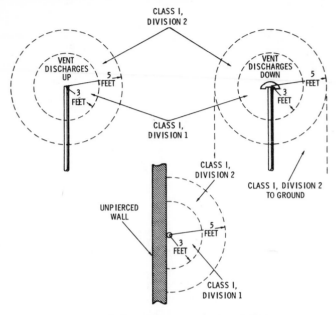

Fig. 514-3. Hazardous areas around vent pipes.

514-3. Wiring and Equipment Within Hazardous Areas—Electrical equipment and wiring in the Class I, Division 1 and Class II, Division 2 locations, as defined in **Section 514-2** of this Article, shall be approved and suitable for these locations. The only wiring methods acceptable (see **Article 501**) are rigid metal conduit and Type MI Cable. General-purpose devices and equipment are not permitted in these locations.

Section 501-13 states that conductors used in these locations shall be approved for the location. There are many conductors under various trade names that are approved for the location. These conductors have a nylon outer covering to protect them from gasoline. The Underwriter's Laboratories have a listing on the conductors that are approved. TW wire, as such, is not approved. However, there is a TW wire with a nylon outer covering that is approved. Also lead-covered cable may be used for the conductors, but is seldom used because of costs and the difficulty of pulling it into conduit. *Exception: Except as permitted in* **Section 514-8.**

514-4. Wiring and Equipment Above Hazardous Areas—Hazardous areas are defined in **Section 514-2** of this Article. **Sections 511-5** and **511-6**

cover wiring methods and equipment for use above hazardous areas. These requirements apply to this Article also. The only wiring methods approved in these locations are metal raceways, and Type MI and Type ALS cable.

514-5. Circuit Disconnects—*Each circuit leading to or through a dispensing pump shall be provided with a switch or other acceptable means to disconnect simultaneously from the source of supply all conductors of the circuit including the grounded neutral, if any.* Although this is very plain, it is often misinterpreted. The intent of the ruling is that, when the supply is disconnected from the source, there shall be no conductors connected that lead to or through a dispensing pump. There are various means of doing this. Special breakers are available that have a pigtail which ties to the neutral bus, and both the hot and the neutral will be disconnected when the breaker is in the OFF position. A double-pole switch may also be used. See Fig. 415-4.

514-6. Sealing—

(a) *An approved seal shall be provided in each conduit run entering or leaving a dispenser or any cavities or enclosures in direct communications therewith. The sealing fitting shall be the first fitting after the conduit emerges from the earth or concrete.* This also is often misinterpreted. Notice the words *first fitting*. This means exactly what it says. There is often an attempt to define a conduit coupling as not being a fitting, but this is not the case—it is a fitting.

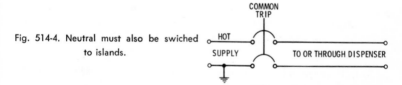

Fig. 514-4. Neutral must also be swiched to islands.

All seals are to be readily accessible. Often someone attempts to install a seal at the edge of the hazardous area and bury it in the earth. This is not allowed. It shall be carried into the building or some other place out of the hazardous area and then installed. If, for instance, the seal goes into the service panel, and there is a hazardous area below the panel, the seal must be 18 inches or more above the floor, and there can be no fitting of any kind between the floor and the seal. See Fig. 514-5.

(b) Additional seals shall be provided as covered in **Section 501-5.** **Section 501-5(a-3)** and **501-5(b-2)** will apply to both horizontal and vertical boundaries between the hazardous and nonhazardous areas.

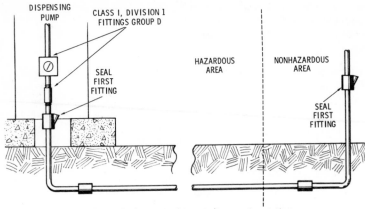

Fig. 514-5. Seals required in gasoline service stations.

514-7. Grounding—*Metallic portions of dispensing pumps, metallic raceways, and all noncurrent-carrying portions of electrical equipment, regardless of voltage, shall be grounded as provided in* **Article 250.** This grounding will extend back to the service equipment and service ground. Care should be taken in grounding properly, for an accidental fault could cause a poor ground connection to arc and cause an explosion.

514-8. Underground Wiring—*Underground wiring shall be installed in rigid metal conduit, or, where buried under not less than 2 feet of earth, may be installed in nonmetallic conduit conforming to the requirements of* **Article 347.** *Where nonmetallic conduit is used, a grounding conductor shall be included to provide for metallic continuity of the raceway system and for grounding of noncurrent-carrying metallic parts of equipment.*

Cable is permitted underground to bulk plants. It was felt, however, that this should not be permitted for service stations because of frequent changes. Therefore, nonmetallic conduit was added to the Code to take the place of metallic conduit and thus relieve the problem of corrosion which might let fumes or gasoline into the conduit. The use of nonmetallic conduit in no way changes the sealing that is required, which remains the same. Metallic conduit is still to be brought up into the dispenser or the nonhazardous location, as the case might be. This is necessary to prevent physical damage.

Exception: Type MI cable may be used when installed in accordance with **Article 330.**

ARTICLE 515—BULK-STORAGE PLANTS

515-1. Definition—*This designation shall include locations where*

428

gasoline or other volatile flammable liquids are stored in tanks having an aggregate capacity of one carload or more, and from which such products are distributed (usually by tank truck).

515-2.   Hazardous Areas—

(a) Pumps, Bleeders, Withdrawal Fittings, Meters and Similar Devices.

(1) This covers adequately ventilated indoor areas containing pumps, bleeders, withdrawal fittings, meters, and similar devices installed in pipelines handling flammable liquids under pressure. The area for a distance of 5 feet in all directions from the exterior surface of any of the fittings or devices mentioned is classified as Class I, Division 2. This same classification will extend 25 feet horizontally and to a height of 3 feet above the floor or ground from these devices. See Fig. 515-1.

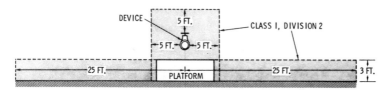

Fig. 515-1. Adequately ventilated indoor area.

Flammable and Combustible Liquids Code, NFPA No. 30, becomes a part of the NEC, and the discussion for factors influencing adequacy of ventilation that is required to prevent the accumulation of hazardous vapor-air mixtures is covered there. This NFPA Code will aid materially in judging conditions of hazards that might be present. This classification is based upon adequate and positive ventilation.

(2) In inadequately ventilated indoor areas containing the same equipment as in (1), the exception is that, instead of being a Class II, Division 2 location, it changes to a Class I, Division 1 location. Fig. 515-1 can be used for this type of location except that Division 2 will change to Division 1.

(3) In outdoor locations containing the same equipment as in (1), the classification is Class I, Division 2 for a distance of 3 feet in all directions from the fittings and devices, and a distance of 10 feet horizontally and 18 inches vertically above grade level from the fittings and devices. See Fig. 515-2.

(b) Transfer of Flammable Liquids to Individual Containers.

(1) This applies to outdoor areas, or to indoor areas where posi-

429

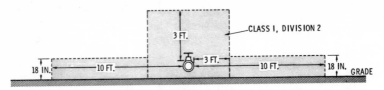

Fig. 515-2. Outdoor area.

tive and reliable ventilation (mechanical) is provided. Again reference is made to the Flammable and Combustible Liquids Code, NFPA No. 30, which becomes a part of the NEC by this reference and will assist in rulings that must be made.

Such areas will be Class I, Division 1 locations in all directions from the vent or fill pipe to a distance of 3 feet. In the area between 3 and 5 feet in all directions, the classification becomes Class I, Division 2. All of this applies to areas where the flammable liquids are being transferred to individual containers.

The area around the fill or vent pipe below the hazardous areas just mentioned will be a Class I, Division 2 location for a horizontal radius of 10 feet, and to a height of 18 inches above the floor or grade level.

(2) On indoor installations where positive and reliable mechanical ventilation is not provided, all of the areas considered in **(1)** become Class I, Division 1 locations.

(c) Loading and Unloading of Tank Vehicles and Tank Cars in Outside Locations.

(1) Loading through an open dome, or from the vent when loading through a closed dome with atmospheric venting, will be Class I, Division 1 for a distance that extends for 3 feet in all directions.

(2) For the conditions in **(1)** above, the classification will be Class I, Division 2 for the area extending between the 3-foot and the 5-foot radius in all directions. See Fig. 515-3.

(3) Other areas around a fixed connection used for bottom loading or unloading, loading through a closed dome with atmospheric venting, or loading through a closed dome with a vapor recovery system shall be considered to be a Class I, Division 2 location for 3 feet in all directions. In the case of bottom loading or unloading, the classification will also include an area within a 10-foot radius of the point of connection, and up to a height of 18 inches above grade.

In arriving at the extent of the hazardous area involved, due consideration shall be given to the total area within which

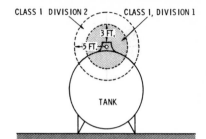

Fig. 515-3. Classification around vents.

the loading or unloading operation may take place. This will include racks, platforms, driveways, etc. Therefore, the dimensions given in this part **(3)** are not a fixed quantity, so the judgment of the inspection authority must also be relied on. See Fig. 515-4.

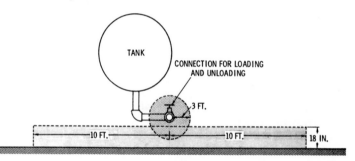

Fig. 515-4. Classification around bottom filler.

(d) Aboveground Tanks.

(1) *The area above the roof and within the shell of a floating roof type tank shall be considered a Class I, Division 1 location.*

(2) With all aboveground tanks, with the exception of the floating roof tank, the area within 10 feet of the shell, ends, or roof of the tank shall be considered as a Class I, Division 2 location. If there are dikes built up around such tanks, the area within the dike and extending up to the height of the dike will also be considered a Class I, Division 2 location.

(3) The area within 5 feet of the vent of an aboveground tank shall be considered as a Class I, Division 1 location. See Fig. 515-5.

(4) Part **(3)** just preceding classified the area within 5 feet around

431

a vent on an aboveground tank as a Class I, Division 1 location. The area between 5 feet and 10 feet shall be classified as a Class I, Division 2 location. See Fig. 515-5.

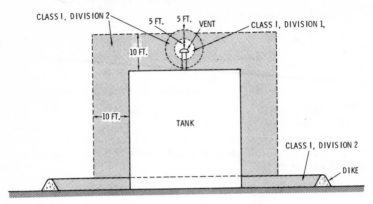

Fig. 515-5. Classification around vertical tank.

Underground tanks are covered in **Article 514**.

(e) Pits.

(1) As with commercial garages **(Article 511)** and filling stations **(Article 514)**, any pits or depressions that lie in hazardous areas shall be considered as Class I, Division 1 locations unless they are provided with positive and reliable ventilation. (See note following **(2)** just below.)

(2) When pits or depressions in hazardous areas, as in **(1)** above, are provided with positive and reliable ventilation, the pit or depression will become a Class I, Division 2 location.

See Flammable and Combustible Liquids Code, NFPA No. 30, for discussion of factors pertaining to positive and reliable mechanical ventilation required to prevent formulation of hazardous vapor-air mixtures.

(3) Pits or depressions that are near aboveground tanks, but which are out of both the Class I, Division 1 and 2 areas, and which contain piping, valves, or fittings, are to be classified as Class I, Division 2 locations.

(f) Storage and Repair Garages for Tank Vehicles. It will be recalled that in Commercial Garages, **Article 511,** where more than three vehicles were in storage, or where repair work was done on these vehicles, the area was classified as a Class I, Division 2 location.

The areas where one or more tank vehicles are stored are to be classified as Class I, Division 2 locations to a height of 18 inches from the floor or grade. This also applies to areas where tank vehicles are repaired.

This part is broad in its coverage, and if in the judgment of the inspection authority there is a greater hazard present, he may classify the area as a Class I, Division 1 location.

(g) **Office Buildings, Boiler Rooms and Similar Locations.** Any office building, boiler room, or similar location in which there will be no handling of or storage of volatile flammable liquids, and no containers for such liquids, will not be considered as a hazardous area. If any of the above areas lap over into a hazardous area, then of course they would be subject to a hazardous classification.

515-3. Wiring and Equipment Within Hazardous Areas—The hazardous areas for bulk storage plants are defined in **Section 515-2.** All wiring and equipment installed in these areas will be subject to the regulations of **Article 501.**

515-4. Wiring and Equipment Above Hazardous Areas—The requirements of this Section are practically the same as for commercial garages The main concern is sparks, arcs, or hot metal particles that might drop into the hazardous area and cause trouble.

Metal raceways and ALS Type cable are approved for installation above hazardous areas. Equipment which might produce arcs, sparks, or particles of hot metal, such as lamps and lampholders for fixed lighting, cutouts, switches, receptacles, motors, or other equipment having make-and-break or sliding contacts, shall be totally enclosed or so constructed as to prevent the escape of sparks or hot metal particles.

Portable lamps or utilization equipment shall be approved and shall conform to the provisions of **Article 501** for the most hazardous location in which they might be used.

515-5. Underground Wiring—

(a) Underground wiring to and around aboveground storage tanks may be:

(1) Installed in rigid metal conduit.
(2) If buried not less than 2 feet deep, it may be installed in nonmetallic conduit or duct.
(3) Direct burial cable may be installed if it is approved for the purpose (one point that might come up here is part **(b)** below; that is, the insulation shall conform to **Section 501-13.** This depends on whether or not there is a possible chance of the insulation being exposed to deteriorating agents.)

433

Where cable is used, it shall be enclosed in metal conduit from the point of the lowest buried cable level to the point of connection to the aboveground raceway. Although not mentioned in the Code, buried cables entering conduits below ground are faced with a frost problem in cold climates. It is recommended that the conduit below ground level be in an ell shape so that the conductors will emerge horizontally through an insulated bushing on the end. Frost heave will not have a tendency to cut or abrade the insulation as much as if the conduit were merely a vertical run. Also, in a rocky ground, rocks may cut the insulation due to normal pressures and to frost heaval. Thus, direct burial cable should be protected below and above by a fine sand bed and covering. See Fig. 515-6.

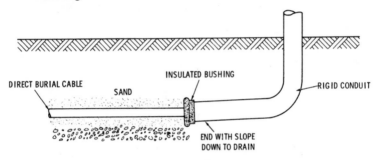

Fig. 515-6. Direct burial cable.

(b) *Conductor insulation shall conform to* **Section 501-13** *of* **Article 501.** Recall that the insulation must be approved for exposure to vapors and liquids.

(c) *Where cable with nonmetallic sheath or nonmetallic conduit is used, an additional grounding conductor shall be included to provide for metallic continuity of the raceway system and for grounding of noncurrent-carrying metallic parts of equipment.*

This is standard procedure for practically all wiring in order to provide grounding protection for raceways and equipment where there is no raceway continuity. The grounding continuity must be complete back to the service equipment and the service ground.

515-6. Sealing—Approved seals are to be installed in the horizontal as well as the vertical boundaries of the defined hazardous areas. Buried raceways under defined hazardous areas shall be considered to be in such areas.

This brings up the use of nonmetallic raceways and direct burial cables, as covered in **Section 515-5(a).** Often, the decision as to where seals are required must, by necessity, come under the authority enforcing the Code. Care must always be taken to prevent vapors and gases from reaching equipment and junction boxes. Therefore, seals are used to stop the transmittal of the gases and vapors. The final answer is a common sense item as to whether there is a hazard presented or not. Check with the inspector if in doubt.

515-7. Gasoline Dispensing—When gasoline is dispensed from a bulk-storage plant, this reverts to **Article 514** which covers the dispensing of gasoline. All applicable requirements of that Article shall be followed.

515-8. Grounding—See NEC.

ARTICLE 516—FINISHING PROCESSES

Two definite conditions must be kept in mind in this Article. One is the vapors from finishing processes and the storage of paints, lacquers, or other flammable finishes, and the other is the residues which accompany finishing processes.

Vapors can be coped with easier than the residues because the residues create a heat problem as well as the hazard created by the vapors. Bear this in mind while reading this Article.

Water-base paints are covered in NFPA 33 which, in essence, states that such paints in mixture are no problem, but when sprayed, the residue may be hazardous.

NFPA No. 33-1969, **Spray Finishing Using Flammable and Combustible Materials,** had considerable information which was not in the NEC. The 1971 NEC has been changed in this Article to be in agreement with NFPA No. 33.

516-1. Definition—*This Article shall apply to locations where paints, lacquers, or other flammable finishes are regularly or frequently applied by spraying, dipping, brushing or by other means, and where volatile flammable solvents or thinners are used or where readily ignitible deposits or residues from such paints, lacquers or finishes may occur.*

Notice that reference is made to NFPA Standard for Spray Finishing Using Flammable Materials (No. 33) and to the NFPA Standard for Dip Tanks Containing Flammable or Combustible Liquids (No. 34). These Standards become a part of this Article by reference.

See NFPA Standard for Blowers and Exhaust Systems, No. 91-1961.

516-2. Hazardous Areas—This Section covers the classification with respect to flammable vapors, with a reference made to **Section 516-3** which covers deposits and residues.

(a) The following are Class I, Division 1, Group D locations:

(1) The interiors of spray booths.

(2) Exhaust ducts.

(3) All space within 20 feet horizontally in any direction from spraying operations that are more extensive than touch-up operations and which are not conducted in spray booths.

(4) All space within 20 feet horizontally in all directions from dip tanks and their drain boards.

(5) All other spaces where hazardous concentrations of flammable vapors are likely to occur.

In reading the above, remember that this Section deals only with concentrations of flammable vapors and that no mention is being made of deposits and residues.

(b) This portion covers open-faced spray booths. *All space within 20 feet horizontally in any direction from the open face of a spray booth, and all space within the room but beyond the limits of Class I, Division 1 as defined in* **Section 516-2(a)** *for extensive open spraying, for dip tanks and drain boards and for other hazardous operations, shall be considered to be Class I, Division 2 locations unless the authority enforcing this Code judges otherwise.*

In other words, the spray portion of an open-faced booth is a Class I, Division 1 location as in (a) above, but the space for 20 feet horizontally in all directions from the open face of the booth is a Class I, Division 2 location. In addition, any part of the room where extensive spraying, dipping, or draining operations take place will also be a Class I, Division 2 location. The inspection authority may judge otherwise, however. The ventilation of the areas involved would most certainly be taken into consideration in any judgement that would be made.

(c) Areas adjacent to (a) and (b) of this Section shall be classified as nonhazardous areas if they meet the following conditions, unless the authority enforcing the Code judges otherwise.

(1) There are tight partitions without communicating openings.

(2) There are areas in which hazardous vapors are not likely to be released.

(d) Drying and baking areas may be judged nonhazardous by the authority enforcing the Code if:

(1) There is adequate positive ventilation provided to prevent the accumulation of concentrations of flammable vapors.

(2) There are interlocks provided to de-energize all electrical equipment (other than Class I equipment) in the event of a failure of the ventilating equipment.

For further information regarding safeguards see NFPA **Standard for Ovens and Furnaces,** *No. 86A-1969.*

516-3.   Wiring and Equipment in Hazardous Areas—

(a) *All electrical wiring and equipment within hazardous areas defined in* **Section 516-2** *shall conform to applicable provisions of* **Article 501.**

Article 501 covered Class I, Division 1 and 2 locations. Remember that such areas are in Group D. Group D covers gases and vapors but not deposits and residues. It will be found that no equipment is approved for use in spray booths for protection involving deposits and residues. For example, a motor may be approved for a Class I, Division 1, Group D location, but the motor cannot be mounted in an exhaust duct from a spray booth because of the deposits and residues from the spraying operation which are highly hazardous from a temperature standpoint. In addition, residues will deposit on the motor and cause a hazard. The same is true of lighting fixtures. A belt used to drive an exhaust fan creates a static electricity problem which must be remembered in designing the system. The NFPA states that the belt shall be enclosed in a nonferrous enclosure and that the fan shall be of nonferrous material. Even if the motor is mounted externally, it is possible to have gases or vapors come into contact with the motor, so it still must be approved for a Group D location.

(b) *Unless approved for both readily ignitible deposits and the flammable vapor location, no electrical equipment shall be installed or used where it may be subject to hazardous accumulations of readily ignitible deposits or residues, as the susceptibility to spontaneous heating and ignition of some residues may be greatly increased at temperatures above normal. Type MI cable and wiring in threaded rigid conduit may be installed in such locations, if the explosion-proof boxes or fittings contain no taps, splices, or terminal connections which may have the possibility of being loose in service and thereby causing abnormal temperatures on external surfaces of boxes or fittings.*

(c) Because there seem to be no lighting fixtures approved for deposits and residues, illumination of readily ignitible areas through panels of glass or other approved transparent or translucent material is permissible only where:

(1) Fixed lighting units are used as the source of illumination.
(2) The panel effectively isolated the hazardous area from the area in which the lighting unit is located. See Fig. 516-1.
(3) The lighting unit is approved specifically for a Class I, Division 1, Group D location.

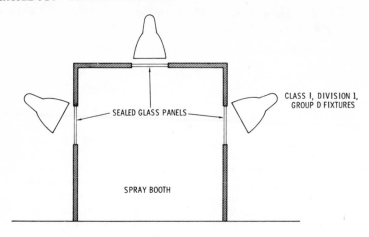

Fig. 516-1. Approved lighting for spray booths.

 (4) The panel is of a material or is so protected that breakage will be unlikely.

 (5) The arrangement is such that the normal accumulation of hazardous residues on the surface of the panel will not be raised to a dangerous temperature by radiation or conduction from the illumination source. See Fig. 516-1. The inspection authority must judge the hazard of the area in which lighting is mounted behind glass.

 (d) Portable lamps and utilization equipment shall not be used in hazardous areas during the finishing operations. They may be used during cleaning or repair operations, but they shall be approved for Class I locations and all of the metal noncurrent-carrying parts shall be grounded.

 (e) *Electrostatic spraying or detearing equipment shall be installed and used only as provided in* **Section 516-4.** NFPA No. 33 becomes a part of the Code by reference, and will give additional details.

 516-4. **Fixed Electrostatic Equipment**—For the requirements of this Section, refer to the National Electrical Code and NFPA No. 70.

 516-5. **Electrostatic Hand Spraying Equipment**—For the requirements of this Section, refer to the National Electrical Code and NFPA No. 70.

 516-6. **Powder Coating**—See NEC.

 516-7. **Wiring and Equipment Above Hazardous Areas**—

(a) All fixed wiring above hazardous areas, as defined in **Section 516-2**, shall be in metallic raceways or shall be Type MI or ALS cable. If cellular metal floor raceways are used, they may only supply ceiling outlets, or extensions to the ceiling, of the area below the hazardous area. They shall have no connections that lead to or through the hazardous area above the floor unless suitable seals are provided. There shall be no systems, piping, etc., installed in the floor ducts carrying electrical conductors.

(b) See NEC.

516-8. Grounding—*All metallic raceways, and all non-current carrying metallic portions of fixed or portable equipment, regardless of voltage, shall be grounded as provided in* **Article 250.**

ARTICLE 517—HEALTH CARE FACILITIES
A.   General

517-1.   Scope—*The provisions of this Article shall apply to health care facilities. See* **Article 660** *for Medical X-ray equipment and* **Article 665** *for therapeutic high-frequency equipment.*

Study diagram on page 70-333 of the 1971 NEC. This gives us a *Typical Diagram for Essential Electrical Systems,* for health care facilities.

517-2.   Definitions—For these definitions refer to this Section of the 1971 NEC. A few of these will be discussed, wherever the author feels than an explanation would be helpful.

Anesthetizing-Location Receptacles. Former **Section 517-4(b)** left something to be desired in regard to receptacles for use in nonhazardous areas of operating rooms, etc. This has been taken care of by designs as shown in the 1971 NEC, Diagrams (a) and (b), pages 70-337 and 70-338.

These receptacles are of a type for use in non-hazardous areas. There are also compatible receptacles for hazardous areas.

Flammable Anesthetizing Locations. *Any operating room, delivery room, anesthetizing room, corridor, utility room, or any other area if used or intended for the application of flammable anesthetics.*

This definition clarifies the areas where flammable anesthetics are likely to be used.

Health Care Facilities. *Buildings or parts of buildings that contain but are not limited to, hospitals, nursing homes, extended-care facilities, clinics, and medical and dental offices, whether fixed or mobile.*

One may readily see that many locations which many of us would never consider, may come under **Article 517.**

Reference Grounding Bus, Patient and **Reference Grounding Bus, Room,** both should be taken quite seriously in both wiring and inspections.

B. General Area Wiring Systems

517-3. Grounding—*All noncurrent-carrying conductive surfaces and equipment that are likely to become energized and are subject to personal contact shall be grounded by one or more of the methods detailed in* **Article 250.**

517-4. Wiring Methods—*Except as modified by this Article, wiring methods shall comply with the applicable requirements of Chapters 1 through 4 of this Code.*

C. Essential Electrical Systems

Part **C** concerns essential electrical systems for hospitals. This material has been taken from NFPA No. 76A-1971 **Essential Electrical Systems for Hospitals.** Also see NFPA No. 20-1971, **Installation of Centrifugal Fire Pumps.**

517-10. General—

(a) This Part **C** only applies to hospitals serving people and does not apply to other types of health care facilities.

(b) The essential electrical system is made up of two parts:

    1. The emergency system.
    2. The equipment system.

These systems shall be capable of supplying a limited amount of lighting and power service considered essential for life safety, life support and effective operation during the time the normal service is interrupted for any reason. See Diagram 517-1.

(c) *Each emergency and equipment system shall have adequate capacity and rating for the operation of all lighting and equipment it serves.*

527-12. Emergency System—

(a) The emergency system may consist of three parts, which shall be limited to circuits considered essential to specific functions:

    1. The life safety branch.
    2. The life support branch.
    3. The critical branch.

(b) *A life safety branch and a critical branch shall be required in all hospitals.*

(1) *The life safety branch shall serve illumination, alarm, and alerting equipment which shall be operable at all times for protection of life during emergencies.*

(2) *The critical branch shall serve lighting and receptacles in critical patient care areas.*

(3) *The life support branch shall serve only power systems, or other equipment meeting the requirements of* **Section 517-51,** *in electrically susceptible patient locations. It shall be installed as a separate branch unless combined with the critical branch at the discretion of the hospital administration and with the approval of the authority having jurisdiction.*

(c) *The feeders for the emergency system shall be physically separated from the normal wiring or protected in such a way as to minimize the possibility of simultaneous interruption.*

If a fault occurs on regular circuits, the systems shall be so installed that the emergency system will not be affected and become inoperable.

(d) The emergency systems composed of the three parts enumerated in **(a),** *shall be run in metal raceways.*

These branches shall be kept entirely independent of all other wiring and equipment and shall not enter the same raceways, boxes or cabinets with each other or other wiring.

Exception No. 1: As permitted in **517-11(b) (3).**

Exception No. 2: In transfer switches.

Exception No. 3: In exit or emergency lighting fixtures supplied from two sources.

(e) **Sections 517-12, -13** and **-14** listing the functions utilizing illumination or equipment are the only functions which are to be connected to the emergency system.

(f) *All branches of the emergency system shall be so installed and connected to the alternate source of power that all lighting and equipment will be automatically restored to operation within 10 seconds after interruption of the normal source.*

517-12. Life Safety Branch—*The life safety branch of the emergency system shall serve the lighting, receptacles and other equipment which are related to the safety of life as follows:*

For additional information see Essential Electrical Systems for Hospitals, NFPA No. 76A-1971.

(1) *Illumination of means of egress, such as lighting required for corridors, passageways, stairways and landings at exit doors, and all necessary ways of approach to exits. See Life Safety Code, NFPA No. 101-1970,* **Section 5-10.**

(2) *Exit signs and directional signs. See Life Safety Code, NFPA No. 101-1970,* **Section 5-11.**

(3) *Alarm systems, including: fire alarms actuated at manual stations, electric water-flow alarm devices in connection with sprinkler systems, automatic fire or smoke or products of combustion detection devices. See Life Safety Code, NFPA No. 101-1970,* **Sections 6-3211, 10-1362,** *and* **10-2344.**

(4) *Alarms required for systems used for the piping of nonflammable medical gases. See Nonflammable Medical Gas Systems, NFPA No. 56F-1970.*

(5) *Hospital communication systems when these are intended for issuing instructions during emergency conditions, including local power requirements for the telephone system.*

(6) *Generator-set location, including task illumination and selected receptacles.*

517-13. Critical Branch—*The critical branch of the emergency system shall serve only the following areas and functions related to patient care:*

(1) *Isolating transformers serving anesthetizing locations in existing hospitals only. See* **Section 517-14** *for new hospitals.* Existing hospitals have thus been taken care of.

(2) Task illumination and selected receptacles:

    (a) Infant nurseries.
    (b) Medication preparation areas.
    (c) Pharmacy dispensing areas.

    (d) Selected acute nursing areas.

    (e) Psychiatric bed areas (task illumination only).

    (f) Nurses station (unless adequately lighted by corridor luminaires).

    (g) Ward treatment rooms.

    (h) Surgical and obstetrical units.

    (i) Locations such as listed in **Section 517-14**.

517-14. Life Support Branch—

(a) Electrically susceptible locations only shall be served by the life support branch of the emergency system. Electrically susceptible locations may be located in the following hospital areas.

1. Aniographic lab.
2. Cardiac catheterization labs.
3. Coronary care units.
4. Delivery rooms.
5. Dialysis rooms.
6. Emergency room treatment areas.
7. Human physiology labs.
8. Intensive care units.
9. Operating rooms.
10. Post-operative recovery rooms.

(b) *The power systems in the above locations may be served by an uninterrupted power system.*

517-20. Equipment Systems—

(a) *The equipment system shall be so installed and connected to the alternate source that equipment listed in* **Section 517-20(d)** *shall be automatically restored to operation at appropriate time-lag intervals following the restoration of the emergency system to operation. This arrangement shall also provide for reconnection of equipment listed in* **Sections 517-20(e)** *and* **(f)** *by either delayed, automatic, or manual operation.*

This tells us about connection of the equipment after an outage on the regular source of power has occured, and that restoration to the standby source may be either delayed, automatic or manual operation.

(b) *The equipment systems may be installed in raceways and boxes with general wiring.*
Before proceeding with this Section on Equipment Systems, it will be well to look at the definition:
Equipment System. *A system of feeders and branch circuits arranged for delayed, automatic or manual connection to the alternate power source and which serves primarily 3-phase power equipment. See Appendix A of* **Essential Electrical Systems for Hospitals,** *NFPA No. 76A-1971.*

(c) *The equipment system shall be connected to equipment listed in* **Sections 517-20(d)** *and* **(e).** *It may be also connected to equipment listed in* **Section 517-20(f).**

(d) *The following components of the equipment system shall be arranged for automatic restoration of operation: (1) Central va-*

443

cuum and medical air systems serving medical and surgical functions; (2) Sump pumps and other equipment including associated control systems and alarms required for the safety of essential apparatus.

(e) The following required components of the equipment system shall be arranged for either automatic or manual connection to the alternate power source.

(1) Heating equipment for heating of operating, delivery, labor, recovery, and patient rooms and intensive care units and nurseries.

Exception: Patient room heating during disruption of normal source under either of the following conditions:

a. The outside air design temperature is higher than —7°C. (+20°F).

This is based on the median of extremes as shown in the 1967 edition of the American Society of Heating, Air Conditioning and Refrigeration "Beginners Handbook of Fundamentals."

b. The hospital is served by at least two utility services, each supplied by separate generating sources or a network distribution system fed by two or more generators. The utility services shall be routed, connected, and protected so that a fault any place between the generators and the hospital will not likely cause an interruption of more than one of the utility services.

(2) Elevator service that will reach every patient floor, ground floors and floors on which surgical suites and obstetrical delivery suites are located. This shall include connections for cab lighting and control and signal systems.

In instances where interruption of power will result in an elevator stopping between floors, it may be desirable to provide throw-over facilities to allow the temporary operation of any elevator to release patients or other persons who may be trapped between floors.

(3) Supply and exhaust ventilating systems for laboratory fume hoods, and surgical suites, obstetrical suites, infant nurseries, and emergency treatment spaces where such areas contain no windows.

(f) The following components of the equipment system may be arranged for either automatic or manual connection to the alternate source:

(1) *Selected autoclaving equipment if electrically heated or controlled.*

(2) *Other selected equipment in locations such as kitchens, laundries, radiological and central refrigeration rooms.*

It is desirable that where heavy interruption currents can be anticipated, the transferred load may be reduced by use of multiple transfer devices. For example, elevator feeders may cause less hazard to electrical continuity if they are fed through individual transfer devices.

517-40. Switching and Overcurrent Protection—This Section is very well done and very much complete. It is felt that it will be clear to you when you read it so it will not be repeated here. See NEC.

D. Electrically Susceptible Patient Areas

517-50. General—This section prescribes the performance criteria and/or wiring methods to minimize shock hazards to patients in electrically susceptible patient areas. Potentials as low as 5 millivolts (0.005 volts) and currents of 10 microamperes (10/1,000,000 of an ampere) can be hazardous to patients connected to instruments or probes.

In a health care facility, it is not feasible to prevent the occurence of a conductive or capacitive path from the patient's body to some grounded object, because that path may be established accidentally or through instrumentation directly connected to the patient. All other electrically conductive surfaces may make an additional contact with the patient, or other instruments which may be connected to the patient, then become possible sources of electrical currents which can traverse the patient's body. When the current path includes a small area of direct contact with the heart, a current in excess of 10 microamperes could be hazardous. Unless special precautions are taken, the power-line-frequency impedance of the patient circuit, which includes the internal conduction path through the small contact area, could be as low as 500 ohms when measured at low-current magnitudes. Under these conditions a voltage difference between the points of patient contact in excess of 5 millivolts also is considered hazardous.

517-51. Performance—

(a) This gives us the criteria for electrical susceptible patient areas. The maximum 60-hertz (cycle) ac voltage between two conducting surfaces, shall not exceed 5 millivolts, when measured across a 500-ohm resistor, during normal operating procedures or in case of failure.

(b) **Special Grounding Requirements.** This goes into detail on grounding necessary to maintain the low amperes and voltage

445

tolerances allowed. Refer to the NEC covering this Section as only a few of the highlights will appear here.

A patient reference grounding bus shall be within 5 feet of the patient's bed, with approved connectors to connect to all metal or conducting furnishings and other nonelectrical equipment for grounding purposes.

A patient reference grounding bus may serve more than one patient, but one patient may not be served by more than one reference grounding bus.

Metallic raceways shall not be relied on for the grounding. see **(b) (2).**

This Section is no doubt one of the most important Sections of **Article 517.** Designers, inspectors, and wiremen should not slight any portion of this Section. Do not merely read it but study it.

E.   Inhalation Anesthetizing Locations

This part is quite similar to **Article 517** as it appeared in the 1968 NEC.

517-60.   Hazardous Areas—

(a) *Any room or space in which flammable anesthetics or volatile flammable disinfecting agents are stored shall be considered to be a Class I, Division 1 location throughout.*

(b) Flammable anesthetizing locations shall be Class I, Division 1 locations to a height extending upwards from the floor to a level of 5 feet. See Fig. 517-1. The definition of Anesthetizing Location is: *Any area which it is intended to administer any flammable or nonflammable inhalation anesthetic agents in the course of examination or treatment and includes operating rooms, delivery rooms, emergency rooms, anesthetizing rooms, corridors, utility rooms and other areas when used for induction of anesthesia with flammable or nonflammable anesthetizing agents.*

517-61.   Wiring and Equipment Within Hazardous Areas—

(a) Hazardous areas, as defined in **Section 517-2,** will be Class I, Division 1, Group C locations. All wiring and equipment in this area shall conform to **Sections 501-1** through **501-15** and to **Section 501-16(a** and **b).** This will include all wiring and equipment that operates at more than 8 volts between conductors and will include:

(1) All fixed wiring.

(2) Fixed equipment.

(3) All portable equipment including lamps and other utilization equipment.

(b) *Where a box, fitting or enclosure is partially but not entirely within a hazardous area, the hazardous area shall be considered to be extended to include the entire box, fitting or enclosure.* An example would be a box in a wall which would be considered to be within the hazardous area of that room.

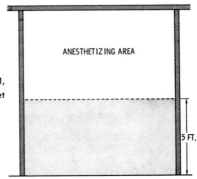

Fig. 517-1. Anesthetizing areas are Class I, Division 1 locations to a height of 5 feet above the floor.

(c) Flexible cords which are or may be used in hazardous locations and have more than 8 volts between conductors shall be:

(1) Approved for extra hard usage.

(2) Shall be of ample length. (This is to keep from adding extensions to them.)

(3) Shall include a grounding conductor.

(4) Shall be stored on a device that will not subject the cord to a bending radius of less than 3 inches.

Cords for use in anesthetizing locations for portable lamps and utilization equipment should not be used for any other purpose. General-purpose cords that are used elsewhere about the hospital should not be used in the operating room. All cords should be inspected periodically and replaced (not repaired) when they show damage or wear.

(d) *Anesthetizing-location receptacles and attachment plugs in hazardous areas shall be of the approved type for services of prescribed voltage, frequency, rating and number of conductors with provision for the connection of the grounding conductor. The attachment plugs shall be designed for use without adapters in Class I, Group C hazardous locations, and shall be interchangeable with locking-type general-purpose receptacles in nonhazardous areas (see* **Diagram 517-2(a)** *and* **(b)** *in the NEC). This re-*

447

quirement shall apply to caps and receptacles of the two-pole, 3-wire grounding-type for single-phase 125-volt AC service.

See **Section 24037** of the Inhalation Anesthetics Standard, NFPA 56A-1971, for further information.

517-62. Wiring and Equipment in Nonhazardous or Above Hazardous Anesthetizing Areas—

- **(a)** Wiring above hazardous areas as defined in **Section 517-60** shall be installed in metal raceways or shall be Type MI or ALS cable.

- **(b)** Equipment which may produce arcs, sparks or hot metal particles, such as lamps and lampholders for fixed lighting, cutouts, switches, receptacles, generators, motors, and other equipment having make-and-break or sliding contacts, shall be of the totally-enclosed type or so constructed as to prevent the escape of sparks or hot metal particles.

- **(c)** *Surgical and other lighting fixtures shall conform to* **Section 501-9(b).**

    Exception No. 1: The surface temperature limitations set forth in **Section 501-9(b) (2)** *shall not apply.*

    Exception No. 2: Integral or pendant switches which are located above and cannot be lowered into the hazardous area need not be explosion-proof.

- **(d)** Approved seals shall be used in horizontal as well as vertical boundaries of hazardous areas and shall conform to **Section 501-5** and **Section 501-5(a) (3),** with the following exceptions:

    Exception: Seals may be located within 18 inches of the point at which a conduit emerges from a wall forming the boundary of an anesthetizing location if all of the following conditions are met. See Fig. 517-2.

    a. *The junction box, switch or receptacle contains a seal-off device between the arcing contacts and the conduit.*

    b. *The conduit is continuous (without coupling or fitting) between the junction box and the sealing fitting within 18 inches of the point where the conduit emerges from the wall. See Fig. 517-2.*

- **(e)** *Anesthetizing-location receptacles and attachment plugs in nonhazardous or above hazardous anesthetizing areas shall be of the approved type for services of prescribed voltage, frequency, rating, and number of conductors with provisions for the connection of the grounding conductor. This requirement shall apply to at-*

tachment plugs and receptacles of the two-pole, 3-wire grounding-type for single-phase 125-volt AC service as shown in Diagram 517-2(a) and (b). These diagrams are in the NEC.

517-63. Circuits in Anesthetizing Locations—

(a) Anesthetizing locations as defined in **Section 517-60** shall be supplied from an isolated system. This system may consist of one or more isolation transformers with no connection between primary and secondary windings, motor generator sets, or batteries. Each circuit within an anesthetizing location, except as provided in **Section 517-63(f),** shall be controlled by a disconnecting means in each circuit conductor. In other words, the circuits in an anesthetizing location are to be ungrounded and separated from the supply system which, of course, will be a grounded system. The isolated system shall supply no location but that for which it is intended.

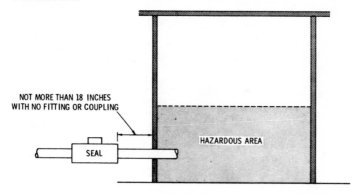

NOT MORE THAN 18 INCHES
WITH NO FITTING OR COUPLING

HAZARDOUS AREA

SEAL

Fig. 517-2. Seals.

(b) Circuits supplying the primaries of isolated systems shall not have more than 300 volts between conductors and shall be provided with proper overcurrent protection. The secondary (isolated circuits) shall not have more than 300 volts between conductors, shall be ungrounded, and shall have the proper overcurrent protection for the conductors that are supplied. Circuits from generators or batteries shall be ungrounded and shall have the proper overcurrent protection. See Fig. 517-3.

(c) *Transformers, motor-generator sets, batteries and battery chargers, together with their overcurrent devices shall be installed in non-hazardous locations, and shall conform to the requirements of this Code for such locations.*

449

(d) *In addition to the usual control and overcurrent protection the ungrounded system shall be provided with a line isolation monitor so arranged that a green signal lamp, conspicuously visible to persons in the anesthetizing location, remains lighted while the system is isolated from ground. An adjacent red signal lamp and an audible warning signal shall be energized when the total current (consisting of resistive and capacitive leakage currents) from either isolated conductor to ground reads 2 milliamperes under normal voltage conditions. The line isolation monitor shall not give warning for a total hazard current less than 1.7 ma. The line isolation monitor shall be designed to have sufficient internal impedance so that, when properly connected to the isolated system, the maximum internal current that can flow through the line isolation monitor, when any point of the isolated system is grounded, is 1 ma. An ammeter, calibrated in the total hazard current of the system, shall be mounted in a plainly visible place on the line isolation monitor with the "alarm-on" (total hazard current = 2 ma) zone at approximately the center of the scale.*

For maintenance tests of the isolation monitor see **Section 3422** *of the* **Inhalation Anesthetics Standard,** *NFPA No. 56A-1971.*

(e) *A branch circuit supplying an anesthetizing location shall supply no other location.*

(f) Lighting fixtures (fixed) in the nonhazardous areas of anesthetizing locations, but not including surgical lighting fixtures or approved permanently installed X-ray equipment, may be supplied from conventional grounded systems, if the following conditions are met:

1. Wiring for the grounded and ungrounded circuits shall not occupy the same raceways.
2. The lighting fixtures and the X-ray equipment (except the enclosed X-ray tube and the metal-enclosed high-voltage leads to the tube) are located at least 8 feet above the floor or outside the anesthetizing location.
3. Switches for the grounded circuits are located outside of the anesthetizing location.

Note 1: For description of approved permanently installed X-ray equipment see **Section 2434** *of the* **Inhalation Anesthetics Standard,** *NFPA No. 56A-1971.*

Note 2: Remote-control stations for remote-control switches may be installed in the anesthetizing location if the remote-control circuit is energized from the ungrounded distribution system.

450

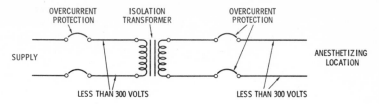

Fig. 517-3. Isolated circuits.

517-64. Low Voltage Equipment and Instruments— See NEC.

517-65. Other Equipment—

(a) The following equipment that is used in hazardous areas shall be approved for Class I locations:

    (1) Suction equipment.

    (2) Pressure equipment.

    (3) Insufflation equipment involving electrical elements.

(b) X-ray equipment that is operated in anesthetizing locations, as defined in **Section 517-60,** shall be provided with approved means of preventing accumulation of electrostatic charges. All control devices, switches, relays, meters, and transformers shall be totally enclosed. Where any of these control devices are located in a hazardous area, they shall be approved for Class I Group C locations. Underwriter's Laboratories Hazardous Area Materials list contains approved items for use in these hazardous locations.

(c) *Equipment for generating high frequency currents or voltages used in electrocautery, diathermy, television, etc., where installed or used in an anesthetizing location, shall conform to* **Sections 517-61** *and* **517-62.**

517-66. Grounding—*In any anesthetizing area, all metallic raceways and all noncurrent-carrying conductive portions of fixed or portable equipment including the conductive floor shall be grounded.*

Exception: Equipment operating at not more than 8 volts between conductors need not be grounded.

F. Communications, Signaling Systems, and Data Systems

517-80. Electrically Susceptible Patient Areas—*Isolation and grounding equivalent to that required for the electrical distribution systems in this Article for these areas shall also be provided. See also* **Articles 725** *and* **800.**

An acceptable alternate means of providing isolation for patient nurse

451

call system is by the use of nonelectrified signaling, communication or control devices held by the patient or within reach of the patient.

Summary

Anesthetizing locations and anesthetics storage locations are susceptible to the smallest electrical discharge. The importance of this may be seen from the fact that all parts of the room and equipment, even though not connected to the electrical supply system, have been provided with precautionary measures. The tile on the floor is of a conductive type and is laid upon metal grids that are grounded. Ground tests of the floor are made and recorded when it is installed, and it is periodically retested.

Anyone working within an anesthetizing location is required to wear over his shoes coverings which are conductive and before entering the room he must stand on a resistance-testing machine to test the resistance to be certain that it is within allowable limis. The patient is grounded, furniture must meet the requirements for these locations, rubber hoses must meet conductive specifications, and all necessary precautions are taken to prevent any spark from occuring, even so far as to the type of garments that may be worn in the room. All of this is covered in NFPA No. 56.

ARTICLE 520—THEATERS AND ASSEMBLY HALLS

A. General

520-1. Scope—*The requirements of this Article shall apply to all buildings, or part of a building, designed, intended, or used for dramatic, operatic, motion-picture or other shows, and night clubs, dance halls, armories, sporting arenas, bowling alleys, public auditoriums, television studios and like buildings used for public assembly.*

520-2. Motion-Picture Projectors—See NEC.

520-3. Sound Reproduction—See NEC.

520-4. Wiring Method—The wiring method shall be metal raceways, Type ALS cable, or Type MI cable. There are exceptions to this which will follow. However, in most places where a City, County, or State has inspections and supplemental Codes to the National Electrical Code, there are seldom any exceptions to these wiring methods.

Exception No. 1. As provided in **Article 640**, *Sound Reproduction, in* **Article 800,** *Communication Circuits, and in* **Article 725** *for Class 2 Remote Control and Signal Circuits.*

Exception No. 2. Where the area intended for public assembly has a capacity of less than 200 persons, Type AC metal-clad cable as provided in **Article 334** *may be used, or for concealed work, concealed knob-and-tube work or nonmetallic sheathed cable as provided in* **Articles 324** *and* **336** *may also be used.*

For recommendations for determination of population capacity, refer to NFPA Life Safety Code (No. 101). This Exits Code actually becomes a part of the NEC if the inspection authority so desires, and in a great many cases it is accepted as the method of calculating the population that may assemble in an assembly hall.

At the time of this writing, the 1966 NFPA Technical Committee Reports are available, which are the advance reports of contemplated changes in various Codes. The figures in this report will be used as a guide for the determination of population of assembly place. It is not the intent of the NFPA that these be hard and fast rules, as this would be impossible since there are many conditions of which the committee is unaware. The NFPA merely establishes a guide line from which the authority responsible for the enforcement of the National Electrical Code can make a final decision. Following are the guide lines:

Occupancy	*Sq. Ft. Per Person*	
Places of Assembly	15	net
Areas of concentrated use without fixed seating	7	net
Standing space	3	net
Store, Street Floor, and Sales Basement	30	gross
Other floors	60	gross
Storage and shipping	100	gross
Educational Occupancies		
Classroom area	20	net
Shops and other vocational areas	50	net
Office, Factory, and Workroom	100	gross
Hotel and Apartment	200	gross
Institutional		
Sleeping departments	120	gross
In-patient departments	240	gross

The above figures, based on counts of typical buildings, represent the average maximum density of occupancy.

From the foregoing it may be readily seen that there are no fixed figures as to the area per person for occupancy. This gives considerable latitude to the enforcing authority to make the final decision.

Exception No. 3. The wiring for stage set lighting and stage effects and other wiring which is not fixed as to location shall be done with approved portable cables and approved flexible cords.

520-5. Number of Conductors in Raceway—Table 1 of Chapter 9 governs the number of conductors for border or stage pocket circuits, or for remote-control conductors, which may be installed in any metal conduit or electrical metallic tubing. For auxiliary gutters or wireways, the sum of the cross-sectional areas of all of the conductors contained therein shall not exceed 20% of the interior cross-sectional area of the gutter or raceway. *The 30 conductor limitation of* Section 362-5 *or* 374-5 *shall not apply.*

520-6. Enclosing and Guarding Live Parts—See NEC.

B. Fixed Stage Switchboard

520-21. Dead Front—See NEC.

520-22. Guarding Back of Switchboard—See NEC.

520-23. Control and Overcurrent Protection of Receptacle Circuits—See NEC.

520-24. Metal Hood—See NEC.

520-25. Dimmers—*Dimmers shall conform to the following:*

(a) **Disconnection and Overcurrent Protection.** When dimmers are installed in ungrounded conductors, the overcurrent for each dimmer shall not exceed 125% of the dimmer rating, and the dimmers shall be disconnected from all ungrounded conductors when the master or individual switch or circuit breaker supplying such dimmer is in an open position.

(b) **Resistance or Reactor Type Dimmers.** It is recommended that resistance or reactance type dimmers be placed in the grounded neutral conductor, but that they do not open the circuit. Resistance or series reactance dimmers may be placed in either the grounded or ungrounded conductor of the circuit.

   Where designed to open either the supply circuit to the dimmer, or the circuit that is controlled by it, the dimmer shall comply with Section 380-1 which requires that no switch shall open the grounded conductor unless the grounded conductor and ungrounded conductor or conductors are simultaneously opened.

(c) **Auto-Transformer Type Dimmers.** Auto-transformer type dimmers shall be supplied by a source that does not exceed 150 volts, and the input and output grounds shall be common as provided for in Section 200-4.

C. Stage Equipment—Fixed

520-41. Circuit Loads—Branch circuits that supply footlights, border lights, and proscenium sidelights shall not carry a load that exceeds 20 amperes. Where circuits have heavy-duty lampholders, an exception is made to provide for these, but the conditions in **Article 210** that cover heavy-duty lampholders must be complied with.

520-42. Conductor Insulation—*Foot, border, proscenium or portable strip lighting fixtures shall be wired with conductors having insulation suitable for the temperatures at which the conductors will be operated and not less than 125°C (257°F).* Insulation temperatures may be found in **Table 310-2(a).**

520-43. Footlights—See NEC. Notice in **Section 520-43(b)** that disappearing footlights shall be arranged so as to automatically disconnect from the circuit when they are in the closed position. Otherwise they would present a great fire hazard if energized while in the closed recess.

520-44. Borders and Proscenium Sidelights—

(a) *Borders and proscenium sidelights shall be constructed as prescribed in* **Section 520-43**, *shall be suitably stayed and supported, and shall be so designed that the flanges of the reflectors or other adequate guards will protect the lamps from mechanical injury and from accidental contact with scenery and other combustible material.*

(b) Cables for Border Lights. Only types S, SO, or ST flexible cords shall be used to supply border lights. These flexible cords shall be suitably supported and used only where flexible conductors are necessary.

520-45. Receptacles—Receptacles that are intended to supply incandescent lamps shall be rated at no less than 20 amperes and shall be supplied by conductors no smaller than No. 12. The plugs for incandescent and arc lamps shall not be interchangable.

520-46. Stage Pockets—Receptacles shall comply with **Section 520-45** when intended for use with portable stage lighting equipment and shall be mounted in suitable pockets or enclosures.

The remainder of **Article 520** needs no explanation. Refer to the National Electrical Code.

ARTICLE 530—MOTION-PICTURE STUDIOS AND SIMILAR LOCATIONS

See NEC.

ARTICLE 540—MOTION PICTURE PROJECTORS

This Article is seldom used by the trade. Therefore, refer to the National Electrical Code for the answer to any questions involving motion picture projectors.

ARTICLE 550—MOBILE HOMES AND
MOBILE HOME PARKS

Many revisions were made in the 1971 NEC to conform with NFPA No. 501B, Mobile Homes. The first Part is **Scope** and **Definitions.** Part **A** covers Mobile Homes and Part **B** covers Mobile Home Parks and includes:

1. Feeder demand factors for lots.
2. Type distribution system.
3. Requirements for mobile home service equipment, each lot.

550-2. Definitions—See the NEC for definitions of:

1. Feeder Assembly.
2. Mobile Home.
3. Mobile Home accessory Building or Structure.
4. Mobile Home Lot.
5. Mobile Home Park.
6. Mobile Home Service Equipment.
7. Park Electrical Wiring System.

Mobile homes have caused much discussion by Code panels and inspection authorities in general. They are built and sold to the public as a complete unit with the walls in place. Thus, local inspection authorities cannot really check to see that the wiring meets the Code requirements. Underwriter's Laboratories have a labeling service that is available to mobile-home manufacturers and the mobile homes come from such factories with the label on them. However, these seem to be in the minority. Some inspection authorities demand an inspection before the units are allowed in their jurisdictional area. Others find that some manufacturers ask for local inspection and label their product accordingly to show that a local inspection has been made, feeling that the public is entitled to purchase a mobile home with adequate and safe wiring. These local labels are often accepted by other inspection authorities. Tennessee has passed a law that is very complete in regard to mobile homes.

Another problem that faces inspection authorities is that so often the wheels are removed and the mobile home is set on a permanent foundation. Local laws will govern whether it stays a mobile home or not. In many localities it may stay a mobile home as long as a license is purchased annually for a mobile home.

There is also a popular mobile home that is built in two or more mobile sections which are hauled to the location and bolted together to become a large home.

All of these are problems which cannot be covered by the National Electrical Code, but become local problems to be answered by local rulings and laws. Basically, the things that the local authority enforcing the Code is interested in is that:

(1) Mobile homes and the electrical panel therein is basically a feeder panel, and that the neutral bus is isolated from the panel enclosure and the equipment grounding. This must be taken care of by an extra conductor for grounding purposes only from the source of supply through the cord or cords supplying the home. See Figs. 550-1 and 550-2.

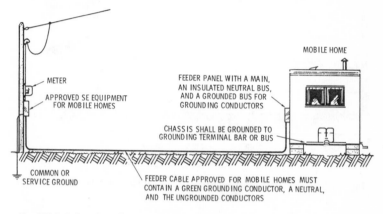

Fig. 550-1. Pole-mounted service-entrance equipment for mobile-home use with the feeder cable above ground.

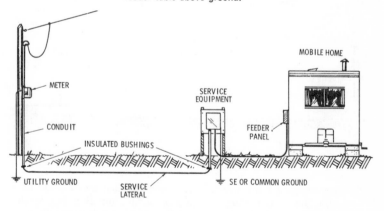

Fig. 550-2. Underground service lateral for use with a mobile home.

(2) If there are two cords supplying the home, the two panels must be treated as entirely separate panels and not interconnected.

457

(3) Supply cord or cords shall be no longer than 36½ feet and no less than 21 feet in length.

(4) Where the calculated load exceeds 100 amperes, or where a permanent feeder is used as a supply, four permanently installed conductors, one being identified as the grounding conductor as required by Code, must be used. See Figs. 550-3 and 550-4.

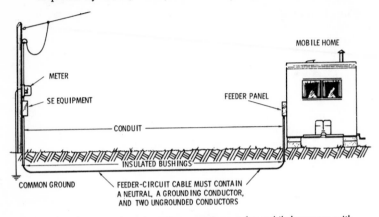

Fig. 550-3. Pole-mounted service-entrance equipment for mobile-home use with the feeder cable buried.

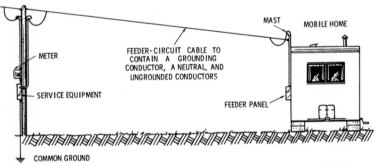

Fig. 550-4. An overhead feeder-cable installation to supply power to a mobile home.

(5) Grounding of both electrical and nonelectrical metal parts in a mobile home is through connection to a grounding bus in the mobile-home distribution panel. The grounding bus is grounded through the green colored conductor in the supply cord or the feeder wiring to the service ground in the service-entrance located adjacent to the mobile-home location. Note this last part—

The service-entrance equipment located adjacent to the mobile home. Neither the frame of the mobile home nor the frame of any appliance may be connected to the neutral conductor in the mobile home.

(6) The chassis shall be grounded. The grounding conductor may be solid or stranded, insulated or bare, and shall be an armored grounding conductor or routed in conduit if it is No. 8 AWG. The conductor, if No. 6 AWG or larger, may be run without metal covering. The grounding conductor shall be connected between the distribution panel grounding terminal and a terminal on the chassis. Grounding terminals shall be of the solderless type and approved for the wire size employed.

In summary, the distribution panel of a mobile home is not service-entrance equipment. It is, in essence, a feeder panel. The service-entrance equipment is located adjacent to the mobile home.

When a mobile home is located and installed as a permanent home, then the picture changes and the necessary alterations must be made in the wiring system to meet the requirements of the Code for a permanent home.

Note under definitions of Mobile Home, that it is *designed to be used as a dwelling unit(s) without permanent foundation.* This to me rules a mobile home out as a "Prefabricated" or "Module Home".

Refer to **Article 550** of the NEC for the complete coverage.

ARTICLE 551—RECREATION VEHICLES AND RECREATION VEHICLE PARKS

This Article has a new title and conforms to NFPA No. 501C. Part **A** applies to wiring systems used in the vehicles. Part **B** applies to recreational vehicle park wiring systems and includes:

1. Type of distribution.
2. Receptacle.
3. Load Calculations.
4. Lot service equipment.
5. Installation requirements for overhead and underground conductors.

It appears that any authority having jurisdiction over the enforcement of the National Electrical Code has a very comprehensive guide for inspection and enforcement of the NEC in regard to recreational vehicles and parks. See **Article 551** of the NEC.

ARTICLE 555—MARINAS AND BOATYARDS

These areas have the possibility of becoming very hazardous, from an electrical aspect. In wiring Marinas and Boatyards, be sure that you follow the prescribed methods as outlined in the NEC.

Chapter 6. Special Equipment

ARTICLE 600—ELECTRIC SIGNS AND OUTLINE LIGHTING

Refer to the National Electrical Code for the answer to any questions involving electric signs and outline lighting.

ARTICLE 610—CRANES AND HOISTS

Refer to the National Electrical Code for the coverage of this Article.

ARTICLE 620—ELEVATORS, DUMBWAITERS, ESCALATORS, AND MOVING WALKS

Refer to the National Electrical Code for the coverage of this Article.

ARTICLE 630—ELECTRIC WELDERS

Refer to the National Electrical Code for the coverage of this Article.

ARTICLE 640—SOUND-RECORDING AND SIMILAR EQUIPMENT

Refer to the National Electrical Code for the coverage of this Article.

ARTICLE 645—DATA PROCESSING SYSTEMS
Refer to the National Electrical Code for coverage of this Article.

ARTICLE 650—ORGANS

Refer to the National Electrical Code for the coverage of this Article.

ARTICLE 660—X-RAY EQUIPMENT

Refer to the National Electrical Code for the coverage of this Article.

ARTICLE 665—INDUCTION AND DIELECTRIC HEATING EQUIPMENT

Refer to the National Electrical Code for the coverage of this Article.

ARTICLE 670—METALWORKING MACHINE TOOLS
Refer to the National Electrical Code for the coverage of this Article.

ARTICLE 680—SWIMMING AND WADING POOLS
A. General

Due to the large usage of underwater lighting and other electrical equipment in conjunction with swimming pools, this has become a very important Article in the Code. The water and conductivity of wet surfaces around the pool have become a very serious hazard, and in designing or installing electrical installations in such locations, special precautions should be taken at all times.

680-1. Scope—*The provisions of this Article apply to the construction and installation of electric wiring for equipment in or adjacent to all swimming and wading pools, whether permanently installed or storable and to metallic appurtenances in or within 5 feet of the pool, and to the auxiliary equipment, such as pumps, filters and similar equipment. No electric appliances or wiring shall be installed in the water or in the enclosing walls of a swimming pool, except as provided in this Article.*

The requirements of **Article 680** *will add to the safety of decorative and therapeutic pools; however, additional safeguards may be necessary.*

680-2. Approval of Equipment—*All equipment shall be approved for the purpose.* It will be found that the Underwriter's Laboratories approval is practically universally acceptable for this equipment.

680-3. Application of Other Articles—The requirements of **Chapters 1** to **4,** inclusive, are applicable to wiring of swimming pools with the exception of the modifications in this Article which are necessary due to the hazards involved. *See* **Section 370-13** *for junction boxes,* **Section 347-3** *for rigid non-metallic conduit, and* **Article 720** *for low-voltage wiring.*

680-4. Definitions—

The NEC covers definitions in this Section. The following are the definitions covered, so refer to the NEC:

(a) Permanently installed swimming or wading pools.

(b) Storable swimming or wading pools.

(c) Forming shell.

(d) Wet-niche lighting fixtures.

(e) Dry-niche lighting fixtures.

(f) Ground-Fault Circuit-Interrupters.

680-5.   Transformers and Ground-Fault Circuit-Interrupters—

(a) Transformers. Transformers and their enclosures that supply fixtures shall be approved for the purpose. The transformers of the two-winding type with a grounded metal barrier between the primary and secondary windings shall be used and check the Green UL Listing Book to be certain that the one you use has been approved.

(b) Wiring. All conductors on the load side of ground-fault circuit-interrupters or transformers (as covered in **(a)**) shall be kept entirely separate from all other wiring and equipment.

680-6.   Location and Protection of Receptacles—Outdoor receptacles shall not be located within 10 feet of the inside walls of the pool. (See Fig. 680-1.)

If the outdoor receptacles are located between 10 and 15 feet of the inside of the pool, the circuit shall be protected by a **Ground-Fault Circuit-Interrupter. Section 400-4** covers the prohibited uses of flexible cords and you are reminded of **Section 210-22(d),** which will require GFCI's on 15- and 20-ampere receptacles used outdoors for residential occupancies and this will become effective January 1, 1973.

680-7.   Cord- and Plug-Connected Equipment—*Fixed or stationary equipment rated 20 amperes or less, other than an underwater lighting*

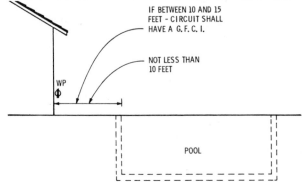

IF BETWEEN 10 AND 15 FEET - CIRCUIT SHALL HAVE A G.F.C. I.

NOT LESS THAN 10 FEET

WP

POOL

Fig. 680-1. Location and protection of all outside receptacles.

463

fixture for a permanently installed pool, may be connected with a flexible cord to facilitate the removal or disconnecting for maintenance or repair. The flexible cord shall not exceed 3 feet in length and shall have a copper equipment grounding conductor not smaller than No. 12 AWG with a grounding-type attachment plug. See **Section 680-24(f)** *for connection with flexible cords.*

680-8. Overhead Conductor Clearances—*The following parts of swimming pools shall not be placed under existing service-drop conductors or any other open overhead wiring; nor shall such wiring be installed above the following:*

(a) *Swimming pool and the area extending 10 feet horizontally from the inside of the walls of the pool.*

(b) *Diving Structure.*

(c) *Observation stands, towers or platforms.*

B. Permanently Installed Pools

680-20. Underwater Lighting Fixtures—

(a) General.

(1) *The provisions of* **Section 680-20** *apply to all lighting fixtures installed below the normal water level of the pool.* See Fig. 680-2.

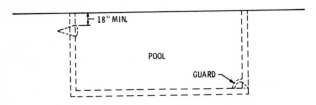

Fig. 680-2. Installation of fixtures below water level.

(2) *Underwater lighting fixtures supplied either directly from a branch circuit or by a transformer meeting the requirements of* **Section 680-5(a)** *shall perform reliably under any likely combination of fault conditions so that there is no shock hazard. Compliance with this requirement shall be assured by one of the following:*

a. *The design and construction of the fixture; or*

b. *The use of a ground-fault circuit-interrupter; or*

c. *Other acceptable means.*

(3) *No lighting fixtures shall be installed for operation at more than 150 volts between conductors.*

(4) *Lighting fixtures mounted in walls shall be installed with the top of the fixture lens at least 18 inches below the normal water level of the pool. A lighting fixture facing upward shall have the lens adequately guarded to prevent contact by any person.* See Fig. 680-2.

Exception: Lights approved for the purpose may be installed at a depth of at least 4 inches below the normal water level of the pool. There may or may not be such lighting fixtures, be sure that you check your Green UL Listing book for approval.

(b) Wet-Niche Fixtures.

(1) Approved metal forming shells shall be:

(a) Installed for mounting of all wet-niche underwater fixtures.

(b) Equipped with provisions for threaded conduit entries.

(c) Metal parts of fixture or forming shell in contact with the water shall be brass or other non-corrosive metal.

(d) Wiring methods shall be rigid metal conduit of brass or other approved corrosion-resistant metal or rigid non-metallic conduit.

(e) Raceway shall extend from the forming shell to a suitable junction box or other enclosure. (See **Section 680-21).**

(f) No. 8 AWG insulated solid copper grounding conductor shall be installed in rigid nonmetallic conduit, from forming shell to the junction box or enclosure.

(2) *The end of the flexible-cord jacket and the flexible-cord conductor terminations within the fixture shall be covered with or encapsulated in a suitable potting compound to prevent the entry of water into the fixture through the cord or its conductors. In addition, the grounding connection within the fixture shall be similarly treated to protect such connection from the deteriorating effect of pool water in the event of water entry into the fixture.*

(3) *The fixture shall be bonded to and secured to the forming shell by a positive locking device which will assure a low-resistance contact and which will require a tool to remove the fixture from the forming shell.*

465

(c) Dry-Niche Fixtures: *A dry-niche lighting fixture shall be provided with:*

(1) provisions for drainage of water; and

(2) means for accommodating one equipment grounding conductor for each conduit entry.

Approved rigid metal or rigid nonmetallic conduit shall be installed from the fixture to the service equipment or panelboard. A junction box is not required, but if used, need not be elevated or located as specified in **Section 680-21(a) (4)** *if the fixture is specifically approved for the purpose.*

Junction boxes mounted above the grade of finished walkways around the pool shall not be located in the walkway unless afforded additional protection such as location under diving boards, adjacent to fixed structures, or the like.

The purpose of this ruling is easy to understand. Junction boxes shall be so located as not to cause a stumbling hazard. The area around the pool is always wet and slippery—if installed without protection, the boxes might be a great hazard and likely to cause falls.

680-21. Junction Boxes and Enclosures for Transformers and Ground-Fault Circuit-Interrupters—

(a) *A junction box connected to a conduit which extends directly to an underwater pool-light forming shell shall be:*

(1) equipped with provisions for threaded conduit entries; and

(2) of copper, brass, suitable plastic or other approved corrosion-resistant material; and

(3) provided with electrical continuity between every connected metallic conduit and the grounding terminals by means of copper, brass, or other approved corrosion-resistant metal that is integral with the box; and

(4) located not less than 8 inches, measured from the inside of

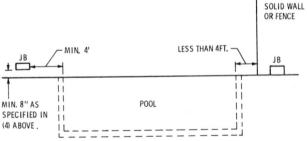

Fig. 680-3. Junction box placement where walls or fence are used.

the bottom of the box, above the ground level, pool deck, or maximum pool water level, whichever provides the greatest elevation, and located not less than 4 feet from the inside wall of the pool unless separated from the pool by a solid fence, wall or other permanent barrier. See Fig. 680-3.

Exception: On lighting systems of 15 volts or less, a flush deck box may be used provided:

a. *An approved potting compound is used to fill the box to prevent the entrance of moisture, and*

b. *The flush deck box is located not less than 4 feet from the inside wall of the pool.*

(b) *An enclosure for a transformer, ground-fault circuit-interrupter, or a similar device connected to a conduit which extends directly to an underwater pool-light forming shell shall be:*

(1) equipped with provisions for threaded conduit entries; and

(2) provided with an approved seal, such as duct seal at the conduit connection, that prevents circulation of air between the conduit and the enclosures; and (see Fig. 680-4)

(3) provided with electrical continuity between every connected metallic conduit and the ground terminals by means of copper, brass, or other approved corrosion-resistant metal that is integral with the enclosures; and

(4) located not less than 8 inches, measured from the inside bottom of the enclosure to the ground level, pool, deck, or maximum pool water level, whichever provides the greatest elevation; and (see Fig. 680-4)

(5) located not less than 4 feet from the inside of the pool unless separated from the pool by a solid fence, wall or other permanent barrier. See Fig. 680-4

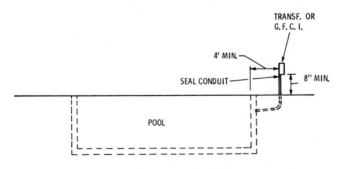

Fig. 680-4. Showing conduit seal.

(c) Junction boxes mounted above the grade of finished walkways around the pool shall not be located in the walkway unless afforded additional protection such as location under diving boards, adjacent to fixed structures, or the like.

The purpose of this ruling is easy to understand. Junction boxes shall be so located as not to cause a stumbling hazard. The area around the pool is always wet and slippery—if installed without protection, the boxes might be a great hazard and likely to cause falls.

(d) *Junction boxes, transformer enclosures and ground-fault circuit-interrupter enclosures shall be provided with a number of grounding terminals which shall be one more than the number of conduit entries.*

680-22. Bonding—

(a) *The following parts shall be bonded together by a solid copper conductor not smaller than No. 8 AWG:* (This formerly was No. 12)

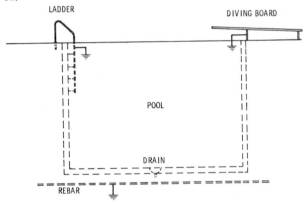

GROUND METAL PARTS, REBAR, LADDER, RAILS,
DIVING BOARDS, DRAINS, OTHER PARTS & EQUIPMENT.

Fig. 680-5. Bonding all metal equipment together by using solid copper wire.

(1) All metallic parts of the pool structure, including the reinforcing steel (See Fig. 680-5).
(2) Forming Shell.
(3) All metallic fittings within or attached to the pool structure.
(4) Metal parts of the electrical equipment associated with the pool water circulating system, including pump motors.
(5) Metallic conduit and metallic piping within 5 feet of the in-

468

side walls of the pool and that are not separated from the pool by a permanent barrier.

(6) All fixed metallic parts that are within 5 feet of the inside walls of the pool and that are not separated from the pool area by a permanent barrier.

Exception No. 1: The usual steel tie wires are considered suitable for bonding the reinforcing steel together, and welding or special clamping will not be required.

Exception No. 2: Structural reinforcing steel or the walls of welded metal pool structures may be used as a common bonding grid for non-electrical parts where connections can be made in accordance with **Section 250-113.**

(b) *For pool water heaters having a rating of more than 50 amperes and having specific instructions regarding the parts of the equipment to be bonded to the other pool components, and the parts of the equipment to be grounded, only those parts designed to be bonded shall be bonded, and only those parts designed to be grounded shall be grounded.*

680-23.   Grounding—*The following equipment shall be grounded:*

(1) Wet-niche underwater lighting fixtures;
(2) Dry-niche underwater lighting fixtures;
(3) All electrical equipment located within 5 feet of the inside wall of the pool;
(4) All electrical equipment associated with the recirculating system of the pool;
(5) Junction boxes;
(6) Transformer enclosures;
(7) Panelboards that are not part of the service equipment and that supply any electrical equipment associated with the pool.

680-24.   Methods of Grounding—

(a) *The following provisions shall apply to the grounding of underwater lighting fixtures, metallic junction boxes, metallic transformer enclosures and other metallic enclosures:*

*(1) Wet-niche lighting fixtures that are supplied by a flexible cord or cable shall have all exposed noncurrent-carrying metal parts grounded by an insulated, copper equipment grounding conductor that is an integral part of the cord or cable. This grounding conductor shall be connected to a grounding terminal in the supply junction box, transformer enclosure or other enclosure. **This grounding conductor shall***

469

be equal in size to the supply conductors but not smaller than No. 16 AWG copper.

(2) The junction box, transformer enclosure or other enclosure in the supply circuit to a wet-niche lighting fixture and the field-wiring chamber of a dry-niche lighting fixture shall be grounded to the equipment grounding terminal of the panelboard. This terminal shall be directly connected to the panelboard enclosure. The equipment grounding conductor shall be installed without joint or splice. See **Fig. 680-6.**

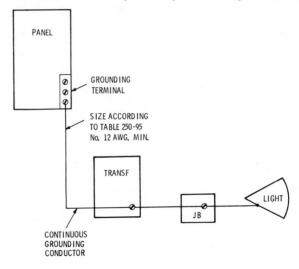

Fig. 680-6. Grounding all electrical equipment to the panelboard.

Exception No. 1: Where more than one underwater lighting fixture is supplied by the same branch circuit, the equipment grounding conductor, installed between the junction boxes, transformer enclosures or other enclosures in the supply circuit to wet-niche fixtures or between the field-wiring compartments of dry-niche fixtures, may be terminated on approved grounding terminals.

Exception No. 2: Where the underwater lighting fixture is supplied from a transformer, and the transformer is located between the panelboard and a junction box connected to the conduit that extends directly to the underwater lighting fixture, the equipment grounding conductor may terminate on approved grounding terminals in the transformer enclosure.

470

(b) *Other electrical equipment shall be grounded to the equipment grounding terminal of the panelboard.*

(c) *A panelboard, not part of the service equipment, shall have an equipment grounding conductor installed between its grounding terminal and the grounding terminal of the service equipment. See Fig. 680-7.*

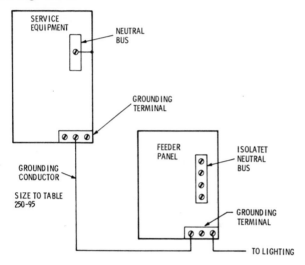

Fig. 680-7. Grounding feeder panel to panelboard.

(d) *An equipment grounding conductor shall be sized in accordance with* **Table 250-95** *but not smaller than No. 12 AWG. It shall be an insulated copper conductor and shall be installed with the circuit conductors in an approved rigid metal conduit or rigid nonmetallic conduit.*

Exception No. 1: The equipment grounding conductor specified in **Section 680-24(a) (1).**

Exception No. 2: The equipment grounding conductor between the wiring chamber of the secondary winding of a transformer and a junction box shall be sized in accordance with the overcurrent device in this circuit. See **Section 680-24(a) (2),** *Exception No. 2.*

Exception No. 3: The equipment grounding conductor between an existing, remote panelboard and the service equipment need not be in conduit if the interconnection is by means of an ap-

471

proved cable assembly with an insulated or covered copper equipment grounding conductor.

(e) *The equipment grounding conductor between the remote panelboard and the service equipment shall be sized in accordance with the overcurrent devices protecting the conductors supplying the panelboard. See* **Table 250-95.** See Fig. 680-6.

(f) *Where fixed or stationary equipment is connected with a flexible cord to facilitate removal or disconnection for maintenance, repair or storage (see* **Section 680-7)** *the equipment grounding conductors specified in* **Section 680-24(a)** *shall be connected to a fixed metallic part of the assembly. The removable part shall be mounted on or bonded to the fixed metallic part.*

C.   Storable Pools

680-30.   Pumps—See NEC.

680-31.   Ground-Fault   Circuit-Interrupters   Required—See   NEC.

Chapter 7. Special Conditions

ARTICLE 700—EMERGENCY SYSTEMS

A. General

700-1. Scope—The provisions of this Article apply to the installation, operation, and maintenance of circuits, systems, and equipment intended to supply power and illumination essential to the safety to life and property, where such circuits are legally required by Municipal, State, Federal, or other Codes, or by any other governmental agency having jurisdiction.

Emergency systems are generally installed in places of assembly where artificial illumination is required, such as buildings subject to occupancy by large numbers of persons, hotels, theaters, sports arenas, hospitals, and similar institutions. Emergency systems may provide power for such functions as essential refrigeration, operation of mechanical breathing apparatus, ventilation when essential to maintain life, illumination and power for hospital operating rooms, fire alarm systems, fire pumps, industrial processes where current interruption would produce serious hazards, public address systems, and similar functions.

Reference is made to NFPA Life Safety Code (NFPA No. 101) for specification of locations where emergency lighting is considered essential to life safety. This No. 101 NFPA Code becomes a part of the National Electrical Code by such reference.

700-2. Other Requirements—The requirements of the National Electrical Code as covered elsewhere in the Code are applicable, except where modified by this Article.

700-3. **Equipment Approval**—*All equipment shall be approved for use on emergency systems.*

700-4. Tests and Maintenance—

(a) *The authority having jurisdiction shall conduct or witness a test on the complete system upon installation and periodically afterward.*

(b) In order to assure proper operation of an emergency system, the authority that has jurisdiction shall require periodic tests to be conducted on the system to assure its maintenance in proper operating condition.

(c) The authority having jurisdiction shall require periodic maintenance on battery systems and unit equipments, including batteries used for starting or ignition on auxiliary engines.

(d) *A written record shall be kept of such tests and maintenance.*

700-5. Capacity—The capacity of the emergency system shall be adequate to handle the requirements of all the equipment that is connected to the auxiliary system.

B. Sources of Power

700-6. Systems—Immediate current supply shall be available to the emergency system in the event of failure of the normal supply of current to the building or group of buildings to supply emergency lighting, emergency power, or both. There are several types of systems for supplying emergency power and these may be one or more of the systems covered in **Sections 700-7** to **700-10.** Unit equipments are covered in **Section 700-22** and shall meet the requirements that are required therein.

The same types of emergency systems might not be suitable in all cases. The conditions must be evaluated as to whether the emergency system will be needed for a long or a short duration. For example, the exit lights in theaters may only be needed for a short time while emptying the theater. In case of an interruption of power to a hospital, either within or from without, the emergency system might be required to furnish power for a long period of time. Each particular condition requires a thorough evaluation of the possible needs, and the system, capacity, etc., shall be arrived at from these evaluations.

700-7. Storage Battery—*One service, in accordance with* **Article 230,** *and a storage battery of suitable rating and capacity to supply and maintain at not less than 87½ percent of system voltage the total load of the circuits supplying emergency lighting and emergency power for a period of at least 1½ hour.* Of course, batteries are not the answer to all conditions, but the requirements of this Section apply where batteries will fulfill the need.

Batteries, whether of acid or alkali type, shall be designed to meet the requirements of emergency service. When of the lead-acid type, they shall meet the following specifications:

(1) Be of a low gravity (1.20 to 1.22 specific gravity) acid type.
(2) Have relatively thick and rugged plates.

(3) Have relatively thick and rugged separators.

(4) Be housed in a transparent jar.

700-8. Generator Set—When supplied from one service in accordance with **Article 230**, a generator powered by some form of prime mover will serve as the source of emergency lighting and power, if the generator has sufficient capacity and is of the proper rating to supply the circuits that carry the emergency illumination and power. There shall be a suitable means of automatically starting the prime mover in case of a power failure. In hospital service, the time of transition from the interruption of the normal source of power to the establishment of the emergency source of power from the emergency generator shall not exceed ten seconds. **Section 700-4** covers test and maintenance and the records that shall be kept.

700-9. Separate Service—Two services will usually suffice as the source of emergency power if installed in accordance with **Article 230**. They should, however, be widely separated electrically and physically to minimize the possibility of simultaneous interruption of service.

700-10. Connection Ahead of Service Disconnecting Means—There are cases where emergency supply is considered to be adequate when connected on the line side of the disconnection means, if the two connections are sufficiently separated so that an interruption of the supply caused by some trouble within the building or group of buildings will not interrupt the supply of both sources. See *Section 230-73*.

700-11. Auxiliary Source—The auxiliary source shall have adequate capacity as called for in **Section 700-5**. The requirements of **Section 700-6** shall also apply to installations where the entire electrical load on a service or subservice is arranged to be supplied from a second source, which can be any one of the sources outlined in **Section 700-6**. A standby power plant will satisfy the conditions required in **Section 700-6**.

700-12. Derangement Signals—*Audible and visual signal devices shall be provided where practicable for the following purposes:*

(a) To give a warning of a derangement or nonfunctioning of the emergency or auxiliary system.

(b) To indicate if the batteries or generator is ready to carry the load if it becomes necessary for the emergency or auxiliary system to take over.

(c) To indicate if the battery charger is functioning properly. The batteries and their condition should also be checked—this will come under the periodic checks required to be taken and written up in the log that is kept of the auxiliary or emergency system.

475

C. Emergency Circuits for Lighting and Power

700-13. Loads on Emergency Branch Circuits—No loads, except those specifically required for the emergency service, shall be connected to or supplied from the emergency supply. Emergency equipment is not intended to take care of the entire load unless designed for this purpose.

700-14. Emergency Illumination—Emergency illumination includes exit lights and auxiliary illumination required for the safe evacuation of a building or buildings. This illumination should also supply sufficient light for the purposes for which it is intended. Many new structures are being built without provisions for illumination from the outside daylight. This condition makes it even more important to have an emergency source of illumination to supply sufficient lighting for the evacuation of the building or buildings. This has been experienced in outages that covered a large area.

Emergency lighting systems should be so designed and installed that the failure of any individual lighting element, such as the burning out of a light bulb, cannot leave any space in total darkness. The burning out of an individual lamp would not, in most cases, cause a total interruption of the lighting source in any one area since most areas are supplied by more than one lamp, but there are installations where this is possible.

There are battery-operated self-contained units which have a trickle charger to keep the battery fully charged. If these are installed, they should be on the emergency supply circuit so that if a breaker should trip or a fuse blow on the regular circuit, the battery could still charge and the unit be operable until the malfunction is corrected.

700-15. Circuits for Emergency Lighting—Branch circuits that are to supply emergency service are to be installed so that an immediate source of emergency supply is available in the event of failure of the regular power supply.

(a) An automatic transfer means is acceptable for transferring to the emergency supply upon failure of the regular source of supply.

(b) Two or more separate and complete sources of power will meet the requirements. If both systems are not regularly used in lighting, there shall be an automatic means of transferring from the regular source to the emergency source of power. Either or both supplies may be a part of the general lighting system, provided that they meet the requirements of the rest of this Article.

700-16. Circuits for Emergency Power—*For branch circuits which supply equipment classed as emergency, there shall be an emergency* *supply source to which the load will be transferred automatically and immediately upon the failure of the normal supply.*

700-17. Independent Wiring—The wiring for emergency circuits shall be kept separated and independent of all raceways, boxes, or cabinets, and other wiring used for the normal supply except:

Exception No. 1. In transfer switches.

Exception No. 2. In exit or emergency lighting fixtures supplied from two sources.

Exception No. 3. In a common junction box attached to exit or emergency lighting fixtures supplied from two sources.

These exceptions are necessary because, in a transfer switch, both supplies must be present to permit switching from one supply to the other. Exit lighting may be supplied from two sources, but each source shall be in a separate raceway.

D. Control

700-18. Switch Requirements—The switch or switches that control emergency circuits are to be accessible only to qualified persons or persons authorized to have control of these circuits.

Exception No. 1. Where two or more single throw switches are connected in parallel to control a single circuit, at least one of these switches shall be accessible only to authorized persons. This means that switches for control of emergency lighting may be paralleled but, if they are, one must be accessible to only authorized persons.

Exception No. 2. There may be additional switches in addition to the one that is controlled by authorized persons, but they shall be arranged so that the unauthorized person may put the lighting into operation but will not be able to disconnect it.

Switches connected in series, or three- and four-way switches shall not be used.

700-19. Switch Location—See NEC.

700-20. Other Switches—

(a) **Exterior Lights.** Lights on the exterior of a building which need not be energized when there is adequate illumination from the daylight may be controlled by light-actuated devices (electric eyes) if approved for the purpose.

(b) **Hospital Corridors.** Switching corridor lighting in the patient areas of hospitals from overhead fixtures to fixtures designed for night lighting is permitted if the switching system is designed so that the switches can only select between two sets of fixtures and so that both sets cannot be extinguished at the same time. In other words, one set of lighting must be connected at all times. It may be either the overhead lighting or the night-light fixtures.

E. Overcurrent Protection

700-21. Accessibility — *The branch-circuit overcurrent devices in emergency circuits shall be accessible to authorized persons only.* This will prevent tampering or interference with the operation of the emergency circuits.

F. Unit Equipments

700-22. Unit Equipments—See NEC.

ARTICLE 710—OVER 600 VOLTS—GENERAL

This Article covers general requirements for installations with voltages over 600 volts. It is suggested that information concerning the particular equipment or the conductors used be obtained from the manufacturer of the product and that their recommendations be closely followed.

In dealing with equipment and conductors used with voltages over 600 volts, it will be found that they are not generally listed by Underwriter's Laboratories. In designing and approving high-voltage equipment and conductors, the National Electrical Manufacturers Association specifications should be secured. These specifications will be found extremely helpful for this type of work.

A. General

710-1. Scope—*This Article applies in general to all circuits and equipment operated at more than 600 volts. For specific installations see the Articles referred to in* **Section 710-2.**

710-2. Installation Covered in Other Articles—*Provisions applicable to specific types of installations are included in:*

Article 230—Services.
Article 346—Rigid Metal Conduit.
Article 347—Rigid Nonmetallic Conduit.
Article 365—Cablebus
Article 430—Motors, Motor Circuits and Controllers.
Article 450—Transformers and Transformer Vaults.
Article 460—Capacitors.
Article 730—Outside Branch Circuits and Feeders.

Article 410—Lighting Fixtures, Lampholders, Lamps, Receptacles and Rosettes.

Article 660—X-ray Equipment.

Article 600—Electric Signs and Outline Lighting.

Article 665—Inductive and Dielectric Heating Equipment.

710-3. Wiring Methods—

(a) Aboveground Conductors. *They shall be installed in rigid metal conduit, in cablebus, in other suitable raceways or as open runs of metal armored cable suitable for the use and purpose.*

In locations accessible to qualified persons only, open runs of nonmetallic sheathed cable, bare conductors and bare bus bars may also be used. For example, transformer vaults would come under this ruling.

(b) Underground Conductors. This is a badly needed portion and should be adhered to closely.

Conductors shall be suitable for the voltage and conditions under which they are installed. Conductors installed in rigid metal conduit or direct burial cable, if of the construction where the energized conductors are surrounded by effectively grounded multiple concentric conductors, closely and evenly spaced circumferentially and meeting the requirements of **Section 250-51** *shall be buried at least 30 inches deep. Where other wiring methods are used the conductors shall be at a minimum depth of 42 inches and preferably at least 6 inches below other utilities.*

Exception No. 1. Under streets or roadways—conductor depth may be reduced to 24 inches if installed in rigid metal conduit.

Exception No. 2. Airport runways—in airport runways, including adjacent defined areas where trespass is prohibited, cable may be buried no less than 18 inches deep and without raceways or concrete encasement.

Exception No. 3. Lesser depths for unusual conditions—the above depths may be reduced 12 inches for each additional 2 inches of protective layer of concrete above the conductors.

710-4. Braid-Covered Insulated Conductors—Open Installation—The following applies to open runs of braid-covered insulated conductors: The braid shall be flame-retardant. If not flame-retardant, the braid shall be made flame-retardant with a saturant for this purpose. The braid shall be stripped back a safe distance at the conductor terminal, according to the operating voltage. This distance should not be less than 1 inch per kilovolt (1000 volts) if practical. (The voltage is the conductor-to-ground voltage of the circuit.)

710-5. Shielding of Solid Dielectric Insulated Conductors—Table 710-5 in the NEC covers shielding of solid dielectric insulated conductors. In using this Table, be sure that the notes that follow the Table are thoroughly read and understood.

Where solid dielectric-insulated conductors for permanent installations operate at voltages higher than those indicated in **Table 710-5** *and under the conditions mentioned, they shall be of a type having shielding for the purpose of confining their dielectric field.* A dielectric field surrounds conductors carrying current. It is of little consequence with low voltages except where high currents are being carried by the conductor. With high voltage, however, the dielectric field is all important in that the electrical stresses created will pin-point and cause breakdown of the insulation. Various forms of conductor shielding will distribute these stresses in an even pattern and prevent the pin-pointing at one spot.

710-6. Grounding of Shielding Tape—In the use of this Section, the manufacturer's specifications should be carefully adhered to when terminating or splicing high-voltage cables. The metallic or other static voltage shield on cables shall be stripped back to a safe distance according to the voltage of the circuit and the manufacturer's specifications.

A suitable termination shall be made at potheads or joints. This termination may be one of many various forms as described in the specifications of the cable for the purpose of stress reduction at the termination of the shield. The metallic shielding tape shall be grounded.

Many high-voltage cables have a conductive tape over the conductor insulation. This is often a cloth tape impregnated with graphite. The graphite residue that might be left on the insulation must be carefully removed by approved methods or there will be a leakage across the insulation and a subsequent breakdown.

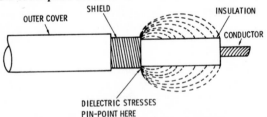

Fig. 710-1. Dielectric stresses in a shielded cable.

The dielectric stresses involved may be seen in Fig. 710-1. These stresses pin-point back to the termination of the shielding and cause undue strain at that point, with accompanying flashovers or breakdowns. The purpose of stress cones, potheads, terminators, etc., is to spread these stresses out and not let them concentrate at one spot on the cable.

710-7. Grounding—See NEC.

710-8. Moisture or Mechanical Protection for Metal Sheathed Cables —See NEC.

B. Equipment—General Provisions

710-10. Indoor Installations—See NEC.

710-11. Outdoor Installations—

(a) In Places Accessible to Unqualified Persons. *Electrical installations which are open to unqualified persons shall conform with* **Article 730.**

> *For Clearances of conductors over 600 volts see National Electrical Safety Code—ANSI C2-1960.*

(b) In Places Accessible to Qualified Persons Only. *Outdoor electrical installations having exposed live parts shall be accessible to qualified persons only and shall conform with* **Section 710-31** *through* **710-34.**

710-12. Metal Enclosed Equipment—The installation of metal enclosed equipments such as metal-clad switch gear, transformers, and the like, need not comply with **Section 710-31** if there are no exposed live parts. Where exposed to damage from vehicular traffic, there shall be suitable guards provided. Where there are ventilating or similar openings, these shall be so designed that any foreign objects that might be inserted will be deflected from live parts.

Metal-enclosed equipment located outdoors accessible to the general public shall be designed so that exposed nuts or bolts cannot be readily removed, permitting access to live parts.

C. Equipment—Specific Provisions

710-21. Circuit Interrupting Devices—

(a) Circuit Breakers.

> **(1)** *Indoor installations shall consist of metal-enclosed units or fire-resistant cell-mounted units except that open mounting of circuit breakers is permissible in locations accessible to qualified persons only.*
>
> **(2)** *Circuit breakers shall be trip-free in all positions.* This means that whether electrically, manually, or mechanically operated, they shall be so designed and installed that, if closed, a short or fault will cause them to trip-free regardless of being operated. In every circuit breaker installation, their rating in respect to closing, carrying, or interrupting capacities shall be no less than the short-circuit duty at the point of application. In other words, the circuit impedance and the fault currents in the circuit that they protect must be considered in

481

the selection of the circuit breaker. They shall be capable of opening under all loads without injury to the operator.

(3) There shall be no circuit breakers mounted inside a vault that contains oil-filled transformers.

(4) A suitable means of indicating the position that the circuit breaker is in (opened or closed) shall be provided at the point or points from which it may be operated.

(5) Oil circuit breakers shall be installed so that approved protection will be provided to any combustible buildings or materials. This may be accomplished by adequate space separation, fire-resistant barriers or enclosures, or trenches with sufficient coarse gravel to drain oil enclosures such as dikes or basins.

(b) Fuseholders and Fuses.

(1) *Fuses which expel flame in opening the circuit shall be so designed or arranged that they will function properly without hazards to persons or property.*

(2) *Fuseholders shall be designed so that they can be de-energized while replacing the fuse unless the fuse and fuseholder are designed to permit fuse replacement by qualified persons using equipment designed for the purpose without de-energizing the fuseholder.* An example of this is with the three-fuse type of operation where, if one fuse blows, the second takes over, etc. In this case, the blown fuse will drop down and may be removed by means of a hot-stick. A new fuse can be inserted and closed, thus cutting out the fuse that took over when the first fuse blew.

Metal-enclosed switchgear and substations which utilize high voltage fuses shall be provided with a gang-operated disconnecting switch. Isolation of the fuses from the circuit shall be provided by either connecting a switch between the source and the fuses or providing roll-out switch and fuse type of construction. The switch shall be of a load-interrupting type, unless mechanically or electrically interlocked with a load-interrupting device arranged to reduce the load to the interrupting capability of the switch.

(3) High-voltage fuses and fused cutouts that are installed in buildings or transformer vaults shall be of a type designed for that purpose. If they are not suitable for opening while carrying full load current, an approved switch or contactor shall be provided which will be capable of opening the full load current. In addition, the cutouts shall be interlocked with an approved interrupter or else bear a conspicious sign reading

DO NOT OPEN CUTOUT UNDER LOAD

The cutouts shall be so located that they may be readily and safely operated and re-fused. Fuses shall be accessible from a clear floor space.

(c) Load Interrupters. Load interrupter switches may be used only if suitable fuses or circuit breakers are also used in conjunction with them and have the capacity to interrupt fault currents. These devices in combinations shall be coordinated electrically so that they will withstand the effects of closing and carrying or interrupting all possible currents up to the assigned maximum short-circuit rating.

710-22. Isolating Means—The equipment shall be provided with a means of completely isolating it for maintenance and repair. It is suggested that a means of grounding also be provided. High-voltage cables with shielding will form a condenser (capacitor) effect and are capable of holding a considerable charge. Caution should be taken to bleed this charge off before touching any parts.

Isolation switches will not be required if there are other approved methods of de-energizing the equipment for inspection or repairs, such as metal-enclosed switchgear units, and removable truck panels. Isolating switches should be interlocked with the circuit interrupting device to prevent their being opened under load, or else they should have signs warning against opening the isolation switches under load. Isolating switches are used only for isolating and are not intended for opening under load.

A high-voltage installation will often have the fuses on a pole, the cables buried underground to the transformers, with isolation switches in the vault. The utility company is usually the only one having access to the vault. In this case, they will open the fuses at the pole and then open the isolation switches in the vault and provide for adequate grounding as an additional safety precaution.

Barriers should be provided on both sides of isolating switches of the indoor type to prevent flashovers. If the fuses and fuseholders are designed for the purpose, they may serve both as the fusing and as the isolation switches.

D. Installations Accessible To Qualified Persons Only

710-31. Enclosure for Electrical Installations—An enclosure in an electrical installation accessible to qualified persons only is defined as being considered an electrical installations in a vault, a closet, or in an area surrounded by a wall, screen, or fence, access to which is controlled by a lock and key or other approved means, and accessible only to qualified persons. The height of the wall, screen, or fence shall not be less than eight feet over-all, except if the enclosure is provided with an equal degree of isolation. In designing the enclosure for a given case, consideration shall be given to the nature and the degree of hazard involved. **Article 450** covers minimum construction requirements for oil-filled transformers. Isolation by elevation is covered in **Sections 710-11** and **710-34.**

710-32. Circuit Conductors—Circuit conductors may be installed in conduit, duct systems, as metal-armored cable or conductors, as bare wire, cable, and buses, or as nonmetallic sheathed cables or conductors as provided in **Sections 710-3** through **710-6.** When bare live conductors are installed, they shall conform to **Sections 710-33** and **710-34.**

In the installation of conductors that carry high-voltage, the sizing of bare conductors must be done with consideration for corona effects.

Insulators, their mountings, and conductor attachments, when used as supports for single-conductor and bus bars, shall be capable of safely withstanding the magnetic forces which will result between two or more conductors in the event of a fault current being imposed on them. The magnetic forces tend to push the conductors apart. The magnitude of the force depends upon the amount of short-circuit current involved, the spacing, etc.

If open runs of lead-sheathed cables are used, they shall be protected from physical damage and electrolysis of the sheath.

710-33. Minimum Space Separation Between Live Parts and Adjacent Surfaces—This Section deals with interior wiring design and construction. It does not apply to the space separation provided in electrical apparatus and wiring devices.

Table 710-33 in the NEC lists the minimum indoor air separation between bare live conductors and between such conductors and adjacent surfaces. These are the minimum values—the spacing may be greater but not less than the spacing shown in the Table. A note following the Table states: *The values given are the minimum permissible space separation under favorable service conditions. They should be increased under unfavorable service conditions or wherever space limitations permit. Proportional values may be used for intermediate voltages.*

710-34. Working Space and Guarding—

(a) **Working Space.** *The minimum clear working space in front of electrical equipment, such as switchboards, control panels, switches, circuit breakers, motor controllers, relays and similar equipment shall not be less than set forth in* **Table 710-34(a)** *unless otherwise specified in this Code.*

(1) *Exposed live parts on one side and no live or grounded parts*

484

on the other side of the working space or exposed live parts on both sides effectively guarded by suitable wood or other insulating materials. Insulated wire or insulated bus bars

Voltage to Ground	Conditions		
	1	*2*	*3*
601-2500	3 ft.	4 ft.	5 ft.
2501-7500	4 ft.	5 ft.	6 ft.
Over 7500	5 ft.	6 ft.	9 ft.

Where the "Conditions" are as follows:

operating at not more than 300 volts shall not be considered live parts.

(2) *Exposed live parts on one side and grounded parts on the other side. Concrete, brick or tile walls shall be considered as grounded surfaces.*

(3) *Exposed live parts on both sides of the work space (not guarded as provided in Condition 1) with the operator between.*

Exception: Working space is not required in back of assemblies such as dead-front switchboards or control assemblies when there are no renewable or adjustable parts such as fuses or switches on the back and when all connections are accessible from other locations than the back.

(b) Separation from Low-Potential Equipment. When there is any low-voltage equipment in the room or enclosure, such as switches, cutouts, or other equipment that operates at 600 volts or less, all exposed live parts or exposed wiring that operates at more than 600 volts must be separated effectively from the low-voltage equipment and wiring by suitable partitions, screens, or fences.

Many utility companies will not permit low voltage in transformer vaults with high voltage, with the exception of low-voltage buses. This does not include lighting and other low voltage that might be required in the operation of the high-voltage equipment.

Exception: Switches or other equipment operating at 600 volts or less and serving only equipment within the high voltage vault, room or enclosure may be installed in the high voltage enclosure, room or vault if accessible to qualified persons only.

(c) Locked Rooms or Enclosures. *The entrances to all buildings, rooms or enclosures containing exposed live part or exposed conductors operating in excess of 600 volts shall be kept locked, except where such entrances are at all times under the observation of a qualified attendant.*

Where the voltage exceeds 600 volts permanent and conspicuous warning signs shall be provided, reading substantially as follows: Warning—High Voltage—Keep Out.

(d) **Illumination.** Adequate illumination shall be provided to properly illuminate the high-voltage area for safe working and the fixtures are to be installed so that there will be no danger to anyone changing bulbs or working on the illumination system. The switching points for this illumination shall be readily accessible and in such a place that, in operating the controls for the illumination, there is no danger of coming into contact with any live parts.

(e) **Headroom.** *The minimum headroom above working spaces about switching equipment where there are live parts exposed at any time shall be not less than 6 1/2 feet.*

(f) **Elevation of Ungraded Live Parts.** The following table gives the minimum working space elevations that are to be maintained where there are unguarded live parts above the working space.

Voltage Between Phases	*Minimum Vertical Clearance of Unguarded Parts*	
	Feet	*Inches*
601-6600	8	0
6601-11000	9	0
11001-22000	9	3
22001-33000	9	6
33001-44000	9	10
44001-66000	10	5
66001-88000	11	0
88001-110000	11	7
110001-132000	12	2

ARTICLE 720—CIRCUITS AND EQUIPMENT OPERATING AT LESS THAN 50 VOLTS

This Article covers systems such as the common "Delco systems", which were used in many homes before electricity was available. Also included are equipments such as 24-volt generators and battery systems and other low-voltage systems used on farms and homes in rural areas. Refer to the National Electrical Code.

ARTICLE 725—REMOTE-CONTROL, LOW-ENERGY POWER, LOW-VOLTAGE POWER AND SIGNAL CIRCUITS

Refer to the National Electrical Code for coverage of this Article.

486

ARTICLE 730—OUTSIDE BRANCH CIRCUITS AND FEEDERS

730-1. Scope—*This Article applies to electrical equipment and wiring for the supply of utilization equipment located on or attached to the outside of public or private buildings, or run between buildings, structures or poles on other premises served.*

For additional information on wiring over 600 volts see the National Electrical Safety Code, ANSI C2-1960 and supplements C2.2A-1965 and C-2.2B-1967.

730-2. Application of Other Articles—*Application of other Articles including additional requirements to specific cases of equipment and conductors, as as follows:*

730-3. Calculation of Load—

(a) **Branch Circuits.** The provisions of **Article 220,** covering the calculation of loads on branch circuits, will apply to this Article. In calculating loads for branch circuits, the ampacities allowable for single conductors in free air must be considered. These ampacities are given in **Table 310-13** for Insulated Copper Conductors, and in **Table 310-15** for Insulated Aluminum Conductors.

(b) **Feeders.** The provisions covering feeders in **Article 220** apply to outdoor feeders also, and **Tables 310-13** and **310-15** apply for feeders for the ampacity of single conductors in free air.

730-4. Conductor Covering—This Section covers the insulation of conductors and where such conductors are required. It must be remembered that these conductors are exposed to the elements and therefore must have an insulation that will withstand these conditions, including ultraviolet light.

Open conductors supported on insulators shall be insulated or covered when located within 10 feet of a building or structure.

Conductors that are in the form of a cable or are in raceways, with the exception of Type MI Cable, shall be of the rubber-covered or the thermo-plastic type. In addition, where they are exposed to water or moisture, they shall comply with **Section 310-5** which states that they shall be resistant to moisture. There must be a "W" in the designation of the type of insulation.

Festoon lighting conductors shall be rubber covered or have a thermo-plastic covering.

730-5. Size of Conductors—See **Section 730-3**.

730-6. Minimum Size of Conductor—

(a) **Overhead Spans.** The length and size of conductors for overhead spans are controlled by the tensile strength and loading from winds, ice, etc. The Code has established: *Overhead conductors shall not be smaller than No. 10 for spans up to 50 feet in length, and not smaller than No. 8 for longer spans*. This ruling is the guide for establishing the size of overhead conductors.

(b) **Festoon Lighting.** Reference is made to **Section 730-25** which covers *Outdoor Lighting Equipment—Lampholders*. The general requirement for festoon lighting is that the conductors shall not be smaller than No. 12 unless supported by messenger wires. It is only natural that for long spans, a larger conductor is required for the proper support.

(c) **Over 600 Volts.** *Overhead conductors operating at more than 600 volts shall not be smaller than No. 6 when open individual conductors nor smaller than No. 8 when in cable.* All conditions must be considered and conductors sized accordingly, using the minimum only as the minimum guide.

730-7. Lighting Equipment on a Pole—

(a) *For the supply of lighting equipment installed on a single pole or structure, the branch circuits shall comply with the requirements of* **Article 210.** In other words, the installation of lights on a pole or structure is considered to be a branch circuit and is subject to all of the conditions and requirements that govern branch circuits. See paragraph (c) below.

(b) *For multiwire branch circuits, a common neutral may be employed for the branch circuits, provided not more than 8 ungrounded conductors are used. Such a common neutral shall have an ampacity of not less than the maximum load of all the ungrounded conductors connected to any phase or polarity.* For example, if a 115/230-volt system is in use, four circuits could be used with a common neutral *if* the ampacity of the neutral corresponded to the total ampacity of all the conductors on one ungrounded leg. Also, if 115-volt branch circuits were used, one neutral could be used if the ampacity of the neutral equalled the total ampacity of the 8 ungrounded conductors.

(c) *The voltage to ground of branch circuits supplying lampholders or lighting fixtures mounted on the outside of buildings or on poles or structures for area illumination of residential, commercial or industrial property shall not exceed 150 volts.*

Exception No. 1. The voltage to ground on branch circuits supplying lighting fixture for illumination of outdoor areas of industrial establishments, office buildings, schools, stores and other commercial or public buildings shall not exceed 300 volts provided;

a. *The fixtures are mounted on the outside of buildings or out of doors on poles or other structures.*

b. *The fixtures are not less than 8 feet above grade or other surface accessible to individuals other than those charged with fixture maintenance and supervision.*

c. *The fixtures are not less than 3 feet from windows, platforms, fire escapes and the like.*

Exception No. 2. The voltage between conductors supplying only ballasts for permanently installed electric-discharge lighting fixtures for area illumination shall not exceed 500 volts provided the fixtures are mounted on poles at a height of not less than 22 feet or on other structures at a height of not less than 18 feet.

730-8. Disconnection—*For branch circuits and feeders, see* **Section 240-18.**

730-9. Overcurrent Protection—

(a) The overcurrent protection of branch circuits shall be governed by **Article 210.** In other words, overhead branch-circuit overcurrent protection must be the same as for other branch circuits, considering of course the ampacity of conductors in free air.

489

(b) This is similar to (a) above, but is governed by the requirements for feeders as covered in **Article 215.**

730-10.   Wiring on Buildings—Wiring for circuits of 600 volts or less may be installed on the outside of buildings as follows:

(1) As open conductors on insulating supports.
(2) As multiple-conductor cable approved for the purpose.
(3) As aluminum-sheathed cable (ALS).
(4) In rigid metal conduit.
(5) In busways, as covered in **Article 364.**
(6) In electrical metallic tubing.

Circuits of over 600 volts are to be treated the same as were the services in **Section 230-101.** Circuits for sign and outline lighting are covered in **Article 600.**

730-11.   Circuit Exits and Entrances—Where branch circuits or feeders enter or leave a building, they are to be treated as service entrances as covered in **Article 230.** There is actually no difference except for the classification of the purpose for which they are used.

730-12.   Open Conductor Supports—*Open conductors shall be supported on* glass or porcelain knobs, racks, brackets, or strain insulators, approved for the purpose.

730-13.   Festoon Supports—It is required that any spans of festoon lighting that are more than 40 feet long shall be supported by messenger wire which shall have approved strain insulators. Neither the conductors nor the messenger wire shall be attached to any fire escape, downspout, or plumbing equipment.

730-14.   Open Conductor Spacings—

(a) **Open Conductors Exposed to the Weather.** The requirements for these are covered in **Section 230-47** which states: *Individual open conductors exposed to weather shall be supported on insulators, racks or other means, placed at intervals not exceeding 9 feet and separating the conductors at least 6 inches from each other and 2 inches from the surface wired over; or at intervals not exceeding 15 feet if they maintain the conductors at least 12 inches apart. For 300 volts or less, conductors may have a separation of not less than 3 inches where supports are placed at intervals not exceeding 4½ feet and conductors are not less than 2 inches from the surface wired over.*

(b) **Open Conductors Not Exposed to Weather.** These are covered by **Section 230-48** which states: *Individual open conductors not exposed to the weather may be supported on glass or porcelain knobs at intervals not exceeding 4½ feet and maintaining the*

490

conductors at least one inch from the surface wired over and a separation of at least 2½ inches between conductors.

(c) **Over 600 Volts.** Refer to **Section 230-101(c).**

(d) **Separation from Other Circuits.** *Open conductors shall be separated from open conductors of other circuits or systems by not less than 4 inches.* This applies to circuits (electrical) such as TV leads, telephone lines, etc. Of course attention must be paid to the voltages involved and the separation spaced accordingly. There will be instances where 4 inches might not be sufficient due to higher voltages involved.

(e) **Conductors on Poles.** This requires that conductors on poles have a separation of not less than 1 foot except when placed on racks or brackets. This again is determined by the voltages involved, with the spacing increased as required for higher voltages.

A horizontal climbing space is to be provided, where conductors are mounted on poles, as follows:

Power conductors, below communication
   conductors ....30 inches
Power conductors alone or above communication conductors:
   Less than 300 volts ....24 inches
   Exceeding 300 volts ....30 inches
Communication conductors below power
   conductors ....same as power conductors
Communication conductors alone or above power
   conductors ....no requirements

730-15. Supports over Buildings—These require the same procedure as for service conductors covered in **Section 230-25.**

730-16. Point of Attachment to Buildings—This requires the same clearances as for services covered in **Section 230-26**—not less than 10 feet above finished grade and a minimum of 18 feet above driveways, alleys, and public roads, with a maximum of 30 feet for the attachment unless more clearance is necessary, and a minimum of 12 feet over residential drives.

730-17. Means of Attachments to Buildings—All of the applicable provisions of **Section 230-27** apply here.

730-18. Clearance from Ground. *Open conductors of not over 600 volts shall conform to the following:*

10 feet—above finished grade, sidewalks or from any platform or projection from which they might be reached;
12 feet—over residential driveways and commercial areas such as parking lots and drive-in establishments not subject to truck traffic;

15 feet—over commercial areas, parking lots, agricultural or other areas subject to truck traffic;

18 feet—over public streets, alleys, roads, and driveways on other than residential property. See Figure 230-8.

730-19. Clearances from Buildings for Conductors not in Excess of 600 Volts—

(a) **Clearance over Roof.** *Open conductors shall have a clearance of not less than 8 feet from the highest point of roofs over which they pass with the following exceptions:* For Exceptions No. 1 and No. 2, see NEC. Also see **Section 230-22(a)** and Fig. 230-6.

(b) **Horizontal Clearances.** *Open conductors not attached to a building shall have a minimum horizontal clearance of 36 inches.*

(c) **Final Spans.** *Final spans of feeders or branch circuits to buildings which they supply or from which they are fed may be attached to the building but they shall be kept 3 feet from windows, doors, porches, fire escapes or similar locations.* The Code does not explicitly state this, but for attachments, it is almost certain that the enforcing authority will base his decisions on the requirements for service drops. The height of spans is specified the same as for service drops. If necessary to get the proper height, the enforcing authority will usually accept masts.

(d) **Zone for Fire Ladders.** *Where buildings exceed 3 stories, or 50 feet in height, overhead lines shall be arranged where practicable so that a clear space (or zone) at least 6 feet wide will be left either adjacent to the buildings or beginning not over 8 feet from them, to facilitate the raising of ladders when necessary for fire fighting.*

Mention is again made of the National Electrical Safety Code. This Code, which covers clearances for conductors over 600 volts, is available from the Superintendent of Documents, Government Printing Office, Washington, D.C. 20402.

730-20.   Mechanical Protection of Conductors—Refer to **Section 230-46** and to the NEC.

730-21.   Conductors Entering Buildings—Refer to **Sections 230-44, 230-49,** and **230-51.** Also refer to **Section 338-3.**

730-22.   Multiple Conductor Cables on Exterior Surfaces of Buildings —The requirements are the same as for service cable covered in **Section 230-50.** Also refer to **Section 338-3** which covers service-entrance cable used for branch circuits and feeders. It is almost certain that it will be necessary to carry an equipment ground or otherwise satisfy the safety requirement of grounding to the satisfaction of the Code enforcing authority.

730-23. Raceways on Exterior Surfaces of Buildings—See NEC.

730-24. Underground Circuits—The requirements for underground branch circuits and feeders are the same as those for services covered in **Sections 230-32** to **230-34.** However, remember that provisions must be made for an equipment or grounding conductor for feeders and branch circuits. This is important because the neutral of a feeder circuit is isolated from the cabinet and equipment, so the continuity of grounding must be provided or the purpose for this isolation will be defeated. If in doubt, check with the inspector before installation.

730-25. Outdoor Lighting Equipment—Lampholders—See NEC.

730-26. Outdoor Lighting Equipment — Location of Lamps — See NEC.

ARTICLE 750—STAND-BY POWER GENERATION SYSTEMS
See NEC.

ARTICLE 800—COMMUNICATION CIRCUITS

Refer to the National Electrical Code for the coverage of this Article.

ARTICLE 810—RADIO AND TELEVISION EQUIPMENT

Refer to the National Electrical Code for the coverage of this Article.

ARTICLE 820—COMMUNITY ANTENNA TELEVISION AND RADIO DISTRIBUTION SYSTEMS

Refer to the National Electrical Code for the coverage of this Article.

Chapter 9. Tables and Examples

This chapter contains many tables and examples which have been referred to in this text by notations to see the NEC.

Major changes have been made in parts of Chapter 9. Tables and changes will not appear here since we are asking you to use this book in conjunction with the official *National Electric Code*. You will find that major and important changes have been made throughout the NEC book for 1971.

Notes

Notes

Notes

Notes

AUDEL BOOKS *practical reading for profit*

APPLIANCES

Air Conditioning (23159)

Brand new from Audel. Domestic, commercial, and automobile air conditioning fully explained in easily-understood language. Troubleshooting charts aid in making diagnosis and repair of system troubles.

Gas Appliances and Heating (23104)

A reliable guide to acquaint repairmen and home owners with the construction, operation and servicing of modern gas-fired appliances such as may be found in the average home.

Home Appliance Servicing (23016)

A practical "How To Do It" book for electric & gas servicemen, mechanics & dealers. Covers principles, servicing and repairing of home appliances. Tells how to locate troubles, make repairs, reassemble and connect, wiring diagrams and testing methods. Tells how to fix electric refrigerators, washers, ranges, toasters, ironers, broilers, dryers, vacuums, fans, and other appliances.

Home Refrigeration and Air Conditioning (23133)

NEW AND UP-TO-DATE. Covers basic principles, servicing, operation, and repair of modern household refrigerators and air conditioners. Automobile air conditioners are also included. Troubleshooting charts aid in trouble diagnosis. **A gold mine of essential facts for engineers, servicemen, and users.**

Oil Burners (23151)

Brand New. Provides complete information on all types of oil burners and associated equipment. Discusses burners—blowers—ignition transformers—electrodes—nozzles—fuel pumps—filters—controls. Installation and maintenance are stressed. Troubleshooting charts permit rapid diagnosis of system troubles and possible remedies to correct them. This book replaces the popular Oil Burner Guide used by thousands of Audel readers in past years.

AUTOMOTIVE

Auto Engine Tune-Up (23181)

New revised edition. This popular how-to-do-it guide shows exactly how to tune your car engine for extra power, gas economy, and fewer costly repairs. New emission control systems are explained along with the proper methods for correcting faults and making adjustments to keep these systems in a top operating condition.

Automobile Guide (23192)

Practical reference for auto mechanics, servicemen, trainees & owners. Explains theory, construction and servicing of modern domestic motor cars. FEATURES: All parts of an automobile—engines—pistons—rings—connecting rods—crankshafts—valve—cams—timing—cooling systems—fuel-feed systems—carburetors—automatic choke—transmissions—clutches—universals—propeller shafts—differentials—rear axles—running gear—brakes—wheel alignment—steering gear—tires—lubrication—ignition systems—generators—starters—lighting systems—storage batteries.

Diesel Engine Manual (23024)

A practical treatise on the theory, operation and maintenance of modern Diesel engines. Explains Diesel principles—valves—timing—fuel pumps—pistons and rings—cylinders—lubrication—cooling system—fuel oil—engine indicator—governors—engine reversing—answers on operation—calculations. AN IMPORTANT GUIDE FOR ENGINEERS, OPERATORS, STUDENTS.

Domestic Compact Auto Repair Manual (23077)

A practical guide covering all phases of service, maintenance and repair of all popular late-model U.S. compact cars. Includes detailed step-by-step instructions on engine tune-up, fuel and carburetor systems, automatic transmissions, power steering and brakes, and electrical systems. Truly a handy reference manual for mechanics, owners, and servicemen.

Foreign Auto Repair Manual (23078)

Contains complete, service and repair data for the most popular imported makes, including Fiat, Hillman Minx, M.G., Opel, Peugot, Renault, SAAB, Simca, Volkswagen, and Volvo. Introductory chapters provide complete data on operation and maintenance of fuel and ignition systems.

Gas Engine Manual (23061)

A completely practical book covering the construction, operation and repair of all types of modern gas engines. Part I covers gas-engine principles; engine parts; auxiliaries; timing methods; ignition systems. Part II covers troubleshootng, adjustment and repairs.

Truck & Tractor Guide (23020)

A shop companion for truck mechanics and drivers—shop foremen—garagemen—maintenance men—helpers—owners—troubleshooters—fleet maintenance men—bus mechanics and drivers—farm tractor operators and mechanics. Covers gas and diesel motor principles—construction—operation—maintenance—repair—service operations—troubleshooting—engine tune-up—carburetor adjusting—ignition tuning—brakes—service of all parts.—1001 FACTS AT YOUR FINGER TIPS.

BUILDING AND MAINTENANCE

Answers on Blueprint Reading (23041)

Covers all types of blueprint reading for mechanics and builders. The man who can read blueprints is in line for a better job. This book gives you the secret language, step by step in easy stages. NO OTHER TRADE BOOK LIKE IT.

Builders Encyclopedia (23178)

Brand New. A book of terms used by members of the building and construction trade. A valuable book for the carpenter, plumber, electrician, steel erector, bridge builder, general contractor, architect, and others in the building and construction industry.

Building Construction and Design   (23180)

New from Audel. A completely revised and rewritten version of Audel's **Architects and Builders Guide.** New illustrations and extended coverage of material makes this treatment of the subject more valuable than ever. Anyone connected in any way with the building industry will profit from the information contained in this book.

Building Maintenance   (23140)

A comprehensive book on the practical aspects of building maintenance. Chapters are included on: painting and decorating; plumbing and pipe fitting; carpentry; calking and glazing; concrete and masonry; roofing; sheet metal; electrical maintenance; air conditioning and refrigeration; insect and rodent control; heating; maintenance management; custodial practices: A MUST BOOK FOR BUILDING OWNERS, MANAGERS, AND MAINTENANCE PERSONNEL.

Carpenters & Builders Library—4 Vols.   (23169)

A practical illustrated trade assistant on modern construction for carpenters, builders, and all woodworkers. Explains in practical, concise language and illustrations all the principles, advances and short cuts based on modern practice. How to calculate various jobs.
Vol. 1—(23170)—Tools, steel square, saw filing, joinery, cabinets.
Vol. 2—(23171)—Mathematics, plans, specifications, estimates.
Vol. 3—(23172)—House and roof framing, laying out, foundations.
Vol. 4—(23173)—Doors, windows, stairs, millwork, painting.

Carpentry and Building   (23142)

Answers to the problems encountered in today's building trades. The actual questions asked of an architect by carpenters and builders are answered in this book. No apprentice or journeyman carpenter should be without the help this book can offer.

Commercial Refrigeration   (23195)

Installation, operation, and repair of commercial refrigeration systems. Included are ice-making plants, locker plants, grocery and supermarket refrigerated display cases, etc. Trouble charts aid in the diagnosis and repair of defective systems.

Do-It-Yourself Encyclopedia—2 Vols.   (23156)

An all-in-one home repair and project guide for all do-it-yourselfers. Packed with step-by-step plans, thousands of photos, helpful charts. A really authentic, truly monumental, home-repair and home-project guide.

Grounds Maintenance   (23186)

New and up-to-date. A comprehensive guide for the homeowner, industrial, municipal, and estate grounds keeper. Information includes proper care of annual and perennial flowers, various house plants, greenhouse design and construction, insect and rodent control, complete lawn care, shrubs and trees, and maintenance of walls, roads, and traffic areas. Various types of maintenance equipment are also discussed.

Masons & Builders Guides—4 Vols.   (23076)

A practical illustrated trade assistant on modern construction for bricklayers, stone masons, cement workers, plasterers, and tile setters. Explains in clear language and with detailed illustrations all the principles, advances and short cuts based on modern practice—including how to figure and calculate various jobs.
Vol. 1—(23072)—Brick work, bricklaying, bonding, designs.
Vol. 2—(23073)—Brick foundations, arches, tile setting, estimates.
Vol. 3—(23074)—Concrete mixing, placing forms, reinforced stucco.
Vol. 4—(23075)—Plastering, stone masonry, steel construction, blue prints.

Plumbers and Pipe Fitters Library—3 Vols. (23155)

New revised edition. A practical illustrated trade assistant and reference for master plumbers, journeyman and apprentice pipe fitters, gas fitters and helpers, builders, contractors, and engineers. Explains in simple language, illustrations, diagrams, charts, graphs and pictures, the principles of modern plumbing and pipe-fitting practices.
Vol. 1—(23152)—Materials, tools, calculations.
Vol. 2—(23153)—Drainage, fittings, fixtures.
Vol. 3—(23154)—Installation, heating, welding.

ELECTRICITY-ELECTRONICS

Electric Generating Systems (23179)

New from Audel. Answers many questions concerning the selection, installation, operation, and maintenance of engine-driven electric generating systems for emergency, standby, and away-from-the-power-line applications. Private homes, hospitals, radio and television stations, and pleasure boats are only a few of the installations that owners either desire or require for primary power or for standby use in case of commercial power failure. THE MOST COMPREHENSIVE COVERAGE OF THIS SUBJECT TO BE FOUND TODAY.

Electric Motors (23150)

New revised edition. Covers the construction, theory of operation, connection, control, maintenance, and troubleshooting of all types of electric motors. A handy guide for electricians and all electrical workers.

Electrical Power Calculations (23050)

275 TYPICAL PROBLEMS WORKED OUT. Presents and explains the mathematical formulas and the fundamental electrical laws for all the everday, practical problems in both AC and DC electricity. EVERY ELECTRICAL WORKER AND STUDENT NEEDS THIS MODERN MATHEMATICAL TOOL.

Guide to the 1971 National Electrical Code (23193)

This important and informative book is now revised to conform to the 1968 National Electrical Code. Offers an interpretation and simplification of the rulings contained in the National Electrical Code. Electrical contractors, wiremen, and electricians will find this book invaluable for a more complete understanding of the NEC. Illustrated.

House Wiring (23190)

New from Audel. Answers many questions in plain simple language concerning all phases of house wiring. A ready reference book with over 100 illustrations and concise interpretation of many rulings contained in the National Electrical Code. Electrical contractors, wiremen, and electricians will find this book invaluable as a tool in the electrical field.

New Electric Library—

For engineers, electricians, electrical workers, mechanics and students. Presenting in simple, concise form the fundamental principles, rules and applications of applied electricity. Fully illustrated with diagrams and sketches, also calculations and tables for ready reference. Based on the best knowledge and experience of applied electricity.
Vol. 1 (23031)—Electricity, magnetism, armature winding, repairs.
Vol. 2 (23032)—Dynamos, DC motors, construction, installation, maintenance, troubleshooting.
Vol. 3 (23033)—Electrical testing instruments, storage battery construction and repairs.
Vol. 4 (23034)—Alternating current principles and diagrams, power factor, alternators, transformers.
Vol. 5 (23035)—AC motors, converters, switches, fuses, circuit breakers.
Vol. 6 (23036)—Relays, capacitors, regulators, rectifiers, meters, switchboards, power-station practice.
Vol. 7 (23037)—Wiring, high-tension transmission, plans, calculations.
Vol. 8 (23038)—Railways, signals, elevators.
Vol. 9 (23039)—Radio, telephone, telegraph, television, motion pictures.
Vol. 10 (23040)—Refrigeration, illumination, welding, X-ray, modern electrical appliances.

Practical Electricity   (23160)

A newly-revised edition of an all-time best-seller. This updated version is a ready reference book, giving complete instruction and practical information on the rules and laws of electricity—maintenance of electrical machinery—AC and DC motors—wiring diagrams—lighting—house and power wiring—meter and instrument connection—transformer connection—circuit breakers—power stations—automatic substations. THE KEY TO A PRACTICAL UNDERSTANDING OF ELECTRICITY.

Questions & Answers for Electricians Exams   (23164)

Newly revised to conform to the 1968 National Electrical Code. A practical book to help you prepare for all grades of electricians' license examinations. A helpful review of fundamental principles underlying each question and answer needed to prepare you to solve any new or similar problem. Covers the National Electrical Code; questions and answers for license tests; Ohm's law with applied examples; hook-ups for motors; lighting and instruments. A COMPLETE REVIEW FOR ALL ELECTRICAL WORKERS.

Wiring Diagrams for Light & Power   (23028)

Brand-new updated edition. Electricians, wiremen, linemen, plant superintendents, construction engineers, electrical contractors and students will find these diagrams a valuable source of practical help. Each diagram is complete and self-explaining. A PRACTICAL HANDY BOOK OF ELECTRICAL HOOK-UPS.

ENGINEERS-MECHANICS-MACHINISTS
Machinists Library   (23174)

Covers modern machine-shop practice. Tells how to set up and operate lathes, screw and milling machines, shapers, drill presses and all other machine tools. A complete reference library. A SHOP COMPANION THAT ANSWERS YOUR QUESTIONS.

Vol. 1—(23175)—Basic Machine Shop.
Vol. 2—(23176)—Machine Shop.
Vol. 3—(23177)—Toolmakers Handy Book.

Mathematics & Calculations for Mechanics   (23026)

Mathematics for home study or shop reference. This work has been arranged as a progressive study, starting with the first principles of arithmetic and advancing step-by-step, through the various phases of mathematics. Thousands of mathematical calculations and tables. New, easy, correct methods covering a complete review of practical arithmetic. Illustrated with examples. A REAL HELP TO ALL MECHANICS.

Millwrights & Mechanics Guide   (23056)

Practical information on plant installation, operation, and maintenance. For millwrights, mechanics, erecting maintenance men, riggers, shopmen, servicemen, foremen, inspectors, superintendents.

Power Plant Engineers Guide   (23052)

A complete steam-engineer's library in one book, with questions and answers. For all Engineers, Firemen, Water tenders, Oilers, Operators, Repairmen and Applicants for Engineers' License Examinations. 1001 FACTS AND FIGURES AT YOUR FINGER TIPS.

Practical Guide to Mechanics   (23102)

A Convenient reference book valuable for its practical and concise explanations of the applicable laws of physics. Presents all the basics of mechanics in everyday language, illustrated with practical examples of their applications in various fields.

Questions & Answers for Engineers and Firemans Examinations (23053)

An aid for stationary, marine, Diesel & hoisting engineers' examinations for all grades of licenses. A new concise review explaining in detail the principles, facts and figures of practical engineering. Questions & Answers.

Welders Guide (23025)

A concise, practical text on operation and maintenance of all welding machines, for all mechanics. Covers electric, oxyacetylene, thermit, unionmelt welding for sheet metal; spot and pipe welds; pressure vessels; aluminum, copper, brass, bronze and other metals; airplane work; surface hardening and hard facing; cutting; brazing; eye protection. EVERY WELDER SHOULD OWN THIS GUIDE.

FLUID POWER

Practical Guide to Fluid Power (23136)

An essential book for the owner, operator, supervisor, or maintenance man concerned with hydraulic or pneumatic equipment. A complete coverage of modern design, application, and repair of fluid power devices. Fully illustrated.

Pumps (23167)

A new and detailed book on all types of pumps from the old-fashioned kitchen variety to the most modern types. Covers construction, application, installation, and troubleshooting.

MATHEMATICS

Practical Mathematics for Everyone—2 Vols. (23112)

A concise and reliable guide to the understanding of practical mathematics. People from all walks of life, young and old alike, will find the information contained in these two books just what they have been looking for. The mathematics discussed is for the everyday problems that arise in every household and business.
Vol. 1—(23110)—Basic Mathematics.
Vol. 2—(23111)—Financial Mathematics.

OUTBOARD MOTORS

Outboard Motors & Boating (23168)

Newly revised and up-dated. Provides the information necessary to adjust, repair, and maintain all types of outboard motors. Valuable information concerning boating rules and regulations is also included.

RADIO-TELEVISION-AUDIO

Handbook of Commercial Sound Installations (23126)

A practical complete guide to planning commercial systems, selecting the most suitable equipment, and following through with the most proficient servicing methods. For technicians and the professional and businessman interested in installing a sound system.

Practical Guide to Auto Radio Repair (23128)

A complete servicing guide for all types of auto radios, including hybrid, all-transistor, and FM . . . PLUS removal instructions for all late-model radios. Fully illustrated.

Practical Guide to Servicing Electronic Organs   (23132)

Detailed, illustrated discussions of the operation and servicing of electronic organs. Including models by Allen, Baldwin, Conn, Hammond, Kinsman, Lowrey, Magnavox, Thomas, and Wurlitzer.

Radiomans Guide   (23163)

A newly-revised and updated Audel best-seller, containing the latest information on radio and electronics from the basics through transistors. Covers radio fundamentals—Ohm's law—physics of sound as related to radio—radio-wave transmission—test equipment—power supplies—resistors, inductors, and capacitors—transformers—vacuum tubes—transistors—speakers—antennas—troubleshooting. A complete guide and a perfect preliminary to the study of television servicing.

Television Service Manual   (23162)

Now completely updated and revised to include the latest designs and information. Thoroughly covers television with transmitter theory, antenna designs, receiver circuit operation and the picture tube. Provides the practical information necessary for accurate diagnosis and repair of both black-and-white and color television receivers. A MUST BOOK FOR ANYONE IN TELEVISION.

SHEET METAL
Sheet Metal Pattern Layouts   (23045)

A practical illustrated encyclopedia covering all phases of sheet-metal work including pattern cutting, pattern development and shop procedure. Developed by experts for sheet-metal workers, layout men, mechanics and artisans, apprentices, and students. A MASTER BOOK FOR ALL THE SHEET METAL TRADES

Sheet Metal Workers Handy Book   (23046)

Containing practical information and important facts and figures. Easy to understand. Fundamentals of sheet metal layout work. Clearly written in everyday language. Ready reference index.

TO ORDER AUDEL BOOKS mail this handy form to

Theo. Audel & Co., 4300 W. 62nd
Indianapolis, Indiana 4626

Please send me for FREE EXAMINATION books marked (x) below. If I decide to keep them I agree to mail $3 in 10 days on each book or set ordered and further mail ⅓ of the total purchase price 30 days later, with the balance plus shipping costs to be mailed within another 30 days. Otherwise, I will return them for refund.

APPLIANCES

- ☐ (23159) Air Conditioning ....$ 5.95
- ☐ (23104) Gas Appliances and Heating 4.25
- ☐ (23016) Home Appliance Servicing 6.95
- ☐ (23133) Home Refrigeration and
  Air Conditioning 6.95
- ☐ (23151) Oil Burners 4.95

AUTOMOTIVE

- ☐ (23181) Auto Engine Tuneup 5.95
- ☐ (23192) Automobile Guide 8.95
- ☐ (23024) Diesel Engine Manual 6.95
- ☐ (23077) Domestic Compact Auto
  Repair Manual 5.95
- ☐ (23078) Foreign Auto Repair Manual 5.95
- ☐ (23061) Gas Engine Manual 4.50
- ☐ (23020) Truck and Tractor Guide 6.95

BUILDING AND MAINTENANCE

- ☐ (23041) Answers on Blueprint Reading 5.25
- ☐ (23178) Builders Encyclopedia 7.95
- ☐ (23180) Building Construction and
  Design 5.95
- ☐ (23140) Building Maintenance 5.50
- ☐ (23169) Carpenters and Builders
  Library (4 Vols.) 18.50
  ☐ Single Volumes sold separately ......ea. 4.95
- ☐ (23142) Carpentry and Building 5.95
- ☐ (23195) Commercial Refrigeration 6.50
- ☐ (23156) Do-It-Yourself Encyclopedia 8.95
- ☐ (23186) Grounds Maintenance 7.95
- ☐ (23076) Masons and Builders Guide
  (4 Vols.) 14.95
  ☐ Single Volumes sold separately ......ea. 4.00
- ☐ (23155) Plumbers and Pipe Fitters
  Library (3 Vols.) 12.50
  ☐ Single Volumes sold separately ......ea. 4.50

ELECTRICITY-ELECTRONICS

- ☐ (23179) Electric Generating Systems 5.95
- ☐ (23150) Electric Motors 5.95
- ☐ (23050) Electrical Power Calculations 4.50
- ☐   Guide to the 1968 National
  Electrical Code 6.95
- ☐ (23190) House Wiring 5.95
- ☐ (23030) New Electric Library
  ☐ Single Volumes sold separately ......ea. 4.00

- ☐ (23160) Practical Electricity ....$ 5.95
- ☐ (23164) Questions and Answers for
  Electricians Exams 4.50
- ☐ (23028) Wiring Diagrams for Light
  and Power 4.95

ENGINEERS-MECHANICS-MACHINIST

- ☐ (23174) Machinists Library (3 Vols.) 16.95
  ☐ Single Volumes sold separately ......ea. 5.95
- ☐ (23026) Mathematics and Calculations
  for Mechanics 5.50
- ☐ (23056) Millwrights and Mechanics
  Guide 7.95
- ☐ (23052) Power Plant Engineers Guide 7.50
- ☐ (23102) Practical Guide to Mechanics 4.95
- ☐ (23053) Q&A for Engineers and
  Firemans Exams 4.95
- ☐ (23025) Welders Guide 5.50

FLUID POWER

- ☐ (23136) Practical Guide to Fluid Power 6.95
- ☐ (23167) Pumps 5.95

MATHEMATICS

- ☐ (23112) Practical Math for Everyone
  (2 Vols.) 8.95
  ☐ Single Volumes sold separately ......ea. 4.95

OUTBOARD MOTORS

- ☐ (23168) Outboard Motors and Boating 4.95

RADIO-TELEVISION-AUDIO

- ☐ (23126) Handbook of Commercial
  Sound Installations 5.95
- ☐ (23128) Practical Guide to Auto
  Radio Repair 4.50
- ☐ (23132) Practical Guide to Servicing
  Electronic Organs 4.95
- ☐ (23163) Radiomans Guide 5.95
- ☐ (23162) Television Service Manual 5.95

SHEET METAL

- ☐ (23045) Sheet Metal Pattern Layouts 11.95
- ☐ (23046) Sheet Metal Workers Handy Book . 4.50

Prices Subject to Change Without Notice

Name _____

Address _____

City _____ State _____ Zip _____

Occupation _____ Employed by _____

☐ **SAVE SHIPPING CHARGES! Enclose Full Payment**
With Coupon and We Pay Shipping Charges. PRINTED IN USA